INTRODUCTION TO ATOMIC PHYSICS

INTRODUCTION
TO ATOMIC PHYSICS

Otto Oldenberg

PROFESSOR OF PHYSICS
HARVARD UNIVERSITY

SECOND EDITION

McGRAW-HILL BOOK COMPANY, INC.

NEW YORK   TORONTO   LONDON

1954

INTRODUCTION TO ATOMIC PHYSICS

Library of Congress Catalog Card Number 54-6729

IV

THE MAPLE PRESS COMPANY, YORK, PA.

To
JAMES FRANCK
Teacher and Friend

PREFACE

The present book grew out of a course, Introduction to Atomic Physics, which the author has been giving at Harvard University. Thorough revision of the text has affected in particular the chapters on nuclear physics and cosmic rays. A brief report on the solid state is added.

The book is intended for readers who have taken a one-year introductory physics course and are familiar with the elements of chemistry. Calculus is not necessary for the understanding of atomic physics on the introductory level. There the difficulty is not of a mathematical nature. The beginner finds it difficult, however, to understand how thoroughly our detailed theory of atomic structure, although apparently remote from observed facts, is based on experimental evidence. Therefore, in this book the relation between theory and observed fact is stressed. The guiding idea of the book is to train the student to *understand* and *judge* atomic theory, rather than to *accept it on authority*. This point of view seems to give the best education to the student of any field of science who wants to judge the results of current research and possibly wishes to do research himself. Wherever possible, the historical approach is used; the histories of the great discoveries are discussed. In a few cases, *e.g.*, in the discussion of Bohr's theory, reports on the advanced theoretical treatment and its comparison with experiment are indispensable for judging the validity of the theory. In many other cases reports of the more advanced development are given, in order to avoid the impression that the treatment given in the book represents the final stage of our knowledge. However, it is felt that detailed qualitative descriptions of such advanced theories as that of black-body radiation or the vector model of the atom leave the beginner student dissatisfied, because he fails to understand the mathematical argument. Such theories, which belong to the more advanced courses, are only briefly reported.

Throughout the book the author has applied a method which he has tried in elementary and advanced courses: Some arguments that are essential parts of the course are relegated to problems. If the problem seems too difficult for a beginner, he is guided by a set of questions. *However, the student is urged to try to find the solution without referring to these hints.* Presenting arguments as problems serves two purposes. First, it stimulates the interest of the student, who is given a chance to participate in the investigation; next, it impresses him with the *physical idea* that underlies the problem, as distinct from the *mathematical per-*

formance through which he is asked to go himself. The method of shifting as many computations as possible to problems removes the display of equations from the text and makes the book appear to be rather unmathematical. However, the reader who goes through these problems will find there the apparently missing mathematical arguments. Some problems are intended mainly for physics majors, while many others are for non-physicists as well. This arrangement makes it easy for the instructor to omit the more difficult arguments and use the book for students who have taken only the conventional one-year introductory physics course. Comparatively difficult problems are the following: 3.9, 3.10, 6.15, 6.16, 6.17, 7.19, 9.2, 10.12, 10.14, 12.7, 12.8, 12.9, 14.15, 14.18, 14.19, 16.13, 17.18, 17.19, 18.15, 19.14, and 20.2.

The notation recommended by a committee of the American Association of Physics Teachers has been adopted.

In the lecture course offered at Harvard University many experiments are demonstrated. Other experiments which take more time are performed by the student in an advanced laboratory course in atomic physics. While the experiments are only briefly described in the text, more technical advice is given in an appendix.

The course from which the present book developed originally covered two semesters. After a reorganization, it was reduced to a one-semester course. For such a short course it is recommended that the instructor give only the briefest outline of the fundamentals of chemistry and the kinetic theory of gases. In later sections, too, some detail may be replaced by summaries.

The author gratefully acknowledges many helpful suggestions offered by Col. B. W. Bartlett of the U. S. Military Academy, Professor Howard Carr of the Alabama Polytechnic Institute, Mr. Frank S. Ham, Professor P. E. Le Corbeiller, Dr. R. H. Milburn, and Mr. J. M. Teem, the last four of Harvard University. Sincere thanks are due to Dr. Cecilia Payne-Gaposchkin of Harvard University for her numerous suggestions.

OTTO OLDENBERG

CONTENTS

PART VI. NUCLEAR STRUCTURE

CONTENTS

INTRODUCTION

When trying to understand atomic theory, we become aware of the contrast between this comparatively new branch and the older branches of physical theory. In *mechanics* the theory gives relations between quantities that are directly observable. In *optics* a definite gap opens up between the observation and the theory. For example, we observe certain regular light and dark fringes and explain them by the theoretical concept of light as a wave motion which is not directly accessible to our senses as the surface waves of water are. In *atomic physics* this gap between observations and theoretical concepts is much wider. This seems to us the greatest difficulty in the study of atomic physics.

Even at the beginning of this century, in the earlier development of atomic theory, the gap seemed so wide that a distinguished chemist, although operating every day with the concept of atoms, warned his students that they should not believe too literally in the existence of atoms, which nobody had ever seen as individual particles. In contrast to this skepticism, we are now asked to believe that we know the parts of the most complicated atoms and how the parts work together. We are told, for example, that each mercury atom consists of a nucleus of known mass and electric charge, a nucleus built of 80 "protons" and about 120 "neutrons" and surrounded by 80 "electrons." We are told also that these electrons are arranged in known groups and that each electron is endowed with a known mass and electric charge and is capable of changing its position when absorbing or emitting light according to known laws that differ widely from the laws studied by the beginner in the introductory course on physics. We even claim that we can describe the nucleus in considerable detail. It is safe to say that if a physicist of the year 1900 were confronted with such modern statements, he would reject them as the results of an uncontrolled imagination; for even now nobody has ever taken apart an individual atom and examined its parts as a watchmaker examines the gears of a watch. Our senses tell us only such facts as that certain colored light is emitted by the electric discharge through mercury vapor.

What is the method of research that leads us so far away from the sound basis of observations? We illustrate it by two historical examples that indicate two opposite approaches. On the basis of our present attitude, both are subject to criticism. Nevertheless, they will help us in understanding the modern approach.

1

In the Islamic world, about a thousand years ago, there was an important development of research in physics. The concave mirror, the convex mirror, refraction of light, and many other phenomena were systematically observed and described. This method of careful description of experiments has led to important discoveries. Could it lead to the discovery of atoms and their properties? This does not seem possible, since atoms are beyond the range of direct observation, except by the present highly refined technique which led in 1951 to the observation of individual atoms.

Nevertheless the idea of atoms is eleven centuries older than Islamic science. This brings us to the example that illustrates the opposite approach. The ancient Greeks aspired to penetrate into mysteries beyond the limit of immediate observation. Around 400 B.C., in a period in which nothing was known of elements, compounds, and the laws of our chemistry and physics, Democritus taught that:

. . . particles infinite in number, indivisible, and different from each other are scattered about and move in the otherwise empty space. When they approach each other and become entangled, some of these aggregations form water, some fire, some plants, and some men. But all things really consist of atoms. There is no generation from nothing, nor any generation from existing things because the atoms do not change. As tragedies and comedies are written with a small set of ever the same letters, thus the infinite variety of all possible events in nature are realized by a small set of ever the same atoms which occupy different positions and perform different motions.

Atomos is the Greek word for indivisible. This, then, was the first appearance of the concept of atoms. Are we justified in saying that Democritus discovered the atomic structure of matter? Our present critical attitude does not allow us to accept that, because he did not offer any evidence proving the truth of his new idea, which was based solely on his intuition and his faith in a simple structure underlying the complexity of everyday observations.

By another example let us illustrate the fact that the indiscriminate use of the intuition may equally well lead in the wrong as in the right direction. This is evident from the Greek ideas of the cosmos. Around 350 B.C. Aristotle taught that the earth does not move and that it lies exactly at the center of the universe. A century later his teaching was opposed by Aristarchus, who claimed that the earth revolves about the sun in the circumference of a circle, the sun lying in the middle of the orbit. Although at present we accept this latter picture of the cosmos, Aristarchus is generally not considered to be the discoverer of the heliocentric system, for he did not offer a proof that demonstrated the superiority of his system over the geocentric system of Aristotle. The Copernican system is the universally accepted name for the new concept.

Copernicus, 1800 years later, applied the same basic idea; but he went a great step further by using this idea for the explanation of certain observations of great complexity. He explained the planetary orbits, which to the terrestrial observer seem very involved, as simple orbits about the sun, seen from one of the planets, the earth. The history of this discovery shows why we do not consider Democritus the discoverer of the atomic structure of matter. He had no way of proving the truth of his idea by correlating it with observed facts. This last step was taken 22 centuries later by Dalton. This criticism, based on more than 2,000 years of further scientific development, does not detract from our admiration for the great step forward in human thought made by the Greek philosophers. They had the freedom of mind to abandon such naïve ideas as that the residence of the human race must be the center of the universe. Beyond the range of the human eye they visualized a realm of nature in which different laws may be in effect, e.g., where the familiar experience that matter is divisible without limit may not be true. They imagined that orderly structures of nature of totally different kinds may exist on the very small and the very large scale. The origin of these ideas is evident from the Greek origin of the words "atom" and "cosmos."

After criticizing the Islamic and the ancient Greek physicists as representatives of two opposite lines of thought, we want to know what we consider to be the most fruitful approach. The answer is, a combination of both these methods. Modern atomic theory is a product of the imagination which has led us very far beyond what we perceive with our senses, but we claim that we have a criterion for the value of a theory. We judge it by its power to make a multitude of observed facts derivable from a unified basis. An example of this point of view will be given by each chapter of the present book. We accept on authority only the observed facts; e.g., spectral lines observed. In the lecture course as many as possible of such facts are demonstrated by experiments. The theory, e.g., Bohr's theory of the hydrogen atom, cannot be derived from the observed facts. Therefore, the theory is by no means so certain as these facts. Even in our introductory treatment we must adopt the critical attitude indispensable in research, judging the value of a theory by its power to give a consistent picture of many observed facts. This point of view will guide us throughout this book. We may state our criterion in a more extreme form: We accept a theory if it allows us to predict the result of an experiment hitherto untried. Thus a discouraged student of atomic theory may gain confidence when he recalls its recent success: The theory predicted that the element uranium, after a most complicated treatment, would lead to a reaction in which an unheard-of energy would suddenly be liberated. The value of this theory is generally recognized.

There is still another aspect in understanding atomic theory. How is it possible that human beings discovered a structure so remote from what the senses perceive? This question suggests the historical approach, which will give answers to the questions: How did one or the other discovery grow out of the preceding discoveries? What was the idea that guided the discoverer? It is our principal aim, however, to make clear the logical structure of elementary atomic physics, *i.e.*, to demonstrate the bearing of each experiment on our theoretical picture. Therefore, we systematically arrange our presentation according to the consecutive steps of theoretical understanding, founding each new step on experimental evidence. This point of view manifests the power of the theory to tie together many apparently unrelated phenomena.

We arrange our discussion from the point of view of the theory. This gives the student practice in invoking experiments from different fields of physics and chemistry in the support of the same theoretical idea. We start from the arguments for atomic structure in the widest sense, the structure of *matter* as revealed in chemistry (Part I) and the study of *gases* (Part II). Next, we study the structure of *electricity* (Part III) and the structure of *light* (Part IV). The following detailed discussion of the structure of individual atoms is naturally subdivided into the structure of the *external electrons* (Part V) and that of the *nucleus* (Part VI). Finally, in Part VII, we give a brief outline of *wave mechanics*, which, instead of Newtonian mechanics, governs the motion of the smallest particles studied in atomic physics.

During his complicated journey through the vast territory of atomic physics, the student should keep in mind the significance within the whole of any detailed view. In this endeavor he will be assisted by the survey printed in the table entitled Atomic Physics. Here the bearing of any group of experiments on our theoretical knowledge is evident from the correlation between the *observation*, given in the left column, and the *theory* in the right column.

In a book devoted to a systematic survey it is not possible to trace the slow development of each new experiment and new idea in full detail. For example, it would be misleading to say that the charge on the electron was first measured in 1909 by Millikan using the oil-drop method. On one hand, this statement disregards the results of the earlier workers using clouds of water drops; on the other hand, it discounts the great difficulties overcome by Millikan and his numerous coworkers during their efforts spread over a decade and resumed much later. This example illustrates the fact that numerous brief historical statements given throughout the book must be taken with a grain of salt.

Atomic Physics

OBSERVATION	THEORY

Part I. Structure of Matter as Revealed in Chemistry

Facts of chemistry	Atoms and their relative weights, Dalton, 1803; Avogadro's rule, 1811

Part II. Gases

Pressure, temperature, specific heat of a gas; Brownian motion	Kinetic theory of gases, beginning 1848

Part III. Structure of Electricity

A. Determinations of e/m	
Electric discharge through liquids; Faraday's laws, 1833	e/m of ions in liquids; existence of a fundamental charge, 1881
e/m of cathode-ray particles	Cathode ray consists of free electrons, J. J. Thomson, 1897
e/m of positive-ray particles	Positive ray consists of free $+$ ions
e/m decreases for high velocities	Mass equivalent to energy, Einstein, 1905
B. Determination of e	
Millikan's oil-drop experiment, 1909	Determination of the fundamental charge; masses of atoms and molecules

Part IV. Structure of Light

Photoelectric effect, 1887, 1916	Light consists of quanta of energy $h\nu$,
Compton effect, 1923	Planck, 1900; Einstein, 1905

Part V. Electronic Structure of Atoms

A. The nuclear atom	
Scattering of α particles	The heavy, positively charged nucleus surrounded by electrons, Rutherford, 1911
B. Electronic structure	
Spectrum of hydrogen atoms	Bohr's theory, 1913
Spectra of heavier atoms	Energy levels of *external* electrons
Methods of observation	Fundamental processes
Periodic table of elements	Stability of rare-gas electronic structure
X rays	The *internal* electron groups
C. Solid state	
Conductivity, specific heat	Quantum theory of solid state

Atomic Physics—(Continued)

OBSERVATION	THEORY

Part VI.   Nuclear Structure

OBSERVATION	THEORY
Isotopes, 1920	Nuclei built of a few types of particle; energies of formation
Natural radioactivity, 1896	Spontaneous disintegration of heavy nuclei
Artificial transmutation of elements, 1919, 1932; artificial radioactivity, 1934; uranium fission, 1939	Artificial transmutation of nuclei; neutrons, 1932
Cosmic rays, 1912	Highest-energy rays of cosmic origin; positrons, 1932; mesons, 1937

Part VII.   Wave Nature of Matter

OBSERVATION	THEORY
Diffraction of electrons, 1927	The motion of matter governed by waves, de Broglie, 1922; Heisenberg, Schrödinger, 1925

PART I
STRUCTURE OF MATTER AS REVEALED IN CHEMISTRY

In the study of atomic physics, we must first make clear the argument which explains certain experiments by the existence of atoms. Conventionally, these experiments and their interpretation are considered as belonging not to physics but to chemistry. We assume that the reader is familiar with the elements of chemistry. Hence we restrict ourselves to a brief review of the complicated argument which, starting from observations, leads to the atomic theory of matter, Avogadro's hypothesis, and the molecular formulas.

CHAPTER 1
THE ATOMIC HYPOTHESIS AND AVOGADRO'S RULE

1.1. Qualitative Analysis; Existence of Elements. Most substances can be analyzed into constituents, as water is analyzed into hydrogen and oxygen. However, a certain group of substances, like hydrogen and oxygen, cannot be analyzed any further. [This statement should be qualified, in view of the more recent discovery of isotopes (Chap. 16). The reader will find that most statements of physics are only approximations valid within a limited range.] Substances that withstand further chemical analysis are called "elements." This argument leads only to the existence of such elements. It does not say whether these elements have a *continuous* or *discontinuous*, *i.e.*, atomic, structure.

1.2. Quantitative Analysis by Weight; Existence of Atoms. When water is analyzed into its constituents, the same ratio of masses is always found, *i.e.*, 2.016 hydrogen to 16.000 oxygen. This is an example of the general *law of constant proportions*, which states that *the same compound always contains the same elements in the same mass proportion.*

There is another compound, hydrogen peroxide, which, when analyzed into hydrogen and oxygen, yields another mass ratio, 1.008 hydrogen to 16.000 oxygen. For the time being we are not interested in the fact that each of these ratios is approximately a ratio of integers ($\frac{1}{8}$ and $\frac{1}{16}$, respectively); this will be discussed in the chapter on nuclear physics (Sec. 16.2). Instead, here we are interested in the fact that one of these ratios is exactly twice as large as the other. Numerous similar results obtained with other compounds have led to the *law of multiple proportions*, which states that, *when the same two elements combine to form more than one compound, the different masses of one of the elements that unite with a constant mass of the other bear a simple ratio to one another.*

Dalton, in 1803, took the great step that led to the basis of theoretical chemistry by introducing the atomic hypothesis and so explaining the two empirical laws just mentioned. He assumed that each element consists of atoms, *i.e.*, very small particles, all of the same kind and of the same mass. In a compound substance a few atoms of different kinds combine. For the above example, Dalton made the simplest assumption that water consists of 1 hydrogen and 1 oxygen atom, abbreviated as HO. Correspondingly, hydrogen peroxide would be written as HO_2. The reader may invent such molecular formulas for the various compounds of nitrogen (N) and oxygen (O) which have been observed in the following proportions: 14:16, 28:16, 14:32, 28:48, or 28:80.

The argument just presented fails to furnish *unique* molecular formulas. HO is only the simplest formula for water. But it would be compatible with the law of multiple proportions to write instead H_2O or HO_2, or any other such combination. In each case the formula for hydrogen peroxide would have to be changed accordingly. Other experiments are needed to eliminate this ambiguity.

1.3. Quantitative Analysis of Gases by Volume; Avogadro's Rule. This new evidence was furnished in 1808 by Gay-Lussac. While the laws concerned with *weights* of substances are independent of the state (solid, liquid, or gaseous) of these substances, Gay-Lussac measured the *volumes of gases*, all at the same temperature and pressure. He found, for example, that 1 cm^3 of hydrogen and 1 cm^3 of chlorine form 2 cm^3 of hydrogen chloride. The general law describing all such experiments states that the *ratios of the volumes of gases used and produced in a chemical reaction are represented by small whole numbers.* This law is interpreted, and, at the same time, the ambiguity of the molecular formulas partly resolved, when we adopt Avogadro's hypothesis (1811), which assumes that *under the same conditions of temperature and pressure equal volumes of all gases contain the same number of molecules.*

The law of Gay-Lussac deals with volumes of gases which may be recorded by the experimenter. Avogadro's rule, however, is of a different character in that it is concerned with molecules, *i.e.*, with something unobservable. This is typical of a hypothesis in atomic physics. While we cannot verify it by direct observation, we can tentatively adopt it, draw conclusions regarding observable facts (here the formation of hydrogen chloride), and compare these conclusions with the observations. Unfortunately we shall find that our present initial discussion of a hypothesis is unusually involved, since Avogadro's rule by itself is insufficient to predict all observed facts but must be supplemented by specific assumptions for one or the other type of molecule (Cannizzaro, 1858).

Adopting Avogadro's rule, we say that 1 cm^3 *of any gas* contains n molecules. Hence in the example given above, *before* the reaction, n hydrogen molecules are present (occupying 1 cm^3) and *after* the reaction $2n$ hydrogen chloride molecules (occupying 2 cm^3). Since the total quantity of hydrogen available remains unchanged, we are forced to assume that each hydrogen chloride molecule contains only half as many hydrogen atoms as each hydrogen molecule. The simplest, but not the only possible, assumption is that each hydrogen molecule contains 2 atoms of hydrogen (written H_2), while each hydrogen chloride molecule contains only 1. Exactly the same argument applies to the relation between chlorine and hydrogen chloride since, as stated above, 1 cm³ of chlorine supplies all the chlorine atoms present in 2 cm³ hydrogen chloride. Thus we obtain the molecular formulas H_2 for hydrogen, Cl_2 for chlorine, and HCl for hydrogen chloride.

This first important result opens the door to the exploration of other molecular formulas, *e.g.*, those of water vapor and oxygen. Here our starting point is the observation that, under the same conditions of temperature and pressure, 2 cm³ hydrogen and 1 cm³ oxygen form not 3 but only 2 cm³ water vapor. On the basis of Avogadro's rule and the formula H_2 for a hydrogen molecule, we argue as follows: (1) Each water molecule contains as many hydrogen atoms as a hydrogen molecule, *i.e.*, 2; in other words, the share contributed by hydrogen to the water molecule must be written H_2. (2) Each water molecule contains only half as many oxygen atoms as an oxygen molecule. Hence the simplest assumption is to write O_2 for the oxygen molecule and H_2O for the water molecule.

This argument does not exclude more complicated formulas. Hence it is an important additional fact that no analysis of a gas has ever been performed that would force us to assume more than 2 atoms in a hydrogen molecule. Therefore, we accept the simplest formulas derived here. Once we accept these molecular formulas, more measurements of the volumes of gases form the basis of similar arguments which lead to the molecular formulas of other gaseous elements and compounds.

Later it will be mentioned that these results regarding the constitution of molecules are well confirmed by three independent groups of observations, dealing respectively with *specific heats* (Sec. 4.2), *spectra* (Sec. 11.2), and *positive rays* (Sec. 6.3). For example, it can be shown that hydrogen, excited by an electric discharge, emits light which, when analyzed in a spectrograph, shows all the properties characteristic of *diatomic* molecules. Therefore there is no doubt that the conventional molecular formulas correctly represent the molecular constitution.

It is evident that Avogadro's argument is by no means a rigorous conclusion from the experimental data. Attention is called to this generally adopted procedure in which a hypothesis is tested by drawing conclusions, which are then compared with observed facts. This first example of the method is unusually complicated by the need for the additional assumptions of molecular formulas. On the other hand, the importance of these formulas and of the elaborate, but not unique, way in which they are derived is evident.

The student who has difficulty in analyzing Avogadro's elaborate argument, which is the basis of all quantitative chemistry, may be comforted by the historical fact that it took the chemists and physicists nearly half a century to adopt the new idea. Up to the middle of the nineteenth century HO was widely written as the formula for the water molecule. The fact that Avogadro's rule leads to a consistent system of chemical formulas covering all chemical compounds was finally recognized to be the proof for the new idea.

Avogadro's rule may be stated as follows: The number of molecules contained in 1 cm³ of any gas under standard conditions (0°C and 1 atm pressure) is a universal constant. "Universal" means applicable to any gas, independently of its chemical properties. Historically this was an unusual situation in which the *existence* of an important universal constant had been inferred without any estimate of its *numerical value*. Avogadro could only argue that the individual molecules are so small that we cannot see them and so light that we cannot weigh them. Therefore, their number per cubic centimeter must be very large. It took more than half a century before the first estimates of their sizes and weights were obtained (Sec. 5.2). Accurate measurements of these quantities have been made, more than a century after Avogadro's discovery (Sec. 7.2).

A summary of this discussion will be found at the end of Chap. 2.

PROBLEMS

1.1. *Molecular formula.* (*a*) 2 cm³ *nitric oxide* is analyzed into 1 cm³ nitrogen and 1 cm³ oxygen. What are the simplest molecular formulas for nitrogen and nitric oxide? Take the formula for molecular oxygen for granted. Explain your answer. (*b*) What ratio of volumes do you predict when gaseous nitrogen tetroxide, N_2O_4, is analyzed into nitrogen and oxygen?

1.2. *Ratio of volumes of gases.* What ratio of volumes do you predict when gaseous hydrogen peroxide, H_2O_2, is analyzed into H_2 and O_2?

CHAPTER 2

SOME RESULTS AND DEFINITIONS
OF CHEMISTRY

2.1. Valence. In chemistry it has been found that sodium (Na) and related elements may form compounds with oxygen (oxides) of the molecular constitution Na_2O, indicating that 1 oxygen atom has the power of binding 2 sodium atoms. However, calcium (Ca) and related elements form oxides described by CaO. Such power of atoms is generally described as their "valence." Oxygen is called "bivalent" and sodium "univalent." A crude picture of the valence of oxygen, just sufficient for the beginner physicist, is given by two little hooks with which each oxygen atom is endowed while each sodium atom carries only one hook. Thus a "saturated" molecule is formed when each of the two hooks of 1 oxygen atom is interlinked with the one hook of a sodium atom. Correspondingly, calcium would be called "bivalent" because it forms the compound CaO. Chlorine (Cl) and related compounds are univalent because with sodium they form compounds of the type NaCl.

For a thorough understanding of chemical compounds this picture of the valence is too primitive because it fails to give an explanation of the fact that some elements manifest different values of valence in different compounds. Later, in our discussion of the periodic table of elements, we shall refine our picture of the valence.

2.2. Atomic and Molecular Weights. Avogadro's rule allows us to measure the ratio of the weight of various kinds of molecules as follows. Suppose we weigh two gases, say first H_2 and next O_2, in the same glass bulb and under the same conditions of temperature and pressure. Since, according to Avogadro's rule, in both cases the bulb contains the same number of molecules, the weights of the gases are proportional to the weights of the individual molecules, or

$$\frac{\text{Weight of oxygen in bulb}}{\text{Weight of hydrogen in bulb}} = \frac{\text{weight of } O_2 \text{ molecule}}{\text{weight of } H_2 \text{ molecule}}$$

The ratio of these weights is measured as 15.87. By this simple method the *relative weights* of all gaseous molecules are determined.

It is convenient to express such ratios on the basis of an arbitrarily selected unit. Historically, two different units have been used. It is obvious that the mass ratio of a hydrogen atom H and a hydrogen molecule H_2 is $1:2$. Since the hydrogen atom is the lightest of all atoms, it may be adopted as the arbitrary unit. In this system H_2 would have the molecular weight 2.000 and O_2 a little less than 32. Instead, at present a slightly different system is universally adopted; it is based on $\frac{1}{16}$ of an oxygen atom as the arbitrary unit. (We shall use the letter M to indicate any molecular weight on this basis.) This gives the oxygen molecule the molecular weight of exactly 32.000 and the hydrogen molecule the molecular weight 2.016. The relative masses of the atoms, called "atomic weights," are accordingly 1.008 for H and, by definition, 16.000 for O. There are two reasons for the curious choice of $\frac{1}{16}$ of an oxygen atom as a unit. First, it has a practical advantage, as many atomic weights have been determined by the analysis of oxides, *i.e.*, by comparison with oxygen atoms. Second, it leads to the strange result, unexplained through more than a century, that many, but not all, atomic weights are whole numbers. This important observation will be discussed in the chapter on isotopes (Sec. 16.2).

The term "atomic weight" makes us believe that we should express this quantity somehow with the help of the familiar unit, the gram. In this respect, however, the universally adopted term "atomic weight" is misleading. This quantity is defined as the *ratio of two masses* (or of two weights). Therefore, it makes no difference in what units the individual weights are measured. The conventional expression for this situation is "the molecular weight has no dimension." (Another familiar example of a quantity that has no dimension is the specific gravity of a substance, defined as the ratio of its density to that of water.)

The atomic weights of all elements are listed in Appendix 4.

2.3. A New Unit of Mass. In chemistry it is convenient to define a new unit of mass replacing the gram. One "gram molecule" or "mole" is defined as the mass of that number of grams to which the molecular weight is numerically equal, that is, M grams. It is evident that the number of grams contained in 1 mole is individually adapted to each substance. An example is 1 mole $O_2 = 32.000$ g O_2. For the application of the new unit mole, the following relation is important. For oxygen, O_2, the same mass is described as

$$96 \text{ g} = 3 \text{ moles}$$

or, in general,

$$\text{Mass (grams)} = \text{mass (moles)} \times M \tag{2.1}$$

where mass (grams) and mass (moles) mean the numbers expressing the same mass in the units gram and mole respectively.

Correspondingly, when dealing with *atomic* weights we define 1 "gram atom" as the mass of as many grams as given by the atomic weight. This definition leads to the analogous relation:

$$\text{Mass (grams)} = \text{mass (gram atoms)} \times \text{atomic weight} \qquad (2.2)$$

The usefulness of the new unit "mole" will be evident when we express the number N of molecules contained in 1 mole, *i.e.*, in M grams.   A certain kind of gas has individual molecules of mass m measured in grams. For this gas let us express the total mass of 1 mole in two ways, first (because of the definition of the mole) as M grams, next as the total mass of all individual molecules, that is, Nm grams.   Since we are dealing with the same mass,

$$M = Nm \qquad \text{or} \qquad N = \frac{M}{m}$$

Next, comparing any two gases, indicated by the subscripts 1 and 2 respectively, we write the same equation for each:

$$N_1 = \frac{M_1}{m_1} \qquad \text{and} \qquad N_2 = \frac{M_2}{m_2}$$

Since the molecular weight M is defined as proportional to the mass m of one molecule, it follows that $M_1/m_1 = M_2/m_2$, hence $N_1 = N_2$.   This result means that the number of molecules contained in 1 mole is the same for any substance.   Now we may omit the distinguishing subscripts 1 and 2 and write this universal constant N_0.   It is called "Avogadro's number."   In the important equation

$$M = N_0 m \qquad (2.3)$$

only M and m are specific for the substance.   This new statement that the *number of molecules N_0 contained in one mole is a universal constant* (as well as the old version, Sec. 1.3) is based on Gay-Lussac's observations, which here serve for the measurement of molecular weights and hence for the definition of the unit mole.   This statement is simpler than Avogadro's rule given above, in which we refer the number of molecules to a unit *volume* because there we have to stipulate standard conditions. Here we refer the number to a unit *mass* (1 mole).   It is obvious that the number so defined is independent of the conditions because a certain mass of a gas does not lose any of its molecules when we cool or compress or liquefy or freeze it.   At the present stage of our argument the numerical value of Avogadro's number N_0 remains unknown (Sec. 7.2).

The usefulness of the mole as our new unit of mass is illustrated by an example.   Suppose a chemist wants to mix hydrogen and oxygen in such a proportion that, when water is formed, each oxygen atom finds the necessary 2 hydrogen atoms as partners.   From the molecular formulas and atomic weights he computes that he must mix 4.032 g H_2 and

32.000 g O_2 in order to produce 36.032 g H_2O. The same result is more easily stated as 2 moles H_2 and 1 mole O_2 form 2 moles H_2O.

The frequent use of the quantities M, N_0, and m makes it worthwhile to consider their *dimensions* and *units*. We imagine that, using any quantity of any gas, we measure Avogadro's number N_0 by counting the absolute number of molecules present and dividing it into the mass measured in moles. Hence the dimension of N_0 is 1/mass and its unit 1/mole. The mass m of 1 atom is simply measured in grams. Hence the molecular weight $M = N_0 m$ has the dimension mass/mass (called "no dimension"), as mentioned in Sec. 2.2. The last equation shows that the unit of the molecular weight M may be called g/mole. This unit amounts to the same as the unit adopted in Sec. 2.2.

The reader can easily prove that the number of atoms in 1 gram atom is the same as the number of molecules in 1 mole, *i.e.*, Avogadro's number N_0.

Occasionally we shall use a closely related concept, the "gram equivalent." The formula H_2O of the water molecule makes it evident that 1 oxygen atom has the same valence or is "equivalent" to 2 hydrogen atoms. Hence we may say that 2 gram atoms of hydrogen represent the equivalent weight of 1 gram atom of oxygen. The "gram equivalent" is defined as the mass of any element equivalent to 1 gram atom of hydrogen. Thus the same mass is described as

10 gram equivalents of oxygen = 5 gram atoms of oxygen

or, in general,

Mass (gram equivalents) = mass (gram atoms) × valence   (2.4)

Here the ways of the chemist and the physicist separate. The chemist studies the various compounds; the physicist, among other problems, studies the behavior of gases, the emission and absorption of light, the effects of electric currents. Through the greater part of a century these two ways seemed to lead into independent realms of science separated so completely that research was carried on in separate laboratories. However, no border line exists at present between chemistry and physics. These two lines of research joined again with the discovery of a theory which describes on a unified basis all properties of atoms, in particular their spectra and their chemical behavior. This theory, which requires advanced mathematics, will be discussed only very briefly in Chap. 22.

SUMMARY OF CHAPTERS 1 AND 2

Quantitative chemical analysis *by weight* leads to two fundamental laws of chemistry: the law of constant proportions and the law of multiple proportions. These laws, summarizing the results of experiments, are understood on the basis of the hypothesis that matter consists of atoms and molecules.

Quantitative analysis *of gases by volume* leads to the law of Gay-Lussac and its interpretation by Avogadro's hypothesis. Molecular formulas are based on this result. Although they cannot be rigorously derived, a consistent system of such formulas (H_2, Cl_2, O_2, H_2O) has been worked out.

The valence of an atom describes its ability to bind one or several other atoms of certain kinds.

The atomic and molecular weights give the weights (or masses) of atoms and molecules in terms of an arbitrary unit, $\frac{1}{16}$ of the weight (or mass) of an oxygen atom.

A new unit of mass is introduced, which simplifies many laws and computations. One gram atom is the number of grams given by the atomic weight, and 1 gram molecule or mole is the number of grams given by the molecular weight.

One gram equivalent is the mass of any element equivalent to 1 gram atom of H. The number N_0 of molecules contained in 1 mole is a universal constant, called "Avogadro's number."

PROBLEMS

2.1. *Molecular weights.* Calculate the molecular weights of helium and chlorine from the following data, all taken under standard conditions: Density of helium = 1.785×10^{-4} g/cm³; density of chlorine = 3.16×10^{-3} g/cm³; density of oxygen = 1.429×10^{-3} g/cm³.

2.2. *Formula of rock salt.* Rock salt is analyzed by weight into 39.3 per cent sodium and 60.7 per cent chlorine. What is its chemical formula? Use Appendix 4.

2.3. *Formula of ethylene.* Ethylene (density under standard conditions = 1.250×10^{-3} g/cm³) is analyzed by weight into 85.62 per cent carbon and 14.38 per cent hydrogen. What is its chemical formula? Given: density of O_2 under standard conditions = 1.429×10^{-3} g/cm³. Use appendix 4.

2.4. *Composition of compounds.* How many grams of nitrogen, N_2, and how many grams of oxygen, O_2, are consumed to produce (*a*) 100 g NO, (*b*) 100 g NO_2, (*c*) 100 g N_2O_3? Use Appendix 4.

PART II
GASES

We are interested in the study of gases for various reasons. Historically, their properties represent the first major field beyond chemistry in which the atomic theory, based on the work of Joule, Clausius, and Maxwell, succeeded in interpreting a vast group of observed facts. The theory culminated in the first determination of the masses and sizes of molecules. This development began about half a century after Dalton's application of the atomic hypothesis to the fundamental laws of chemistry. In many chemical investigations of gases, results of the kinetic theory are applied. Furthermore, the study of gases is important for spectroscopic investigations, since only in gases are the individual atoms effectively separated from their neighbors and their individual properties exhibited by sharply defined spectral lines. The properties of gases must be known for the study of electric discharges through gases. Such discharges, which exhibit cathode rays and positive rays, yield important results on the nature of electricity and matter. In astrophysics, the kinetic theory of gases enters into the consideration of stellar atmospheres. Finally, the flow of electricity through metals and from glowing metals is understood by the comparison of the electricity contained in the metal with a gas.

CHAPTER 3

EXPLANATION OF PRESSURE
AND TEMPERATURE

3.1. Experiments. The first aim of the theory of gases is the interpretation of the ideal-gas law. This law itself represents an empirical equation and, therefore, is independent of any theory. To begin with, we describe the set of experiments leading to that law. The experimenter has methods for measuring the pressure of a gas, its volume, its mass, and its temperature. The pressure p is measured with a mercury manometer (barometer). From the height h of the mercury column the *pressure p* (in dynes/cm²) is computed as $p = $ height $\times$ weight per unit volume of mercury. From the volume and mass of the gas we compute its *specific volume v* = volume/mass, measured in cm³/g; v is the reciprocal of the more familiar *density*. The *temperature t*, finally, is defined as the quantity measured by the mercury thermometer, calling its readings for water at the ice point 0 and at the boiling point 100 degrees centigrade (written 100°C). These experiments lead to the result that at a constant temperature the pressure is inversely proportional to the specific volume (Boyle's law); furthermore that the product pv is a linear function of the temperature (Charles' law). In an equation, this experimental result is stated as

$$pv = r(t + 273)$$

where r is a constant of proportionality specific for the gas under investigation. The same addend 273 shows up in the corresponding equations for all gases. Therefore, it is convenient to introduce a new letter $T = t + 273$. This we call the absolute temperature, measured in degrees Kelvin (written °K).

In the next group of experiments, we compare the values of r (the specific gas constants) for various gases and find that r is inversely proportional to their molecular weights M. This is written as an equation $r = R/M$, where R is a constant of proportionality correlating the various gases. Hence R is not *specific* for one gas but is a *universal* constant called the "universal gas constant." Now we write the ideal-gas law as

$$pv = \frac{R}{M} T \tag{3.1}$$

or

$$\frac{p \times \text{volume} \times M}{\text{mass (g)}} = RT$$

Since, according to Eq. (2.1), mass (g)$/M$ = mass (moles), the ideal-gas law may be written

$$\frac{p \text{ volume}}{\text{mass (moles)}} = RT$$

or, introducing the letter V for the "molar volume" (= volume/mass in the unit cm³/mole),

$$pV = RT \qquad (3.2)$$

The numerical value of the universal gas constant R may be computed by introducing into this equation any set of values of p, V, and T measured for any gas (avoiding excessively high densities). All quantities must be measured in the same system of units; we choose the cm, g, sec system (see Appendix 1). For example, air (average molecular weight $M = 29.0$) at 0°C and a pressure of 1 atm = 1.013×10^6 dynes/cm² has a specific volume 770 cm³/g = 2.23×10^4 cm³/mole. This leads to

$$R = 8.31 \times 10^7 \text{ ergs/(mole degree)}$$
$$= 1.987 \text{ cal/(mole degree)}$$
$$= 0.0820 \text{ liter atm/(mole degree)}$$

The unit follows from Eq. (3.2), since the product $p \times$ volume has the dimension of force $\times$ distance or energy.

Equation (3.2) shows that the volume per mole of any gas, $V = RT/p$, depends only on p and T, not on the nature of the gas, because the molecular weight M, which characterizes an individual gas, does not enter into this expression for V. A figure familiar to every chemist is the volume occupied by 1 mole of any gas under standard conditions. This figure is easily computed by introducing $T = 273°$K and $p = 1$ atm = 1.013×10^6 dynes/cm² into Eq. (3.2). The result is 22.4 liters. This is called the "molar" volume or "gram-molecular" volume of gases.

We must examine the validity of the ideal-gas law more closely. Our definition of the temperature is limited to the range of the mercury thermometer and, therefore, fails below −39 and above about 550°C. Outside these limits, the statement $pv = RT/M$ cannot be based on measurements, because we have not defined what we mean there by the word "temperature." All we can do is arbitrarily apply the same statement; in other words, use the same equation as the *definition* of the temperature.

3.2. Kinetic Theory of Gases. It is an obvious picture that in the solid body each atom is bound to a certain position about which it vibrates. When heating the solid body, we reach the melting point where the motion becomes so violent that the atoms and molecules are free to move but are still in touch with one another. When we heat and finally evaporate the liquid, the atoms and molecules form a vapor or a gas. Since the density of the gas is much smaller than that of the liquid, we must assume that in the gas the molecules do not touch each other but are separated by distances large as compared with their own diameters. Now their heat motion enables them to shoot in straight lines until they collide with one another or the walls of the container. We assume that these are elastic collisions. Furthermore, we assume that there are no mutual forces acting between the molecules except for the repulsion acting while the molecules are in actual collision. Hence between collisions each molecule will travel in a straight line (neglecting the parabolic curvature of its path caused by the gravitational force). For the sake of convenience we shall call the smallest particles "molecules," although in some gases they are individual atoms.

For the interpretation of the ideal-gas law we want to understand the pressure of a gas. This, in the kinetic theory, is interpreted as the bombardment of the wall by molecules, a bombardment so rapid that we have no chance of distinguishing the individual molecular impacts but notice only their over-all effect as the pressure. The molecules are assumed to bounce back elastically.

The result of a simple computation, which is given in many introductory textbooks of physics, is as follows: When N particles per second of mass m and velocity u are incident perpendicularly on a wall and bounce back, the force

$$F = 2mNu \qquad (3.3)$$

is exerted on the wall. This formula when applied to molecules of a gas leads to the final, simple result of the theory:

$$pv = \frac{u^2}{3} \qquad (3.4)$$

In order to check the validity of our *theory*, we compare its result, *i.e.*, the last equation, with the result of the *experiments*, *i.e.*, the ideal-gas law $pv = RT/M$. Here we are disappointed because the two equations are not identical. Hence, as far as this argument goes, we have no reason to believe that the basic idea of our theory is correct. Our next endeavor will be to make, on the basis of the theory, predictions that may be checked by experiments. This is the subject of the next chapter. For the time being, all conclusions from our theory are tentative, subject to the condition, "if our theory is correct." If the theory is correct, we can equate the left sides of the ideal-gas law and the theoretical Eq. (3.4). Thus we conclude that

$$\frac{u^2}{3} = \frac{R}{M} T \qquad (3.5)$$

This result gives us a chance of computing the numerical values of the speed of molecules. The result, *e.g.*, for oxygen at 0°C, is

$$u = 460 \text{ m/sec}$$

a surprisingly large value, larger than the speed of sound in air.

On this basis we easily express the kinetic energy of each molecule (mass m) as

$$W_k = \frac{1}{2} mu^2 = \frac{3}{2} m \frac{R}{M} T$$

or, remembering $M = Nm$ [Eq. (2.3)],

$$W_k = \frac{3}{2} \frac{R}{N_0} T \tag{3.6}$$

Since R and N_0 are both universal constants, we conclude that, if our theory is correct, at the same temperature all molecules have the same kinetic energy although their masses and speeds may differ widely. (The quotient R/N_0, meaning the gas constant computed not per mole but per molecule, is called the "Boltzmann constant k.") For example, the kinetic energy of any atom or molecule at 0°C is 56.6×10^{-15} erg.

The last equation gives us an understanding of the physical significance of the temperature. The absolute temperature is proportional to the kinetic energy of the rectilinear motion of the molecules. Originally we introduced the absolute temperature, $T = t + 273$, only for the mathematical simplification of the ideal-gas law [Eq. (3.1)]. Here we find that on the absolute scale (or "Kelvin scale") the zero has a physical significance; it means the ultimate disappearance of molecular motion.

3.3. Maxwellian Velocity Distribution. Here we shall give a brief report on an important further development, omitting the advanced mathematical treatment. In the theory of the ideal-gas law we simplified the treatment by the assumption that all molecules have the same velocity. This obviously does not agree with the properties of the real gas. When 2 molecules (or billiard balls), both with the same velocity, collide, they will have different velocities after the collision, except in some special cases. Therefore, in the real gas, collisions among the molecules should have the effect of bringing about a distribution of velocities, presumably without sharp limits at low or high velocities. Maxwell (1860) derived the law expressing this distribution of velocities. Suppose that we were able to explore a very large number N of molecules by measuring the velocities u of the individual molecules picked out at random. Their directions do not show any preference; therefore, we pay attention only to the absolute values of their velocities. We divide the whole range of speed arbitrarily into very small steps Δu. For each of these steps we may imagine that we count the number of molecules ΔN having this particular speed. $\Delta N/N$ is the fraction of molecules belonging to each step. We may call $\Delta N/N$ the probability of finding a molecule having the speed associated with a certain small step.

Although there is no such technique by which we may explore the speeds of individual molecules in the manner here described, Maxwell succeeded in deriving the mathematical law for this probability as a function of the velocity. We refrain from reporting the complicated formula and instead describe the law by the family of curves given in Fig. 3.1. In our approximation (Sec. 3.2) we found that the one and only molecular

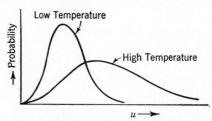

FIG. 3.1. Maxwellian velocity distribution.

speed u introduced into the theory is completely defined by the temperature and the molecular weight, $u = \sqrt{3RT/M} = 1.73\sqrt{RT/M}$ [Eq. (3.5)], irrespective of the pressure. Correspondingly Maxwell found that the temperature and the molecular weight completely define the velocity distribution. The arithmetical average speed is derived from the distribution law as $\bar{u} = \sqrt{8RT/\pi M} = 1.59\sqrt{RT/M}$, a result not very different from the one speed we postulated in our approximation.

We are sure, to start with, that the approximation would not contain, *e.g.*, the factor T, whereas the correct formula would have $\sqrt{T}$. This would make the dimensions of the approximate formula wrong and could only be the result of a blunder, not an approximation. But even the numerical factor of our approximation is nearly correct.

Figure 3.1 gives the curves for two different temperatures. For the further illustration of the distribution law, Table 3.1 gives the percentage of oxygen molecules at 0°C to be found in the various ranges of velocity.

Table 3.1. *Velocity Distribution of Oxygen Molecules at 0°C*

Velocity Range, m/sec	Per Cent of the Molecules
0–100	1.3
100–200	8.1
200–300	16.7
300–400	21.5
400–500	20.3
500–600	15.2
600–700	9.2
Above 700	7.7

Later, in the theory of electrons in metals, we shall be concerned with the fact that Maxwell's distribution curve has no sharp upper limit.

Hence for any given high speed there is always a certain probability of finding some molecules, although this probability is very small for speeds far exceeding the average. This probability increases rapidly with increasing temperature.

SUMMARY OF CHAPTER 3

The ideal-gas law, $pv = RT/M$, applies, in a good approximation (except for high densities), to any gas. It follows that the volume per mole of any gas under standard conditions is $V = RT/p = 22.4$ liters. In the kinetic theory, the pressure exerted by a gas on a wall is represented by the rapid bombardment of the wall with molecules, which leads to the theoretical result $pv = u^2/3$. The comparison of the two similar equations furnishes the formulas for the speed $u = \sqrt{3RT/M}$ and the kinetic energy $W_k = 3RT/(2N_0)$ of the molecules. The last equation shows that the temperature of a gas measures the kinetic energy of the molecules. Maxwell's velocity distribution is given as a family of curves representing the probability distribution of all possible velocities among the molecules of a gas.

PROBLEMS

3.1. *Ideal-gas law.* A bulb of 5.00-cm radius contains 0.400 g of nitrogen at 20°C. Compute the pressure (in atm).

3.2. *Composition of air.* Under standard conditions the density of oxygen is 1.4290×10^{-3}, that of nitrogen 1.2507×10^{-3}, and that of air 1.2928×10^{-3} g/cm³. Compute the percentages, by volume, of oxygen and nitrogen present in air, assuming that air contains no other gas.

3.3. *Mass of air.* (a) Compute the total mass of air contained in a lecture room, 5 m high, 12 m wide, and 15 m long at a pressure of 1 atm and a temperature of 20°C. (For density of air see preceding problem.) (b) Air contains argon (atomic weight 39.9), one of the "rare gases," in a concentration of 0.94 per cent of volume. Compute the total mass of argon present in the same room.

3.4. *Force exerted by bombardment, elastic collisions.* Construct a demonstration apparatus in which a rapid bombardment by steel balls produces a force on the pan of a balance. Under the assumption of elastic reflection, from what height h must $n(= 10)$ steel balls be dropped per second to produce the same force F as a 2.5-g weight resting on the pan if each ball hits the pan only once? Take the mass of each steel ball $m = 0.4$ g and neglect friction due to air.

3.5. *Force exerted by bombardment, inelastic collisions.* A sandbag is bombarded by a machine gun shooting horizontally; $m =$ mass of each bullet; $n =$ number of bullets per second; $(c) =$ velocity of bullets. Compute the force F exerted on the sandbag.

3.6. *Unit of universal gas constant.* Check the units of the universal gas constant R as stated in the text.

3.7. *Value of universal gas constant.* Calculate the value of the universal gas constant from the following data: Under standard conditions (see Sec. 3.1) the density of helium is 1.785×10^{-4} g/cm³. Helium is a monatomic gas of atomic weight $M = 4.00$.

3.8. *Speed and energy of molecules.* Calculate the speed and the kinetic energy W_k of helium atoms, He, and nitrogen molecules, N_2, (a) at 0°C; (b) at 100°C. Use Appendix 4.

3.9. *Isothermal atmosphere (calculus problem).* On the basis of the ideal-gas law compute the pressure p in the atmosphere as a function of the height h above sea level, assuming constant temperature T. The earth is considered to be flat. Assuming a temperature of 0°C and a molecular weight $m = 29$, compute the height h in meters at which the pressure p has one-half the value of the pressure p_0 at sea level.

HINT: *a.* Consider a horizontal slice of the atmosphere (area A, thickness Δh, density ρ) so thin that the pressures at the lower and upper surfaces differ only slightly; the difference is called Δp. The differential equation must express the fact that the weight of the air contained in the slice equals the difference of the forces (= pressures $\times$ area) exerted by the air on the lower and upper surfaces of the slice.

b. With the help of the ideal-gas law express the density ρ and introduce this expression into the last equation. The equation so obtained will express the pressure difference Δp as a function of the increment Δh of the height. The sign must express the fact that the pressure is *decreasing* with *increasing* height.

c. Rearrange the equation so that p appears only on the left and h only on the right side.

d. Integrate the equation, not omitting the constant of integration C.

e. The significance of C becomes evident when you write the equation for the special case of sea level ($h = 0$), where p is called p_0.

f. Write the pressure p as a function of the height h in the form of an exponential function.

3.10. *Density of upper atmosphere at nonuniform temperature (calculus problem).* In the real atmosphere the temperature is far from uniform. Above 100 km the temperature T may be represented by a linear dependence on the height h (defining $h = 0$ at 100 km): $T = a + bh$ where a and b are defined by the following data: T at 100 km $= 0$°C; T at 400 km $= 2000$°C. (a) Derive the equation representing the pressure p in terms of the height h. (b) Calculate p (in mm mercury) and the density ρ (in g/cm³) at 400 km, assuming $p_0 = 10^{-3}$ mm mercury at 100 km ($h = 0$) and an average molecular weight $m = 20.0$.

HINT: Starting from the same idea as in the preceding problem, assume that T is not a constant but $T = a + bh$.

CHAPTER 4

EXPERIMENTAL TESTS OF THE KINETIC THEORY

In the preceding chapter we failed to derive a theoretical equation for the pressure of a gas agreeing with the ideal-gas law which represents the experiments. There is no contradiction between theory and experiment, but the theory fails to introduce the concept of the temperature and, instead, predicts molecular speeds. Our next concern is to test the kinetic theory by experiments. This is the purpose of the present chapter discussing the direct measurement of these speeds, specific heats of gases, and Brownian motion.

4.1. Measurement of Molecular Speeds. Molecular speeds were first measured by Stern (1920) about sixty years after the theoretical predic-

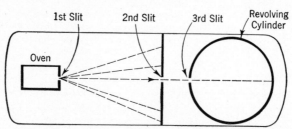

Fig. 4.1. Stern's measurement of molecular velocities, using a drum revolving at high speed.

tion of these speeds outlined in the preceding chapter. This large time interval indicates the great technical difficulty of the experiment.

For this measurement Stern developed the "atomic beam" method (Fig. 4.1), which in recent years has found other important applications in atomic physics. We shall describe the experimental arrangement used later by Zartman. A small capsule containing a little silver is placed in a highly evacuated chamber and heated by an electric oven to such a high temperature that the silver evaporates. The vapor atoms shoot out of a narrow slit (first slit) into the high vacuum and there continue their straight paths. Most of the silver atoms are deposited on the walls of the container. Some atoms, however, shoot through a second slit, mounted parallel to the first slit, in the middle of the chamber, and continue their paths as a narrow beam. They, in turn, are incident on the outside wall

of a metal cylinder with the axis parallel to the slits, which can be rotated
at high speed about its axis.   Into the wall of this cylinder a third slit is
cut parallel to the axis.   Suppose the cylinder is at rest and adjusted so
that the atomic beam just passes through its slit.   Then, gradually, a
deposit of silver is formed at the rear inside wall of the cylinder, exactly
opposite to the slit.   Next let us assume a rapid revolution of the cylinder.
Then, most of the time, the silver arriving in the beam is deposited on the
outside wall of the cylinder and wasted for our experiment.   We are
interested in the small fraction of the silver atoms that happen to pass
through the third slit in the moments when it just faces the beam.   These
atoms need some time (diameter/speed of atoms) to travel to the opposite
wall of the cylinder.   During this brief time interval the cylinder rotates
by a small angle so that now the deposit is formed not opposite the slit
but in a *position slightly shifted* by the distance s.   The same time
interval just mentioned may be expressed as s/speed of surface.   Hence,

$$\text{Speed of atoms} = \text{speed of surface} \times \frac{\text{diameter}}{s}$$

Stern's results agree within the limit of his accuracy with the theoretical
prediction giving an outstanding confirmation of the kinetic theory of
gases.   Since in Stern's measurement of molecular speeds the difficult
technique was not yet fully developed, only a rather inaccurate determination of the average speed could be made.   Later Zartman refined the
method and measured the distribution, obtaining good agreement with
Maxwell's theoretical prediction.

4.2. Specific Heats of Gases.   The specific heat of any substance is
defined as the quantity of heat required to raise the temperature of a unit
mass of the substance 1°C.   For our purpose it will be useful to choose
the mole as the unit of mass.   Thus we write the definition

$$\text{Specific heat} = \frac{\text{increase of heat energy of 1 mole}}{\text{increase of temperature}} \tag{4.1}$$

It has been found that the specific heats of gases depend upon the
method of measurement.   We may measure them either at constant
pressure or at constant volume.   The different values are experimentally
found as follows.   Suppose the gas is contained in a cylinder closed by a
piston.   We keep its *volume* constant by keeping the piston at a fixed
position, or, instead, we keep its *pressure* constant by placing a certain
weight on the piston but leave it free to move.   Such measurements lead
to the result that the specific heat c_p of a gas at constant pressure is
larger than the value c_v obtained at constant volume.   The difference
was explained as early as 1842 by J. R. Mayer, who assumed that when
heating a gas *at constant volume* we simply impart heat energy to its

molecules. However, when heating a gas *at constant pressure*, while imparting the same energy to its molecules, in addition we perform mechanical work by raising the piston. (This important argument furnished the first determinations of the mechanical equivalent of heat, since here heat energy is partly changed into mechanical work. We are not concerned, however, with this aspect.) Since in our present argument we are interested in the energy content of the molecules, we do not pay attention to the work required to raise the piston and simply consider c_v, the specific heat of the gas at constant volume.

We begin with the results of experiments. In Table 4.1 we list a few representative values of c_v. This table makes it evident why we prefer to

Table 4.1. *Specific Heats of Gases*

Gas	c_v cal/(mole degree)
He	3.02
A	2.95
Hg vapor	2.94
O_2	5.00
N_2	4.98
CO	5.01
HCl	4.90

express the specific heats in terms of 1 mole instead of 1 g; it brings out a simple relation. All gases known to the chemist as monatomic, *i.e.*, as having molecules identical with single atoms (the rare gases, mercury vapor), have specific heats of nearly 3 cal/(mole degree) although they differ widely in their atomic weights. Most gases consisting of diatomic molecules have specific heats near 5 cal/(mole degree). A further fact is that these values of c_v are independent of the temperature and pressure. These are the observed facts we wish to explain.

The kinetic theory suggests the idea that the heat energy required to raise the temperature of the gas is stored in the heated gas as kinetic energy of the individual molecules. This idea leads to a simple theoretical prediction based on the theoretical expression for the kinetic energy of 1 molecule [Eq. (3.6)].

$$W_k \text{ of 1 molecule} = \frac{3}{2}\frac{R}{N_0} T$$

Consequently the total heat energy of 1 mole (or N_0 molecules)

$$W_k \text{ of 1 mole} = N_0 \frac{3}{2}\frac{R}{N_0} T = \frac{3}{2} RT$$

The specific heat c_v is computed as the increase of this energy when we heat the gas from T_1 to T_2, divided by this increase of temperature [Eq. (4.1)]; hence,

$$c_v = \frac{\frac{3}{2}R(T_2 - T_1)}{T_2 - T_1} = \frac{3}{2}R \qquad (4.2)$$

In terms of calculus the definition of the specific heat, corresponding to Eq. (4.1), reads:

$$c_v = \frac{d(W_k \text{ of 1 mole})}{dT}$$

which leads to the same result:

$$c_v = \frac{d(\frac{3}{2}RT)}{dT} = \frac{3}{2}R$$

This is a surprisingly simple result. It correctly states that the specific heats of gases are independent of the pressure and the temperature, as p and T do not enter into the last equation. Beyond that, the last equation gives the numerical value

$$c_v = \frac{3}{2} \times 1.987 = 2.98 \text{ cal/(mole degree)}$$

This theoretically predicted value of c_v agrees within the limits of error with the specific heats measured for the monatomic gases and thus supplies a strong confirmation of the kinetic theory. The equivalence of heat and mechanical energy represents one of the great discoveries of the nineteenth century. Here, for the special case of monatomic gases, the kinetic theory makes a more specific statement by identifying heat energy and kinetic energy of the atoms.

This agreement, however, seems marred by the larger values of c_v which are measured for the diatomic gases and indicate that we must refine our assumptions. The further progress, which requires more advanced mathematics and represents one of the important developments of physics within the first third of the present century, will be only qualitatively reported.

The diatomic gases like O_2 show values of c_v in the neighborhood of 5 cal/(mole degree) whereas the monatomic gases have values of nearly 3. These figures indicate that each diatomic molecule is a larger container of energy. This is explained by the idea that the diatomic molecule is able to *rotate* in addition to the rectilinear motion which was the only mode of motion considered in our above theory. How much energy is required to produce rotation of diatomic molecules? The answer is given by a general theorem, the "equipartition theorem," which states that on the average each "degree of freedom" contains the same amount of *kinetic energy*. Any individual atom or molecule is attributed as many "degrees of freedom" as are independent figures required to describe its position and configuration. This definition attributes to each *atom* (considered to be a point) three degrees of freedom and to each *diatomic molecule* (considered to consist of two points connected at a certain fixed mutual distance) five degrees of freedom, more specifically three describing the position of its center and two additional degrees of freedom describing its direction in space (which is uniquely described by two angles). Thus the equipartition theorem attributes to the diatomic gas a specific heat larger than that of the monatomic gas in the ratio 5:3, *i.e.*, 4.96 cal/(mole degree)—a result in good agreement with the observation.

This, then, is the difference between the two experiments in which the kinetic energy of molecules manifests itself: In the *specific heat* of a gas we consider the *total energy content* of the molecule, including rectilinear motion and rotation; but the *pressure* of a gas is fully explained by the *rectilinear motion* alone of the molecules impinging on a wall, where single atoms and diatomic molecules produce the same effect.

Much more complex is the behavior of the specific heat c_v of hydrogen gas, H_2. Although near room temperature it has the standard value of any diatomic gas [nearly 5 cal/(mole degree)], at much lower temperatures the value decreases toward 3; on the other hand, at high temperatures the value exceeds 5. For the explanation, quantum theory of molecules has to be invoked. Quantum theory points out that the equipartition theorem is only an approximation which is valid for modes of motion completely described by the laws of Newtonian mechanics. As a matter of fact, however, rotation (but not rectilinear motion) is limited by quantum rules which prescribe that a molecule can contain rotational energy only in discrete amounts characteristic of the molecule. As long as such energy quanta are very small compared to the average energy of each degree of freedom, each molecule contains very many quanta of energy and the gas does not noticeably deviate from the behavior predicted by the equipartition theorem. Hydrogen, however, as the lightest molecule (see Sec. 11.2), shows unusually large characteristic energy quanta of rotation. At very low temperatures the average energy is smaller than these quanta, so that the rotation is not excited by thermal collisions. Then the rotation becomes inactive, and c_v of hydrogen gas approaches the value typical for a monatomic gas.

On the other hand, at very high temperatures another aspect of our theoretical picture breaks down. The very intense collisions produce *vibration* of the diatomic molecule along the internuclear axis. This new mode of motion is also limited by quantum rules. Here, however, the quanta are so large that even at room temperature they are practically not excited at all. As a result the vibrational degree of freedom may be disregarded at room temperature but gradually comes into play at increasing temperature. Altogether, quantum theory gives a complete account of the specific heat as a function of the temperature.

Historically, quantum theory is based on a hypothesis which has been introduced for the interpretation of two apparently widely different fields, spectroscopy and specific heats. The same energy quanta which we invoked for the theory of specific heats show up with vastly finer detail in molecular spectra (Sec. 11.2). The gradual development of the theory of specific heats is typical for the history of a theory. When we find that the theory only partly represents the facts, we do not discard it but try to refine it by additional assumptions. The fundamental hypothesis of the quantum theory has had a vast success which we shall later discuss at great length.

4.3. Brownian Motion. The last experiment to be cited in support of our theory has a wider importance in that it demonstrates the perpetual heat motion of the smallest particles in gases as well as in liquids. As early as 1827, just after the introduction of achromatic lenses, the Scottish botanist Brown discovered that small dust particles suspended in water, when viewed through a microscope, show a perpetual, entirely irregular motion. The same type of motion can be seen in a gas when we observe through a microscope a small oil drop slowly falling down. This irregular motion, incidentally, is observed in Millikan's oil-drop experiment (Chap. 7). Only the larger drops are falling uniformly, while the smaller ones appear to perform an irregular dance about the average line of their fall.

Long after the observation made by Brown, this mysterious irregular motion was identified with the heat motion common to all particles. Why is it noticeable only in the smallest drops? Individual *gaseous molecules* have sizes so small and speeds so high that there is not the slightest chance of observing them under the microscope. The *smallest oil drop* just observable under intense illumination through the microscope behaves like a giant molecule. Since it has a mass ever so much larger than that of the ordinary molecule, its random heat motion is so much slower that it is clearly discernible. On the other hand, the *larger oil drops*, more easily observed under the microscope, have such low speeds of heat motion that this motion is not noticeable. It is a fortunate coincidence that there exists a range where the drops are large enough to be visible and small enough to have an easily observed heat motion. In the Brownian motion of tiny crystal fragments suspended in liquids one can distinguish the violent motion of the smallest fragments and the slower motion of the larger fragments. Odd-shaped fragments show a rotation as well as a linear motion. These motions take place only over the smallest distances observable under the microscope. Hence the rotation is not observed over several revolutions but only over a few degrees followed by another short random rotation.

Brownian motion can be well demonstrated by microscopic projection. This is the most direct and striking demonstration of heat motion.

SUMMARY OF CHAPTER 4

The kinetic theory of gases is confirmed (1) by Stern's direct measurement of molecular speeds; (2) by its application to the specific heats, which in the simplest case of the monatomic gases agree with the theoretical value $c_v = \frac{3}{2}R$; (3) by Brownian motion.

PROBLEMS

4.1. *Measurement of molecular speed.* In his refinement of Stern's method (Fig. 4.1), Zartman used a drum of radius $r = 5.0$ cm revolving at the rate of 241 rps. The shift between the zero position and the average displaced position of the metal deposited was measured as 1.8 cm. To what molecular velocity does this correspond?

4.2. *Effect of gravity on atomic beam.* A narrow beam of silver atoms is ejected from a source at 800°C. The beam starts in the horizontal direction and travels a distance of 1 m. How far below its original level does it arrive as a result of the effect of the gravitational force?

4.3. *Specific heat.* Calculate the heat (in calories) required to heat 100 g N_2 from 0 to 100°C. Answer the same question for He. Use Table 4.1 and Appendix 4. (1 cal = 4.18×10^7 ergs.)

CHAPTER 5

MEAN FREE PATH;
REPORT ON FURTHER DEVELOPMENT

5.1. Mean Free Path. So far we discussed *velocities* of molecules, which allow us to interpret the pressure of a gas and its specific heat. We disregarded *collisions* between molecules. They will be discussed in the present chapter.

Early in the history of the kinetic theory the mean free path was introduced on the basis of the following argument. If we uncork an ammonia bottle in one corner of a room, we might expect the ammonia smell to be noticeable instantaneously all over the room, since the theory tells us that the molecules have a speed of several hundred meters per second. As a matter of fact, however, the propagation of the vapor, made evident

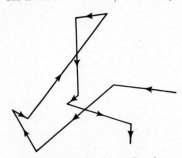

by the smell, takes a time interval of, say, 1 min. This delay was explained by Clausius, who assumed that each molecule, although endowed with high speed, travels only a short distance in a straight line until, by a collision with another molecule, it is deflected. Therefore, its path may look like the crooked line sketched in Fig. 5.1. Mutual collisions retard the propagation across a room. The figure indicates the meaning of the

Fig. 5.1. Path of a molecule.

free path between collisions. As we cannot observe an individual free path of a molecule, all we can do is define its average, called the "mean free path," and correlate it with the various properties of the gas.

Without computation it is evident that the mean free path l decreases when the number of molecules per unit volume or their radius r increases. This relation is quantitatively expressed as follows (see Fig. 5.2). As an approximation we suppose that only one molecule is moving, all other molecules being at rest. This molecule, when moving over an arbitrary distance d, carves out a volume = cross section × distance = $\pi r^2 d$. How many other molecules does it hit on its way? It hits not only those whose centers are in the volume carved out, but in addition those which intrude into the carved-out volume with any small part of their volumes.

34

The centers of all these molecules are located in the volume with twice the radius of a molecule, *i.e.*, the volume $\pi(2r)^2d$. If we call N the number of molecules per cubic centimeter, there are $N\pi(2r)^2d$ molecules. This is the number of collisions suffered by the molecule moving through the distance d. Hence the number of collisions in the unit distance is

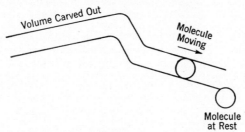

Fig. 5.2. Free path of a molecule.

$4\pi Nr^2d/d = 4\pi Nr^2$, and its reciprocal is the mean distance between consecutive collisions, which is identical with the mean free path l.

$$l = \frac{1}{4\pi Nr^2} \tag{5.1}$$

The equation shows that the mean free path is inversely proportional to the number of molecules per cubic centimeter N, hence inversely proportional to the density of the gas. For a given gas at a certain density the mean free path is a geometrical property, *i.e.*, it does not depend upon the speed of the molecules. We shall give the numerical values of the mean free path after discussing molecular masses and diameters (Sec. 7.2).

The long mean free path prevailing at very low pressure can well be demonstrated by the evaporation in "high vacuum" of an aluminum bead (see Appendix 2). An obstacle placed in the path of the evaporating atoms throws a sharp shadow, which is observed on the aluminum deposit on the glass wall.

5.2. Estimate of Masses and Sizes of Molecules. Since the measurements of the masses and sizes of molecules based on the kinetic theory of gases are superseded by later methods (Chap. 7), we shall only briefly report earlier results. The mean free path l of a gas is related to its viscosity. This quantity, which we shall discuss again in Millikan's oil-drop experiment, is defined as follows. We consider two large parallel plates (area A, distance s) between which there is the gas or liquid to be investigated. When one plate is moving in its plane with respect to the other with the velocity u, the other plate is subjected to a force

$$F = \eta A \frac{u}{s} \tag{5.2}$$

where η is an empirical factor of proportionality, called the "coefficient of viscosity." For air under standard conditions the experiment in which we measure F, A, u, and s leads to the result

$$\eta = 1.82 \times 10^{-4} \text{ cm}^{-1} \text{ g sec}^{-1}$$

Here η is defined by simple measurements apart from any molecular theory.

The interpretation of η on the basis of the kinetic theory of gases leads to a simple relation between the mean free path l and the viscosity η of a gas. This relation allows the calculation of l on the basis of the measurement of η. Here it can only be reported that the earliest evidence on the masses and sizes of molecules was based on the measurement of the viscosity of gases and a few other quantities (Loschmidt, 1865). The results, although far inferior to our present results, give the correct order of magnitude, e.g., the mass 10^{-22} g for an air molecule. This discovery marked a great progress in a period in which it was known only that a molecule is much lighter than any weight that we can determine on a balance. Avogadro's number was derived with the same limited accuracy.

PROBLEM

5.1. *Mean free path.* In the text the mean free path of molecules moving among other molecules *of equal size* is considered. Later we shall consider electrons moving through a gas, or neutrons colliding with uranium nuclei—in general, very small particles moving among irregularly located particles *of much larger size*. For this case express the mean free path l in terms of n and r, as in Sec. 5.1. We shall apply the result in nuclear physics (Prob. 19.2).

PART III

ELECTRONIC STRUCTURE OF ELECTRICITY

After studying the atomic structure of *matter* as manifest in chemistry and later applied in the theory of gases, we turn to experiments that reveal a similar structure of *electricity*. Our first aim is to find the mass and charge of the smallest observed particles. Our argument will follow the historical development. We shall begin with the determination of the ratio of charge to mass of electrically charged atoms in solutions. The same quantity will be measured by different methods for the particles which constitute cathode rays and positive rays. Finally, Millikan's oil-drop experiment will furnish an accurate determination of the charge of individual electrons, which will be identified with cathode-ray particles. The combination of these measurements will give the charges and masses of the various fundamental particles and Avogadro's number.

CHAPTER 6

DETERMINATIONS OF e/m

6.1. Faraday's Law of Electrolysis. We shall discuss electrolytic conduction, *i.e.*, electrical conduction through certain liquid solutions. We shall be interested in this phenomenon only in so far as it leads to evidence for the structure of electricity. We shall discuss only briefly the experimental evidence expressed in Faraday's laws of electrolysis, as we presuppose that the student has studied this subject in an introductory course.

Suppose two platinum electrodes are dipped into a solution of hydrogen chloride, HCl, and are connected with an electric power supply of a few volts. We observe that hydrogen gas bubbles out at the negative electrode, the "cathode," and chlorine gas at the positive electrode, the "anode." Faraday observed that the volumes of the gases so liberated are equal and that they are proportional to the quantity of electricity (= current × time) which has passed through the solution. In another experiment, water is decomposed by an electric current. In this case the same quantity of electricity used for the decomposition of HCl liberates the same volume of hydrogen at the cathode, but only one-half this volume of oxygen at the anode. The two results have in common the fact that the gases liberated at the cathode and anode are equivalent in the sense that when they are recombined, the original substances, HCl and H_2O, are formed without any residue.

Here we are not concerned with secondary reactions occurring at one or the other electrode. In the case of the separation of HCl the chlorine gas fails to bubble out at the anode in the beginning of the experiment, because it is dissolved in water. Only after the water is saturated does the full amount of chlorine gas bubble out. Furthermore, in the decomposition of water we disregard the fact that pure water barely conducts current at all and that we must dissolve, for example, sulfuric acid, H_2SO_4, in the water to make it conducting. The H_2 bubbling out at the cathode results from the dissociation of H_2SO_4, whereas its partner SO_4 migrates to the anode and there liberates oxygen by a secondary reaction.

Hydrogen atoms and all metallic atoms are liberated or deposited at the *negative* electrode. As this indicates that they carry *positive* charges, they are called "electropositive." Correspondingly, chlorine, oxygen, and related atoms that are liberated at the *positive* electrode are called "electronegative."

39

Faraday correlated these observed facts in the general law

$$\frac{\text{Mass liberated}}{\text{Quantity of electricity}} = \frac{1}{F} \times \frac{\text{atomic weight}}{\text{valence}} \tag{6.1}$$

Here the mass is measured in grams, not gram atoms. $1/F$ is a constant of proportionality indicating that *for any substance* the ratio mass/quantity of electricity (called "electrochemical equivalent") is proportional to the atomic weight and inversely proportional to the valence. F represents a new universal constant called the "Faraday constant." The significance of this constant F is evident when we rewrite the equation as follows:

$$F = \frac{\text{quantity of electricity (coulombs)}}{\text{mass (grams)}} \times \frac{\text{atomic weight}}{\text{valence}}$$

Here the units in the parentheses indicate that these are the units applied for the determination of the numerical value of F given below. We simplify this equation by expressing the mass first in terms of gram atoms by Eq. (2.2) and next in terms of gram equivalents by Eq. (2.4).

$$\begin{aligned} F &= \frac{\text{quantity of electricity (coulombs)}}{\text{mass (gram atoms)}} \times \frac{1}{\text{valence}} \\ &= \frac{\text{quantity of electricity (coulombs)}}{\text{mass (gram equivalents)}} \end{aligned} \tag{6.2}$$

This equation shows that the Faraday constant F gives the quantity of electricity (in coulombs) carried by 1 gram atom of a univalent substance. One gram atom of a bivalent substance carries twice this amount, etc. The most accurate determination of this universal constant yields the value $F = 96,520$ coulombs/gram equivalent (see Appendix 3).

So far we have discussed Faraday's law as it was discovered in 1834, although we have used modern terminology. We shall understand this law better when, following Stoney (1874), we ask: How large a quantity of electricity is carried by one individual atom? The answer is based on Avogadro's rule, which states that the number of atoms in 1 gram atom is a universal constant (called N_0):

N_0 atoms of a univalent substance carry the quantity F
1 atom of a univalent substance carries the quantity F/N_0
1 atom of a bivalent substance carries the quantity $2F/N_0$, etc.

The striking result is that *any* univalent charged atom, irrespective of its other chemical properties, carries the same quantity of electricity. This is unexpected because one might guess that different atoms would represent electrical carriers of different capacity. It is still more unexpected that any bivalent charged atom carries exactly twice this amount, etc.

This led Stoney to the conclusion that here is a manifestation of a fundamental property of electricity: Electric charges can be subdivided only into discrete quantities, each of the value F/N_0. These units of electric charge Stoney called "electrons." Hence,

$$\text{Charge of electron} = \frac{F}{N_0} \qquad (6.3)$$

Here the question remains open whether these electrons discovered in electrolysis are positive or negative charges or whether electrons of both signs exist and form compounds with the originally neutral atoms. On the basis of this new concept we can briefly restate Faraday's law: *Each valence of a charged atom carries one electron.* The reader may verify that, starting from this statement, we may derive the previous form of Faraday's law.

As far as this argument goes, the value of the electronic charge is unknown because the value of Avogadro's number N_0 has not yet been determined. Here we refrain from introducing the crude estimate of N_0 based on investigations of gases. Instead we shall use the last equation for the computation of N_0 after discussing Millikan's independent determination of the charge on the electron.

Considering the present emphasis on atomic physics in which all possible properties of matter are interpreted in terms of properties of atoms, it is a strange historical fact that it took as much as forty years to find that in electrolysis the atoms carry electric charges represented by simple multiples of a fundamental charge. This important theoretical conclusion is based only on Faraday's law (1834), Avogadro's rule (1811), and, we may add, the assumption that the total charge observed is equally distributed over the atoms deposited.

Finally we must express Faraday's results in different terms in order to make them comparable with the results of later experiments on gases and vapors. Faraday measured the electrochemical equivalents, mass (g)/quantity of electricity (coulombs), of the various elements. As this ratio is characteristic for any element, it should be the same for any amount of the element, in particular for the smallest amount that exists, *i.e.*, the individual charged atom. Thus we have determined the ratio of mass to charge (in g/coulomb) called m/e of the charged atoms responsible for the conductivity of the solution. In investigations of the various electrical rays, it is conventional to characterize them by the reciprocal ratio e/m, called "specific charge." In electrolysis, for charged hydrogen atoms (written H$^+$), this ratio is computed as

$$\left(\frac{e}{m}\right)_{\mathrm{H^+}} = 9.578 \times 10^4 \text{ coulombs/g}$$
$$= 9.578 \times 10^3 \text{ emu/g}$$

It is evident that this is the largest value of e/m observed in electrolysis because all other atoms have larger masses; their atomic weights cover the range from unity for hydrogen, the lightest atom, to 238 for uranium, the heaviest atom found in nature.

We shall discuss only briefly Arrhenius's theory of electrolytic conduction (1887). Arrhenius assumed that in a solution, although as a whole it is neutral, charged atoms (called "ions," *i.e.*, migrators) like H^+, Cl^-, exist in equal concentration and are pulled by the electric field to the respective electrodes. Are such ions present once and for all in the solution or do we generate them by applying the electric field between the two metal electrodes? It has been observed that, even for the weakest electric fields, the conductivity of the solution has its full value. Hence we must assume that such ions do exist once and for all. Water solutions in particular have high conductivities. Therefore, we must attribute to water a particular power of breaking up neutral molecules like HCl or NaCl into equal numbers of positive and negative ions.

One may ask how the water molecule is able to tear apart the constituents, *e.g.*, tear apart HCl into H^+ and Cl^-. This ability is attributed to the fact that the water molecule, although neutral as a whole, carries positive and negative charges at appreciable distances within its structure. Therefore, it is surrounded by electric fields which attack the charged constituents of the HCl molecule. The final effect is that these constituents H^+ and Cl^- separate and go into more stable configurations by attaching themselves to neutral water molecules H_2O and so forming the ions $(H_3O)^+$, called "hydronium," and $(ClH_2O)^-$. This attachment process is called "hydration."

In the present discussion of electrolysis we limit ourselves to the simplest cases. In textbooks of chemistry more complicated phenomena are discussed which are caused by the occurrence of more complex ions and secondary reactions at the electrodes.

6.2. e/m of Cathode-ray Particles. In electric discharges through gases at low pressure there are observed cathode (or negative) rays and positive rays, both of which are found to be of corpuscular nature. By an experimental technique entirely different from electrolysis, the ratio of charge to mass, e/m, of these corpuscles is determined and compared with the values obtained in electrolysis.

a. Electric and Magnetic Deflection. Figure 6.1 shows an electric discharge tube consisting of two spherical bulbs connected through a narrow neck. The discharge is produced in the right bulb between the anode (the plate connected with the positive terminal of a power supply) and the cathode (the cylinder occupying the neck, connected with the negative terminal). The function of the left spherical bulb will be discussed in the section on positive rays (Sec. 6.3). A power supply provides several thousands or tens of thousands of volts. The gas consists, for example, of hydrogen or mercury vapor at a pressure of a few thousandths of a

millimeter.   A discharge fills the whole right bulb uniformly with dim
light.   Furthermore, there is a straight ray, brighter than the discharge,
emanating from the front surface of the cathode, crossing the bulb, and
producing fluorescence of the opposite glass surface.   This ray is called
a "cathode" ray.   An obstacle placed in its path casts a shadow on the
glass surface and so confirms the fact that the phenomenon is a ray
coming from the cathode.

The nature of this ray is revealed when a magnet is brought near by.
Even the weak magnetic field surrounding a steel magnet causes a deflection of the cathode ray.   When in the apparatus of Fig. 6.1 the north
pole of the magnet is placed near the front of the tube, the cathode ray is
deflected *downward*.   If an electric current in the conventional sense, consisting of *positive* charges, were to emanate from the cathode, it would be

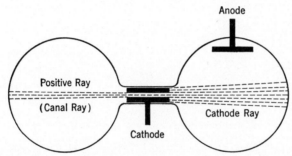

Fig. 6.1. Electric discharge (in right bulb) with cathode ray and positive ray.

deflected *upward*.   We conclude that the cathode ray consists of *negatively* charged particles.   This is confirmed when we let the cathode ray
pass through the space between two parallel metal plates connected to a
battery.   (The potential difference supplied to these plates should be
much smaller than that feeding the discharge; otherwise another independent discharge would be started.)   The electric field between the
metal plates deflects the cathode ray in a direction which indicates that
negative charges are coming from the cathode.

It is apparently absurd that the cathode ray, after leaving the cathode, simply shoots
in a straight line and does not follow the electric field which would pull it toward the
anode.   This anomaly is explained by the fact that the total potential difference
between cathode and anode is by no means uniformly distributed between these metal
plates.   As will be described in Sec. 12.2, a very concentrated potential drop occurs
right in front of the cathode.   If, for example, the total potential difference is 2,000
volts, it may be that 1,900 volts are concentrated within ½ in. in front of the cathode.
Thus the particles emanating from the cathode are strongly accelerated and shoot in
straight lines away from the cathode, hardly affected by the residue of the potential
difference of 100 volts which is too weak to give them a noticeable deflection to the
anode

Simple rules describing the deflection of a current by a magnetic field and the current induced by a field, respectively, are as follows.   Apply the vectors to thumb, forefinger, and middle finger of your *right* hand in the following order: "Current through field causes motion," or "Motion through field causes current."

A quantitative study of the deflections caused by magnetic and electric fields was made by J. J. Thomson.   By way of introduction let us review the forces exerted by such fields on electric charges.   (1) The *electric* field E between plane plates of a condenser (distance s) connected with a battery of electromotive force V is $E = V/s$.   The force exerted by this field E on the charge e is Ee; it is directed parallel to E.   (2) A wire of length l carrying a current I when placed in a magnetic field directed perpendicular to the wire is acted upon by the force $= ilB$, where B = magnetic induction.   The direction of this force is perpendicular to that of the wire and that of the magnetic field.   We want to apply this

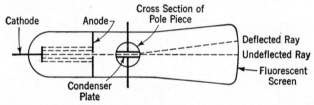

FIG. 6.2. Electric and magnetic deflection of a cathode ray (J. J. Thomson).   The magnet is indicated by the circular cross section of the two pole pieces located in front of and behind the plane of the figure.

fundamental law to the cathode ray, which represents a current although it does not flow through a wire.   We suppose that this special current consists of many charged particles shooting along the ray.   By a computation which is relegated to a problem, we derive the force exerted by the magnetic induction B on the charge e moving with the velocity v perpendicular to B:

$$\text{Force} = evB \qquad (6.4)$$

Again the force is perpendicular to both v and B.

Attention is called to the fact that some laws of electrodynamics contain the velocity of light as a factor of proportionality depending on the system of units applied.   Our equation, force = evB, holds in absolute electromagnetic units.   We shall use this system throughout the book (see Appendix 1).

For his quantitative study of the magnetic and electric deflection of the cathode ray, Thomson (1897) applied uniform fields limited to a well-defined space.   A schematic diagram is given in Fig. 6.2.   The electric discharge through a gas at low pressure takes place in the left part of the tube.   The cathode ray hits the anode, which consists of a metal plate with a small hole at its center which transmits a narrow section of the cathode ray into the right part of the tube.   There the ray is not sub-jected any more to the strong electric field acting between cathode and anode.

This field-free space is better understood when we assume that the whole inside glass surface on the right side of the anode is covered by a conducting layer, say, a gauze screen, connected with the anode; technically this screen is not necessary, since the glass surface is somewhat conducting.   Thus the inside has the same potential as the anode and hence is free of electric fields anywhere except between the condenser plates to be described presently.

Beyond the perforated anode the ray continues its path with uniform velocity in a straight line except in the limited space indicated in the diagram where a vertical *electric* field may be applied between a pair of condenser plates or a *magnetic* field with lines of force normal to the plane of the paper.   (The south pole of the magnet would be in front of the paper, the north pole behind the paper.   In Fig. 6.2 the circle indi-cates the cross section of these pole pieces.)   We presuppose that both these fields are uniform within a limited space and zero outside.   With such an arrangement the cathode ray can be deflected at will upward or downward by either the electric or the magnetic field.   The cathode ray is only dimly visible, but its direction can be well demonstrated by the fluorescence it produces on the opposite glass wall which is made brighter if this glass wall is covered with a fluorescent screen.

J. J. Thomson's experiment consists of two consecutive measurements (subscripts 1 and 2).   For the first measurement the cathode ray is deflected by a certain electric field E_1.   Next, by a magnetic induction B_1 adjusted to the proper value and direction, the cathode ray is brought back into the position it had without any field.   For this adjustment of the two fields the resulting force is zero, hence the forces exerted by the one and the other fields are equal and opposite.   Hence,

$$E_1 e = e v B_1 \qquad\qquad (6.5)$$

As the fields E_1 and B_1 can be measured, we derive the velocity v as the unknown, $v = E_1/B_1$.   The numerical result is a very high velocity of many thousand kilometers per second, the value depending on the condi-tions of the experiment, in particular the potential difference applied between cathode and anode.

For the second measurement only a magnetic induction, B_2, is applied. For this case the theory predicts a circular path of the charged particles within the range of the magnetic field.   Outside this field, of course, the ray travels in a straight line.   The circular path is explained by the fact that the mechanical force exerted by the magnetic field on the moving electric charges is always perpendicular to their instantaneous velocity. Hence the absolute value of the velocity remains unchanged; only its direction is affected.   A mechanical analogue is the path of a motorboat with the motor running uniformly and the rudder straight.   A man sitting in the bow paddles uniformly in the direction perpendicular to the instantaneous velocity.   He does not affect the absolute value of this velocity, but its direction.   Thus the boat runs in a circle.

This is the difference between the two fields applied in these experiments: The *electric* field exerts a mechanical force *fixed in space;* this field when applied alone bends the path of charged particles into a parabola, like the path of a bullet shot horizontally.   On the other hand, the *magnetic* field exerts a mechanical force *turning with the instantaneous velocity;* this field bends the path of the charged particles into a circle.

For the circular path in the magnetic induction B_2 the following condition holds: Centripetal force (or mass $\times$ centripetal acceleration) = force exerted by the magnetic induction; or, when r = radius of curvature and m = mass of particle,

$$\frac{mv^2}{r} = evB_2 \tag{6.6}$$

We apply so weak a magnetic induction that the charged particles are by no means bent into a full circle but only slightly deflected from their originally straight path.   We observe this deflection on the fluorescent screen and, by a simple geometrical consideration, compute the radius of curvature r of their path; the velocity v has been determined by the first experiment.   So here we have one equation with two unknowns, e and m. All we can do is derive one unknown, e/m, called the "specific charge" of the particles.

$$\frac{e}{m} = \frac{v}{rB_2} \tag{6.7}$$

Thomson's important result is that the specific charge of cathode-ray particles is always the same; in particular it does not depend upon the nature of the gas or the metals contained in the apparatus.   The numerical result obtained by the most accurate recent measurements is

$$e/m = 1.75888 \times 10^7 \text{ emu/g}$$

This result reveals the nature of the cathode ray.   The ray does not consist of charged gaseous atoms; otherwise e/m would depend upon the nature of the gas.   We are led to a positive statement when we compare the value of e/m with the largest value obtained for charged atoms in electrolysis, which is the value for hydrogen: 9.578×10^3 emu/g.   We notice that for cathode-ray particles the order of magnitude is much larger, 1,837 times the largest value obtained for charged atoms in electrolysis.   Should we interpret this large value of e/m by a large value of the charge e or a small value of the mass m?   The answer can only be guessed as follows: In electrolysis we found that all charged atoms carry the *same fundamental electric charge* or small multiples of it. Their values of e/m, however, differ because the *masses* differ. We infer that for cathode-ray particles, too, the charge is the same, presumably the fundamental charge. Then the large value of e/m must be attributed to a small mass, of magnitude only $1/1,837$ that of the hydrogen atom. This excessively small value indicates that here we are dealing with particles fundamentally different from the atoms known in chemistry. Thomson concluded that the cathode ray consists of *free electricity* and thus gives evidence of *free electrons*. The process in the electric discharge that causes the emission of free electrons from the cathode will be discussed in the chapter on Fundamental Processes (Sec. 12.2).

In these experiments the free electrons are always observed as *negatively* charged particles, while in electrolysis some atoms carry positive, others negative charges. Recognizing the negative charge as an essential property of free electricity, we come to a new interpretation of charged atoms: Positively charged atoms have *lost* one or several electrons from their neutral structure. Negatively charged atoms have *gained* electrons.

The discovery of free electrons is due to the concentrated effort of several physicists devoted during the same period to the same problem, the nature of the cathode ray. A few months before Thomson's publication and without his knowledge, Wiechert reported experiments from which he concluded that the cathode ray consists of "electric atoms" which have a velocity of 3×10^9 cm/sec and a mass between $\frac{1}{200}$ and $1/4,000$ of the mass of hydrogen atoms and, therefore, are fundamentally different from the familiar "chemical atoms." Thomson stated the bearing of his observation on our concept of matter as follows: "Thus on this view we have in the cathode rays matter in a new state, a state in which the subdivision of matter is carried much further than in the ordinary gaseous state: a state in which all matter—that is, matter derived from different sources such as hydrogen, oxygen, etc.,—is of one and the same kind; this matter being the substance from which all the chemical elements are built up." Thomson's outstanding conclusion is "that *atoms are not indivisible* for negatively electrified particles can be torn from them by the action of electrical forces."

This picture of atoms losing electrons was revolutionary at the time of Thomson's discovery (1897) because it involves the new idea that the electron is an essential part of a neutral atom, a part which in electric discharges or in electrolytic solution may be torn off. The facts of electrolysis are not sufficient to establish this picture because, before Thomson's discovery, it could be assumed that in solution the originally neutral atoms form compounds with positive or negative charges. We need the new concept of free electricity as consisting of *negative* charges in order to conclude that the positively charged atom has *lost an electron*.

Of historical interest is the opposition Thomson's revolutionary view of the nature of matter met. Democritus's original idea of the atom as an indivisible entity had had such overwhelming success in the physics and chemistry of the nineteenth century that the indivisible character of the atom had been raised to the status of a dogma. In a letter Thomson writes, "At first there were very few who believed in the existence of these bodies smaller than atoms. I was even told by a distinguished physicist who had been present at my lecture that he thought I had been pulling their legs."

Is free electricity a special kind of matter? This is only a question of words. Free electricity certainly has in common with atoms the property that each elementary particle has a well-defined mass which, at high velocity, shows the characteristic increase predicted by Einstein's principle. Therefore, we may well recognize electrons as well as positive ions as a kind of matter.

More important is the fact that in our argument we attributed a certain variation of e/m to a variable *mass m*. This implies that we considered the *charge e* as constant. Throughout physics, including nuclear physics, the conservation of electric charge, which here is assumed, is a principle never violated.

FIG. 6.3. Electron emission from a glowing filament (T. A. Edison).

b. Electric Acceleration and Magnetic Deflection. Next we shall describe a related experiment that leads to an alternative determination of e/m of free electrons. In 1883, T. A. Edison, during the development of the incandescent lamp, discovered that glowing filaments of carbon or metal give off electricity. This is demonstrated by an incandescent lamp which carries inside the glass bulb a metal plate, insulated from the glowing filament and supported by a wire which is sealed through the glass (Fig. 6.3). When the plate is made positive with respect to the filament, a current flows through the vacuum and is registered on a sensitive meter. There is no current flow when the plate is made negative.

The nature of this current is explored by the following experiment, which is easily demonstrated* (Fig. 6.4). A straight glowing filament F is mounted along the axis of a small metal cylinder A, insulated from the cylinder. This cylinder and filament are placed in a large glass bulb, which is evacuated except for a very low residual pressure of mercury vapor. When the filament is heated and made negative with respect to the cylinder, a current flows from the filament to the cylinder. A narrow slit along the wall of the cylinder, parallel to its axis, transmits a narrow ray of electric charges coming from the filament, shooting out in a straight direction. As in Thomson's experiment, the space outside the slit is free of electric fields. The low-pressure mercury vapor has only the function of making this electric ray dimly observable. The whole glass bulb is placed between coils of wire so constructed that the electric current through the wire produces a uniform magnetic field perpendicular to the direction of the ray described. When we turn on this field, we observe that the ray is bent in a circular path of which the radius r is easily measured. While in Thomson's experiment, given in Fig. 6.2, the low-

---

* Bainbridge, K. T., *Am. Phys. Teacher*, **6**, 35 (1938).

pressure gas is essential for the production of the ray of electrons by processes to be discussed later, in the present experiment, given in Fig. 6.4, the negatively charged particles are emitted from the glowing filament irrespective of the presence of the gas. Here the gas has only the auxiliary purpose of making visible the path of the otherwise invisible ray of charged particles.

What is the nature of the particles that constitute the ray? They are negatively charged as they are pulled to the positively charged cylinder.

FIG. 6.4. Determination of e/m of electrons emitted from a glowing filament. (*Courtesy of K. T. Bainbridge.*)

Their specific charge e/m is determined by the measurement of the accelerating voltage (between filament and cylinder) and the magnetic field.

To begin with, we compute the velocity of the charged particles (charge e, mass m) coming from the filament and arriving at the plate under the effect of a potential difference V. In order to simplify the computation, we disregard the cylindrical symmetry and rather treat the case of two plane and parallel condenser plates (distance s) one of which emits electrons. (We neglect the inhomogeneity of the field at the edges.) The argument is the same as in the treatment of the free fall in the gravitational field. The electric charges, which are supposed to start from one of the plates with negligible velocity, gain kinetic energy W_k while they lose potential energy, which is computed as force × distance:

$$\text{Force} = Ee = \frac{V}{s} e$$

$$W_k = \frac{1}{2} mv^2 = \text{force} \times s$$

or

$$W_k = \frac{1}{2} mv^2 = Ve \tag{6.8}$$

The last equation, correlating the kinetic energy W_k with a potential difference V, although derived from the case of plane-parallel electrodes, applies as well to any shape of electrodes. This is proved as follows: By definition the potential V is correlated with the electric field E by the equation

$$E \cos \theta = -\frac{dV}{ds}$$

where θ is the angle between the direction of E and the arbitrarily selected path element ds. (A *positive* charge is driven by the field to regions of *lower* potential.) When a charged body (charge q) is driven by the field along the distance Δs, it picks up the kinetic energy

$$\Delta W_k = q \times \text{field component} \times \Delta s = -q \, \Delta V$$

where ΔV is negative. Hence the total energy picked up by the transit from one electrode (potential V_a) to another (potential V_b) is

$$W_k = \int_{V_a}^{V_b} q \, dV = q(V_a - V_b)$$

Next we represent the effect of the magnetic induction B by the same argument as applied to Thomson's experiment:

$$\frac{mv^2}{r} = evB \tag{6.9}$$

The last two equations contain two unknowns, v and e/m. These are expressed in terms of measurable quantities as follows:

$$v = \frac{2V}{Br} \tag{6.10}$$

and

$$\frac{e}{m} = \frac{2V}{B^2 r^2} \tag{6.11}$$

The numerical result is $e/m = 1.759 \times 10^7$ emu/g. Here we recognize the same particles identified earlier by Thomson as *free electrons*.

The reader is familiar with the great technical importance of electron emission from glowing filaments, as applied in radio tubes. This process will be discussed more in detail in Chap. 15; in the present chapter we are interested only in the determination of e/m.

The previous statement that glowing filaments give off only *negatively* charged particles is not completely accurate. Occasionally, there is also observed a weak emission of *positively* charged particles, which are detected, of course, only when the polarity of the glowing filament with respect to the plate is reversed so that no free electrons can go over. By the determination of e/m of these positive particles it has been found that they consist of positive ions, usually of sodium and chemically related metals. This emission of positive ions is limited to filaments carrying impurities. As a rule, after a short period of time the supply is exhausted, and the positive current stops—unlike the current of the opposite polarity, the electron current, which is never exhausted. The emission of positive ions is of minor importance.

Let us compare the two methods for the determination of the specific charge e/m of electrons. Thomson's original method has the advantage of applying to any well-defined ray of charged particles, irrespective of its origin. This method is indispensable for the investigation of alpha rays and beta rays, which we shall discuss in the section on radioactivity. As these rays are emitted from radium atoms, it is not in our power to accelerate them starting from zero velocity. On the other hand, the acceleration of electrons from a filament combined with the magnetic deflection is of great practical importance in numerous laboratory experiments performed with glowing filaments. Furthermore, after discussing the charge on the electron, we shall see that this method provides us with a new unit of energy, the electron volt, which is commonly used in atomic physics (Sec. 7.3).

c. Helical Method; Electron Microscope. Finally, we shall discuss a third method, the helical method (Busch, 1922), for the determination of e/m of the charged particles emitted from a glowing filament. Although this method is related to the preceding one, it is of special interest because it introduces the idea of *focusing a divergent electron beam.*

This process is analogous to focusing a divergent beam of *light*, emitted from any object, by a lens and so producing a real image. The discovery that a diverging *electron* beam may be brought to a focus is the basis of the electron microscope. For the time being, however, we are concerned with the formation of a nonenlarged image.

In high vacuum a glowing cathode gives off electrons (Fig. 6.5a) which are then accelerated by a potential difference of several thousand volts to an anode plate and are incident there at various angles, within a small angular range. A narrow hole at the center of the anode transmits a slim beam of electrons which, beyond the anode, enters into a space free of electric fields. There the beam diverges within a small solid angle which is defined by a diaphragm. Each particle travels along its own straight path, and all of them together produce a blurred fluorescence on the screen. All electrons leave the hole with the same velocity v given to them by the potential difference V between cathode and anode. From Eq. (6.8) we compute this velocity as

$$v = \sqrt{\frac{2eV}{m}} \tag{6.12}$$

Let us consider a particular ray leaving the hole within a small angle α, measured about the axis of the apparatus. We express its velocity components parallel and normal to the axis as

$$v_a = v \cos \alpha \qquad \text{and} \qquad v_n = v \sin \alpha$$

For small angles α, we replace these expressions by the approximations

$$v_a = v \qquad \text{and} \qquad V_n = v\alpha$$

In order to make the originally diverging beam converge at a focus, we apply a uniform magnetic field parallel to the axis of the tube, which is

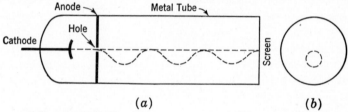

FIG. 6.5. Determination of e/m of electrons, helical method. Focusing of an electron beam. (a) Side view; (b) front view.

easily produced by a long solenoid. We shall treat the effect of the magnetic induction B on the two velocity components separately. B does not affect the *axial* component V_a, because this is parallel to B. The effect on the *radial* velocity component v_n has been computed in the preceding section; the induction B bends the component into a circular path of radius r defined by Eq. (6.6):

$$\frac{mv_n{}^2}{r} = ev_n B \qquad \text{or} \qquad v_n = \frac{eBr}{m}$$

As before, the induction B does not affect the absolute value of v_n, only its direction. The time τ required for one full circle is

$$\tau = \frac{2\pi r}{v_n} = \frac{2\pi}{B} \frac{m}{e}$$

It is important that the time τ is independent of the radius r, since the faster particles travel over proportionally larger circles. [The same fact will be the basis of the construction of the cyclotron (Sec. 18.6).]

The complete path of an electron, which emerges from the hole under a small angle α with the axis, consists of the superposition of the uniform straight motion parallel to the axis and the revolution in a plane perpendicular to the axis. Hence this path is a helix. For two particular electrons the helical paths are sketched in Fig. 6.5b, in which, however, the angles α against the axis are exaggerated. Each helix touches the axis at the hole and later touches it again once for each turn. The lower helix represents an electron that passes through the hole at a smaller angle α and, therefore, performs a narrower helix. An electron that happens to pass exactly in the direction of the axis simply continues along the same straight line. The complete family of helices emerging under various angles (actually small angles) α from the hole form a pattern symmetrical to the axis. Next we want to prove that all helices emerging from the hole come together periodically at the same points of the axis—in other words, that they form an image of the hole. At what distance s from the hole does a helix touch the axis? s is computed from the common axial velocity of each electron $v_a = v$ [given by Eq. (6.12)] by using the time τ of one complete revolution. Hence

$$s = v_a \tau = \sqrt{\frac{2eV}{m}} \times \frac{2\pi}{B}\frac{m}{e} = \frac{2\pi}{B}\sqrt{2V\frac{m}{e}} \qquad (6.13)$$

The fact that the angle α does not enter into this equation proves that for all angles α, i.e., for all helices, the rays come back to the axis at the same distance s from the hole. This mathematical result suggests the following procedure. For a given apparatus, i.e., for a given distance s, B is varied until the well-defined value of B that produces a sharp spot on the fluorescent screen is found. If above this hole we drill a second hole through the anode plate and have it exposed to the slightly diverging electron rays from the same source, hence incident with the same velocity, the screen shows a corresponding bright spot above the first. Altogether the electron rays form on the screen a real image of the various holes. However, the process by which the diverging rays of electrons are made to converge to a focus is entirely different from the process by which lenses form optical images.

The comparison of this effect with the focusing of light by a lens makes the importance of this new device clear. It is true that pictures can be taken without a lens in the pinhole camera. There we rely only on the rectilinear propagation of narrow pencils of light. This compares with the sharp spot of light produced by a sufficiently narrow pencil of cathode rays and is demonstrated by the cathode-ray oscilloscope. But we can build optical instruments of some refinement only when we use a lens to focus on one point a bundle of rays diverging from one point of the object. This is comparable with the apparatus described. Therefore, this application of the magnetic field is called a "magnetic lens."

This apparatus may well serve for the determination of e/m. The magnetic induction B is adjusted until the image on the screen is sharp. Then e/m is computed from Eq. (6.13) and yields a numerical result in good agreement with those of the preceding methods. The outstanding interest of this method lies in the formation of images by the magnetic lens. Although the long solenoid acting as a magnetic lens furnishes only full-size images, a flat coil is not subject to this restriction. Without further computation this is illustrated by Fig. 6.6a, in which the uniform

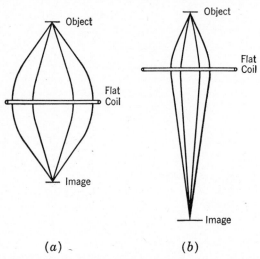

(a) (b)

FIG. 6.6. The flat coil as a magnetic lens focusing electrons. (a) Full-size image; (b) enlarged image. The object, a thin specimen, transmits fast electrons. The diagram does not show that the paths of the electrons are twisted by the magnetic field.

field of a solenoid is replaced by the nonuniform field of a flat coil. When the object is placed closer to the coil, this focuses the rays at a greater distance (Fig. 6.6b). The analogy with the optical lens indicates that here a *magnified* image is produced. (The figure simplifies the path of the electrons since the helical path cannot be fully represented by a plane figure.) In this respect the focusing of electrons by a magnetic lens is not so simple as the focusing of light by a glass lens. In the electron microscope, schematically represented by Fig. 6.7 (Ruedenberg, 1931), a beam of electrons accelerated by, say, 60,000 volts, is made to converge in high vacuum on the object, which must be a specimen of a thickness as small as 10^{-6} or 10^{-5} cm to transmit electrons. The specimen scatters and diffracts the electrons to such an extent that we consider it to be the source of electrons which continue their paths with the same speed. The first "objective lens" forms a magnified image, the second objective lens a still much more magnified image of the specimen. Instead of magnetic lenses electrostatic lenses (Fig. 6.8) may serve for image formation. A great advantage of the electron microscope over the ordinary optical microscope is evident. It is known that the wave nature of light, because of diffraction, sets a limit on the resolving power of the optical microscope.

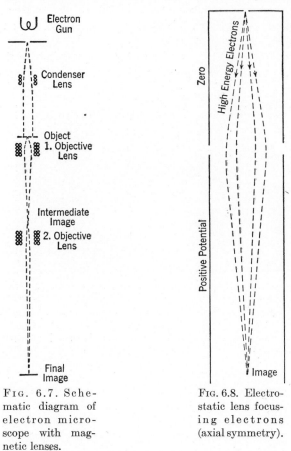

FIG. 6.7. Schematic diagram of electron microscope with magnetic lenses.

FIG. 6.8. Electrostatic lens focusing electrons (axial symmetry).

This limit is about ½ wavelength of light, hence for visible light about 3×10^{-5} cm. Although cathode rays, too, are to a certain extent subject to diffraction, as will be discussed in the chapter on wave mechanics (Chap. 22), this practically does not limit the resolving power of even the best electron microscopes constructed.

The superior resolving power of the electron microscope is evident in Fig. 6.9, which is a picture of zinc oxide smoke particles enlarged 30,000 times. For the sake of comparison we compute the resolving power of the *ideal* optical microscope using, say, yellow light; the picture taken through this instrument, when enlarged to the scale of the figure, would be so badly blurred that no detail finer than 7 mm could be resolved. The wealth of new detail resolved by the electron microscope is striking. Its outstanding drawback is the fact that the specimen under investigation must be placed in high vacuum and, without supporting glass plate, be subjected to a beam of high-energy electrons. There are many objects that cannot stand this treatment although they can be investigated through the optical microscope.

The electron microscope finds important applications in the investigation of the structures of very small bodies. Most important are the

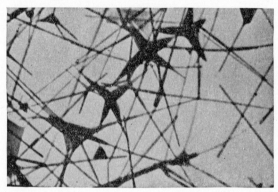

Fig. 6.9. Electron micrograph of zinc oxide smoke particles. Linear magnification 30,000 ×. The figure shows the superior resolving power of the electron microscope. A micrograph taken through the best optical microscope and enlarged to the same scale would be so blurred that no detail finer than 7 mm could be resolved. The figure is a section from an original that covers an area 10 times as large with equally good definition. (*Courtesy of Radio Corporation of America.*)

medical applications where the structures of bacteria have been investigated. The microscopical study of viruses started with the advent of the electron microscope; thus the viruses of influenza and infantile paralysis have been photographed.

d. Field Electron Microscope: Observation of Individual Atoms. A special instrument, the "field electron microscope," has been built for the exploration of metal surfaces. These investigations have led to images, although blurred ones, of single atoms.

The field electron microscope (E. W. Müller, 1937) forms a real image of a metal surface by a strikingly simple process. The sharp point of a metal needle is placed at the center of a highly evacuated glass bulb whose inside is covered by a fluorescent screen. A very thin metal cover makes the surface of the screen conducting. A potential difference of, say, 5,000 volts is applied between the needle and the screen, making the needle negative.   This arrangement produces so strong an electric field at the needle point that it pulls electrons out of the metal surface even though the needle is not heated.   The emission of electrons under the effect of strong electric fields (10^6 volts/cm or more) is called "field emission."

For the computation of the electric field at the surface of the needle point we keep in mind that, under the highest magnification, even the sharpest needle point obtainable appears as a round surface.   Hence let us describe the apparatus as a very small sphere, the needle point, placed at the center of a large sphere, the glass bulb.   The capacitance (in emu) of this "spherical condenser" is $C = r/c^2$ (r = radius of small sphere; c = speed of light); hence the charge on the inner sphere $Q = CV$, where V is the potential difference applied.   The electric field E at the distance r follows from Coulomb's law (using emu):

$$E = c^2 \frac{Q}{r^2}$$

At the surface of the needle, fields as high as 5×10^7 volts/cm, high enough to extract electrons, are reached.   These electrons behave entirely differently from light emitted from a surface.   While light spreads into all directions, these electrons are pulled by the strong electric field, which just extracted them, exactly in the radial direction, so that each spot of the small central sphere aims its electrons at one definite spot of the fluorescent glass bulb, $i.e.$, the spot located on the same radius. Hence the fluorescence of the glass bulb gives a real image of the small central sphere, $i.e.$, the needle point.   Thus if one spot of the needle point is distinguished by copious electron emission, the corresponding spot of the glass bulb will show intense fluorescence.   It is evident that the image formed on the screen shows only the spots of *intense electron emission*.   The magnification of the field electron microscope is simply given by the ratio of the radii.   It may be as high as several hundred thousand.

A striking demonstration performed with the field electron microscope is as follows (Müller, 1951): Traces of barium, which makes electron emission from glowing metals more copious, are gradually deposited on the needle point.   (In this experiment barium metal is slowly evaporated from an auxiliary device contained in the same highly evacuated glass bulb.)   The image on the screen shows that the arrival of barium on the needle promotes electron emission from some selected spots.   With an increasing but still very small amount of barium deposited, these spots adjust themselves on the surface until they form a regular pattern (Fig. 6.10).   It is plausible to assume that the barium atoms deposited on the spherical tungsten surface find their stable positions, which are defined not only by properties of the tungsten surface but also by properties of the barium atoms.   Hence the bright spots are images of single barium atoms.   Müller's discovery is important as representing the only known

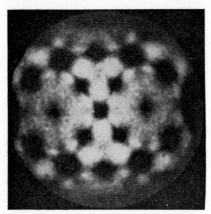

formation of an image of individual atoms.   Furthermore, his method gives a new and powerful tool for the exploration of metal surfaces.

  e. Cathode-ray Oscilloscope.   The cathode-ray oscilloscope (Braun, 1897; Fig. 6.11) represents an important application of an electron beam from a glowing filament, accelerated by a potential difference. A small hole in the anode transmits a narrow beam, which shoots in succession through two small plate condensers, the first pair of plates deflecting the beam up and down in the figure, the second pair, as

FIG. 6.10. Crystal structure of tungsten needle point with a deposit of barium atoms (photographic positive).

indicated in the figure, deflecting the beam backward and forward, *i.e.*, in a direction perpendicular to the plane of the figure.   When a rapidly variable potential is connected with one or the other pair of plates, the ray follows instantaneously and so, by its deflection, indicates the variable potential.   Ordinarily one pair of plates is connected with a "sweep circuit," *i.e.*, a circuit that imposes a deflection proportional to the time,

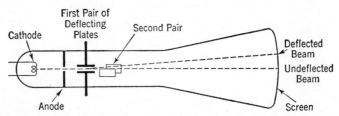

FIG. 6.11. Cathode-ray oscilloscope.   The first pair of plates deflects the beam up or down.   The second pair deflects the beam in the direction normal to the plane of the figure.

say, in the *horizontal* direction.   When the extreme deflection is reached, the ray instantaneously returns to the initial position and repeats the process.   The other pair of plates, say, the pair responsible for the *vertical* deflection, is connected to the variable potential difference to be investigated.   Suppose we want to investigate a periodic, variable potential difference, *e.g.*, that supplied by a generator.   When we periodically repeat the sweep in phase with the potential difference we observe a *steady* curve on the screen representing the potential difference as a function of the time.

The great advantage of this device is its lack of inertia, which makes it applicable to radio frequencies where the mechanical oscillograph built with coils and little mirrors completely fails.   Hence, the cathode-ray oscilloscope is one of the most useful and versatile measuring devices for radio-frequency circuits.   It is an essential part of radar indicators.   It is indispensable for circuit analysis.   In television sets, the scanning in both the pickup device and the viewing tube is carried out by special forms of cathode-ray oscilloscopes.   Furthermore, the oscilloscope is extensively used for recording transient phenomena like sparks, explosions in guns, combustion in gas engines.   In biology, oscilloscopes are used in studies of heartbeats and nerve response.

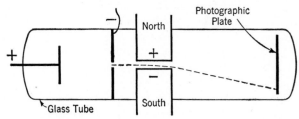

FIG. 6.12. Determination of e/m of positive-ray particles, parabola method.

6.3. e/m of Positive-ray Particles.   As a supplement to the description of the electric discharge (Fig. 6.1) let us consider what happens when an axial canal has been drilled through the cylindrical cathode that fills the narrow neck between the two large spherical bulbs.   While in the right bulb the discharge and the cathode ray are in operation as before, we now observe in the left bulb a new ray, called the "canal ray" because it comes from the axial canal.   If the steel magnet that caused the marked deflection of the *cathode* ray is brought near the left bulb, it fails to affect the *canal* ray, but this is due only to the insufficient field strength.   A stronger magnetic field produced by an electromagnet deflects the ray and, by the sense of the deflection, indicates its nature as a stream of *positively* charged particles.   The corresponding effect is observed for a strong electrostatic field.

J. J. Thomson determined the specific charges e/m of positive-ray particles by the parabola method (Fig. 6.12).   As in the cathode-ray experiment of Fig. 6.2, the positive ray passes through a combination of electric and magnetic fields.   While again both fields are *normal to the ray* (going from left to right), here, in contrast to Fig. 6.2, the two fields are in the same direction (both from top to bottom of the figure).   This is accomplished by the arrangement schematically given by Fig. 6.12, in which the ray passes between the pole pieces of an electromagnet whose faces carry insulated plates to be connected to a d-c power supply.   Let us assume that the ray consists of particles all of the same value of e/m and that the electric field deflects the particles downward.   If all particles had the same velocity, the trace due to the *electric* field alone would be a sharp spot.   Actually the trace is a line pointing *downward*, which indicates that the positive ray consists of particles of a wide velocity range.   The theory predicts the smallest electric deflection for the fastest particles.   In the experiment the ray is simultaneously subjected to a *magnetic* field which, if acting alone, would deflect the particles out of the plane of the paper (in the example of Fig. 6.12 in the direction behind the plane of the diagram) and hence would spread the trace on the plate into a *horizontal line*.   Again, the smallest magnetic deflection belongs to the fastest particles.   Both fields acting together produce simultaneous deflections downward and out of the plane of the diagram.   The theory (see Prob. 6.15) predicts that on the photographic plate whose plane is perpendicular to the velocity of the ions all particles of the same e/m are located on a parabola, the fastest particles hitting closest to the origin (Fig. 6.13).   The equation of the parabola

$$x^2 = y \times \left(\frac{e}{m} \frac{B^2}{E} \frac{l^2}{2} \right)$$

where x = magnetic deflection
$\quad\quad y$ = electric deflection
$\quad\quad l$ = length of path in the fields

allows the computation of the specific charge e/m of the particles, while the intensity distribution along the parabola gives evidence of the velocity distribution of the particles belonging to this value of e/m. Figure 6.13 shows that the intensity along any one parabola shows up only along a limited range, indicating that the positive ray carries particles only within a limited velocity range.   In particular, the parabolas are not continued to their origins since very fast particles are absent.

The numerical results depend upon the gas present in the discharge tube.   Although the velocities spread over a wide continuous range, the values of e/m are sharply defined, as is evident from the good definition of the parabolas.   In hydrogen, for example, the canal ray, or positive ray, splits up into two constituents with the values

$$\frac{e}{m} = 9.58 \times 10^3 \text{ emu/g}$$

and

$$\frac{e}{m} = 4.79 \times 10^3 \text{ emu/g}$$

respectively.

By comparison with the results of electrolysis, we recognize the larger value as belonging to positively charged hydrogen atoms H^+, called "protons." The smaller value indicates a ray of positively charged hydrogen molecules H_2^+. No other positive rays of comparable intensity are observed in hydrogen. We referred to this observation in our discussion of molecular formulas (Sec. 1.3) when stating that the positive-ray analysis confirms the structure of hydrogen as consisting of diatomic molecules. The presence of charged *atoms* in the positive ray, in addition to the diatomic *molecules*, is explained by the effect of the electric discharge which dissociates some hydrogen molecules into atoms. Corresponding values of e/m are obtained by the positive-ray analysis of other gases. In many experiments several types of ion show up by their parabolas. In gases other than hydrogen, ions are observed with two or more positive charges (see the figure).

We shall discuss the origin of the positive ray in the section on electric discharges (Sec. 12.2b). In similar experiments, not described here in detail, it has been observed that certain gases form negative ions like atomic chlorine Cl^-, or atomic oxygen O^-, or molecular oxygen O_2^-. Such negative ions, although less important for the understanding of the electric discharge, have great interest for the theory of the periodic system of elements, as we shall see below (Sec. 13.4).

For the purpose of the present chapter the outstanding result of positive-ray analysis is the fact that it reveals

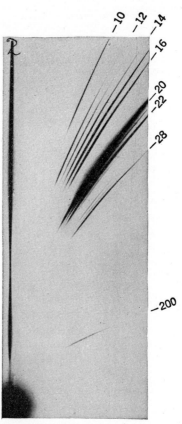

FIG. 6.13. Parabolas. The numbers indicate atomic weights per unit charge (in electronic charges). 10 is Ne doubly charged; 12 is C; 13 is CH; 14 is CH_2 and N; 15 is CH_3; 16 is CH_4 and O; 20 and 22 are Ne; 28 is N_2; 200 is Hg. (*Courtesy of K. T. Bainbridge.*)

the *nature of the positive ray* and so indicates the presence in the electric discharge of charged atoms and molecules which, together with the free electrons, are responsible for carrying the electric current. The two neon parabolas evident in Fig. 6.13 (marked 20 and 22) lead to conclusions of a different kind, which are presented in the discussion of nuclear physics (Chap. 16).

6.4. Equivalence of Mass and Energy. Throughout the study of atomic physics the reader will become accustomed to the historical fact that over and over again an apparently well-established law has turned out to be only an approximation, valid within a limited range. This is true for the constancy of the specific charge e/m of electrons, the numerical value of which was given above with five significant figures. Before long (1901) a certain decrease of this value for *high-velocity* electrons was noticed. For example, electrons accelerated by a potential difference of 80,000 volts are observed to have a velocity of about 1.5×10^{10} cm/sec and a specific charge e/m about one-eighth smaller than the standard value.

Shall we attribute this deviation to a decrease of the charge or an increase of the mass? Such an increase of the mass with the velocity has been predicted by a theory which was not introduced for this purpose but largely for the explanation of Michelson's famous investigation of the velocity of light, *i.e.*, Einstein's theory of relativity. It does not seem advisable here to give a superficial outline of this theory. Instead, we shall first take for granted a certain formula given by Einstein and next explicitly state what we, for the limited purpose of the present book, accept as the fundamental hypothesis.

From his hypothesis of relativity, Einstein derived the statement that the mass m of any body, which at negligible velocity has the "rest mass" m_0, at the velocity v has the larger mass

$$m = \frac{m_0}{\sqrt{1 - v^2/c^2}} \tag{6.14}$$

where c = velocity of light. At the velocities common in daily life this increase of mass with the velocity is far below the limit accessible to observation. However, for an electron that, by a high potential difference, is given a velocity as high as 1.5×10^{10} cm/sec, *i.e.*, one-half of the velocity of light, the change of mass becomes noticeable. In order to estimate this change, we simplify Eq. (6.14) by the binomial theorem, omitting the higher members of the series, and write

$$m = m_0 + \frac{m_0 v^2}{2} \frac{1}{c^2} = m_0 + \frac{W_k}{c^2} \tag{6.15}$$

(Here we identify $m_0 v^2/2$ with the kinetic energy W_k, which again, according to Einstein's theory, is only an approximation.) Applying the last equation to our example, *i.e.*, to electrons with one-half of the velocity of light, we find

$$m = m_0(1 + \tfrac{1}{8})$$

in sufficient agreement with the observed decrease of e/m. Einstein's theory applies to all matter, but only with particles of very small mass is it possible to attain high enough velocities to make the effect measurable.

Einstein's theory has led to the more general result that *any energy*, not only kinetic energy, stored in a body is noticeable as an *increase of its mass*. The quantitative relation is a generalization of Eq. (6.15):

$$\text{Change of mass} = \frac{\text{change of energy}}{c^2} \qquad (6.16)$$

Again we do not reproduce Einstein's derivation of this equation from the hypothesis of relativity.* However, for our limited purpose, we could equally well have chosen the last equation (6.16) to be the fundamental hypothesis. This is in accord with the procedure in theoretical physics in which, at the start of the theory, an equation is established, which serves as the fundamental hypothesis. For example, Newton's equations of motion represent the fundamental hypothesis of mechanics; they are proved to be valid (at least for velocities small as compared with the velocity of light) by their power of correctly predicting the observable facts. Likewise we shall test our fundamental hypothesis, the *equivalence of mass and energy* as stated in the last equation, by comparing conclusions with observed facts. We notice the first success of this hypothesis in that it satisfactorily represents the increase of the mass of cathode-ray particles with the velocity.

In order to estimate the effect of the energy W stored in a body, we rewrite Eq. 6.16:

$$m = m_0 \left(1 + \frac{W}{m_0 c^2} \right)$$

Here $m_0 c^2$ represents the energy that would be made available if the *total* mass of the body were, say, changed into energy of radiation (Sec. 18.5). The energy $m_0 c^2$ is characteristic of the particle and called its "self-energy" (see Prob. 7.20). The equation shows that the energy W stored in a body of mass m_0 has a noticeable effect on the mass only if W is not too small as compared to the self-energy of the body. For the special case of kinetic energy, this is true if the speed of the particle approaches that of light. In modern accelerators ions are given velocities in this range. The most effective of these machines, the synchrotron, even utilizes the effect of relativity for the acceleration of ions (Sec. 18.6*f*). In spectroscopy the accuracy of measurements is so high that a slight relativity effect is observed even for comparatively slow electrons. In nuclear physics, however, we shall deal with energies so large that numerous effects of the energy on the mass are found, most striking the "anni-

---

* A simple derivation, which, however, presupposes the hypothesis of light quanta (Sec. 14.3), is given in Appendix 7.

hilation" of a positron-electron pair whose mass completely changes into energy of radiation (see problems in Chaps. 16, 18, and 19).

An early application of Einstein's principle was tentatively made on the basis of the atomic weights. The atomic weight of hydrogen is nearly 1 and that of helium 4. It was early inferred that the helium atom consists of 4 hydrogen atoms bound together by unknown forces. However, a more accurate determination of the atomic weights (H = 1.008; He = 4.00) revealed that 4 hydrogen atoms have a mass almost 1 per cent larger than 1 helium atom. This was interpreted by the idea that the excess mass produced by taking apart 1 helium into 4 hydrogen atoms is a measure of the energy stored in the 4 hydrogen atoms. Conversely, the combination of 4 hydrogen atoms to form 1 helium atom would liberate this energy. We refrain from giving numerical values, since the quantitative treatment presupposes a more detailed knowledge. However, the preliminary treatment correctly anticipates the vast order of magnitude of the energy so liberated. An example is given by the energy liberated if all the hydrogen contained in a glass of water were combined to form helium; the amount is as large as the energy needed to drive a large steamship across the ocean (Prob. 19.11).

The fundamental importance of this new idea is evident from the fact that it affects the age-old principle of conservation of mass. The mass of a body or a system of bodies is no longer considered as constant but is increased by the amount energy/c^2, when energy is stored in the body.

SUMMARY OF CHAPTER 6

In electrolytic conduction the measurable quantities (mass deposited, atomic weight, valence, and quantity of electricity) are correlated by Faraday's law [Eq. (6.1)]. In this law the Faraday constant F, a universal constant, represents the quantity of electricity carried by 1 gram atom of a univalent substance.

From this law it follows that any individual univalent charged atom (ion) carries the same quantity of electricity F/N_0, each bivalent ion twice this amount, etc. This indicates that electricity can be subdivided only down to this smallest charge F/N_0. These smallest units of electric charge are called "electrons." The reciprocal of the electrochemical equivalent has the significance of charge to mass (e/m) of the individual ion. The largest value of e/m observed in electrolysis is that of the hydrogen ion H+, i.e., 9.578×10^3 emu/g.

The *cathode ray* is a ray consisting of negatively charged particles leaving the surface of the cathode. The specific charge e/m of these particles, determined by a combination of electric and magnetic deflections, has the value 1.7588×10^7 emu/g. This far exceeds any value of e/m known for atoms in electrolysis and has been interpreted by J. J.

Thomson as indicating free electrons. The fact that free electrons are always observed with negative charges leads to the conclusion that *positively* charged atoms have *lost* one or several electrons and that *negatively* charged atoms have *gained* electrons.

Glowing filaments give off negative charges which by the determination of e/m are recognized as free electrons.

A bundle of electrons passing through a hole in a metal plate with uniform velocity but in directions varying within a small solid angle can be focused by a uniform magnetic field placed in the direction of the bundle. The formation of an image by a magnetic lens is the starting point for the construction of the *electron microscope*.

In the field electron microscope an image is formed of a metal surface (needle point) from which electrons are extracted by a strong electric field. The image shows single barium atoms by their local effect on the electron emission.

In the *cathode-ray oscilloscope* the electric deflection of the cathode ray indicates rapidly varying potential differences without any noticeable inertia.

The *canal ray* observed behind the cathode through which an axial canal is drilled consists of positive ions of the gas contained in the discharge tube (positive-ray).

High-velocity electrons show a decrease of e/m. This is interpreted on the basis of Einstein's theory of relativity as an increase of their mass. This result can be represented as a special case of Einstein's law of equivalence of mass and energy.

PROBLEMS

(Study Appendix 1, "Units.")

6.1. *Silver plating.* In an electrolytic solution silver is deposited by an electric current of 0.5 amp. Compute the mass deposited upon the negative plate during a 90-min run. Atomic weight of silver = 107.9; valence of silver = 1.

6.2. *Production of electrolytic hydrogen.* How long does it take to produce 1 liter hydrogen under standard conditions by a current of 5 amp? How much oxygen is produced during the same time at the other electrode?

6.3. *Force exerted by a magnetic field on an electron.* In the discussion of cathode-ray experiments we started from the familiar expression, force = iLB. (The electromagnetic system of units is assumed.) From this expression derive the force on an electron, charge e, moving with the velocity v through a magnetic induction B. Use the following argument: Suppose a current consisting of a stream of electrons, with a density of n electrons per centimeter length, and moving with the velocity v passes through a magnetic induction B perpendicular to the velocity v. At any instant the electrons that are about to move within the next time interval Δt through a certain cross section occupy a certain length.

   a. What is this length?

   b. State the number of electrons passing a cross section during Δt.

c. Express the current as (the number of electrons passing this cross section per second) × (electronic charge).

d. Introduce this expression into the equation, force = iLB.

e. How large is the force on one individual electron?

6.4. *J. J. Thomson's measurement of e/m.* In the first experiment the cathode ray passes between condenser plates 1 cm apart, connected with a power supply of 790 volts; the electrostatic deflection is compensated by a magnetic induction of 30.00 gauss. In the second experiment the same cathode ray is bent by a magnetic induction of 12.50 gauss into a circular path of 12.00 cm radius. Compute e/m of the cathode-ray particles.

6.5. *Electric acceleration and magnetic deflection.* Electrons are accelerated from a glowing filament toward a plate by a potential difference of 100 volts. After passing through a slit, they enter a space free of electric fields in which they are subjected to a magnetic induction of 3.00 gauss directed perpendicular to their velocity. Find their linear velocity v behind the slit and the radius R of their path in the magnetic field.

6.6. *Focusing of an electron beam.* Electrons, after being accelerated by 1,200 volts, are diverging from a narrow hole. How large an axial magnetic induction is required to focus the beam on a screen placed at a distance of 40 cm from the hole?

6.7. *Positive ions.* Sodium is a univalent electropositive element with the atomic weight 23.0. How large a specific charge e/m is it expected to show in the positive-ray experiment?

6.8. *Deflection of positive ions.* Solve Prob. 6.5, replacing the electrons by singly charged sodium ions.

COMMENT: The magnetic deflection would not be measurable. The result demonstrates that the deflection of *ions* requires a much stronger magnetic induction than that of *electrons.*

6.9. *Atomic weight of electron.* From the values of e/m calculate the atomic weight of the electron (Sec. 6.2a).

6.10. *Velocity selector.* A narrow beam of positive ions of various values of e/m travels through the combination of electric and magnetic fields which J. J. Thomson used in the experiment of Fig. 6.2. A narrow hole is placed in such a position that it transmits only *undeflected* ions. Satisfy yourself that it transmits ions of a well-defined velocity v irrespective of their specific charge e/m. Calculate this velocity for $E = 1,000$ volts/cm and $B = 1,000$ gauss.

6.11. *Field electron microscope.* The essential parts of a field microscope are a needle point surrounded by a conducting enclosure. For the computation of the electric field this apparatus is described as a spherical condenser whose inner sphere is as small as the needle point. (*a*) Assuming that an electric field $E = 4.0 \times 10^7$ volts/cm is needed to produce "field emission" from the needle point, calculate the radius r of the needle "point" (the inner condenser sphere) for the following data: radius R of outer condenser sphere = 3.0 cm; potential difference between the spheres $V = 4,000$ volts. Neglect r when subtracted from R. Given: capacitance of spherical condenser (inner radius r; outer radius R) = $Rr/(R - r)$ nearly = r. (*b*) Calculate the magnification R/r of this field microscope.

HINT: Express the charge q on the small sphere and the electric field E at its surface in terms of V.

6.12. *Loss of mass by the sun.* The solar constant (1.96 cal cm^{-2} min^{-1}) gives the energy of solar radiation received per minute per square centimeter at the earth. By radiation the sun is expected to lose mass. How large is this loss of mass per year? (Distance earth to sun = 1.490×10^{13} cm.) See related Prob. 19.11.

6.13. *Electric deflection of charged particles.* Charged particles are traveling across an evacuated parallel-plate condenser (potential difference V; plate distance d), entering in a direction parallel to the plates (z direction) with a given velocity v. See Figs. 6.2 and 6.12.

a. Calculate the path of the particles in the condenser, expressing the y coordinate (normal to z) in terms of z and the quantities given.

b. Calculate the deflection y of electrons ($v = 1.000 \times 10^9$ cm/sec) that have traveled the distance $z = 5.00$ cm across a condenser ($d = 0.500$ cm) connected with $V = 5.00$ volts.

c. Calculate the deflection y of protons, H^+, for $v = 6.03 \times 10^8$ cm/sec; $V/d = 2.380$ volts/cm; length of path in condenser $= 8.00$ cm.

6.14. *Magnetic deflection of charged particles.* A positive ray of given e/m enters a magnetic induction B as in Fig. 6.12. Calculate the deflection x (in centimeters) of the ray when it leaves the induction in terms of e/m, B, the path length z, and the velocity v of the ions. Although the magnetic induction exerts a force in a direction not fixed in space but turning with the velocity of the ion (Sec. 6.2*a*), we assume deflections so small that this force can be considered to be fixed in space, normal to the plane of Fig. 6.12. Thus we compute the magnetic deflection x by the method we used for the electric deflection y in the preceding problem. Calculate the deflection x of protons; $B = 400$ gauss; length of path in magnet $= 8.00$ cm; $v = 6.03 \times 10^8$ cm/sec. Notice that fast ions are less subject to electric and magnetic deflections than slow ones.

6.15. *Parabola method.* A positive ray is deflected in the vertical direction (y direction) by an electric field V/d and simultaneously in the horizontal direction by a magnetic induction B, both acting over the same length of the path as in Fig. 6.12. A photographic plate is placed in the path of the ray right behind the deflecting fields. Compute the shape of the trace on the photographic plate made by ions of a common e/m but different velocities v, *i.e.*, the shape of the curves of Fig. 6.13. Calculate the specific charge e/m and identify the type of ion for the following data: $V/d = 2,380$ volts/cm; $B = 2,000$ gauss; path length z in the fields $= 8.00$ cm; $x = 0.300$ cm; $y = 0.400$ cm. Which part of the trace is due to fast and which to slow ions?

HINT: In the preceding problems the two equations are derived representing the electric deflection y and the magnetic deflection x. For a given value of e/m both deflections are variable because of the wide range of velocities v of the ions present in the positive ray. By eliminating v from the two equations you will derive the equation representing y in terms of x for any value of e/m, that is, the equation representing the curves of Fig. 6.13.

6.16. *Cathode-ray oscilloscope (calculus problem).* (*a*) Find the slope of the path of the electrons described in Prob. 6.13 at the point of their emergence from the condenser. (*b*) You are asked to build a cathode-ray oscilloscope using all the data of Prob. 6.13. Beyond the electric field the electrons travel in a straight line. You want the deflection of the ray as observed on the screen to be 3.00 cm. How far behind the condenser must you place the screen?

6.17. *Accuracy of result (calculus problem).* When determining e/m of ions by the parabola method, you measure corresponding values of x and y on a parabola. (*a*) Suppose you measure the electric (vertical) deflection y with an accuracy of 1 per cent. How large is the corresponding per cent error in e/m? (*b*) Answer the same question supposing that the magnetic (horizontal) deflection x, the potential difference V, or the magnetic induction B are measured each with an accuracy of 1 per cent.

HINT: Use the derivatives.

CHAPTER 7

DETERMINATION OF THE CHARGE
ON THE ELECTRON

7.1. Millikan's Experiment. After the determination of e/m for free electrons we turn to the next important step, the determination of the charge e on the electron by Millikan's oil-drop experiment (1909). The reader may well approach this subject by forgetting all he has just learned of atoms and electrons. This implies that the new experiment will give entirely *independent* evidence of the structure of electricity.

The first determinations of the electric charges carried by small drops were made by J. J. Thomson and H. A. Wilson. They measured charges carried by water droplets which are formed in a cloud chamber (C. T. R. Wilson; see Sec. 17.2a). These preliminary experiments were developed into a high-precision measurement by Millikan, who measured the

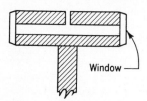

charges on the smallest bodies that can be investigated, ultramicroscopic drops. He used oil because it does not noticeably evaporate. The small drops generated by an atomizer fall under the effect of gravity, the rate of fall being slowed down by friction in air as is the fall of the small water droplets constituting a cloud. Some oil drops are allowed to fall through a small hole in the upper plate of a horizontal plate condenser (plate distance s; Fig. 7.1). Between the plates, the fall of the drop, carefully shielded from air currents, is observed through a microscope. When a potential difference V is applied to the plates of the condenser, some drops move upward, some downward, a fact which indicates that almost all drops carry electric charges. Presumably the charges are produced by friction in the nozzle of the atomizer. The drops, originally falling under the effect of gravity, may be lifted by the application of a sufficiently strong electric field, $E = V/s$.

Window —

Fig. 7.1. Millikan condenser.

We measure the charge on a drop in either one of two ways. The simpler way consists of adjusting the upward force qE until the drop just stops falling; *i.e.*, until the forces acting upward and downward are equal. Then $qE = mg$ where q and m are the charge and the mass of the oil drop.

The other method is more commonly used.   First we use the electric field to lift the drop, and next, before it reaches the upper plate, we turn off the electric field and allow the drop to fall under the effect of gravity. The motion of the tiny drops is strongly retarded by friction in the air in the same way as the fall of the tiny water drops constituting a cloud is retarded.   Therefore a constant force gives to a drop not a uniform *acceleration* (as it would in high vacuum) but instead a uniform *velocity*, which is determined by the friction provided by the "viscous medium." The velocities upward v_u and downward v_d are measured through a microscope.   The velocity of a body moving through a viscous medium, like that of a boat moving through water, is proportional to the driving force acting on the body: in the case of the *falling* drop the gravitational force alone (mg) and in the case of the *rising* drop the electric force counteracted by gravity $(qE - mg)$.   This argument leads to the equation

$$\frac{v_u}{v_d} = \frac{qE - mg}{mg} \qquad (7.1)$$

If we know the mass m of the oil drop, we can use the last equation for the computation of its charge q, since g is known and v_u, v_d, and E are measured.   Unfortunately we cannot use the microscope to measure the size of the drop, since its diameter is of the same order of magnitude as the wavelength of visible light; therefore this diameter is too close to the limit of the resolving power of the microscope.   However, this does not prevent us from seeing the drop.   Under intense illumination from the side against a dark background, it shows up like a star which we can see although we cannot measure its diameter because of the limited resolving power of all optical instruments.   Millikan determined the diameter of the drop by observing the rate of fall under the effect of gravity and viscosity and by applying a well-known law that correlates the velocity of fall of a sphere through a viscous medium with its radius.   This law, discovered by Stokes (1845), states that

$$v = \frac{2gr^2\rho}{9\eta} \qquad (7.2)$$

where v = velocity
g = gravitational acceleration
r = radius of drop
ρ = density of the oil
η = coefficient of viscosity of air (defined in Sec. 5.2)
When v, g, ρ, and η are measured, the radius r and the mass m of the oil drop, assumed to be of spherical shape, are computed.

We are unable to reproduce Stokes' original derivation, which is based on hydrodynamics.   Instead we assume that this law has been established by experiments performed with larger spheres for which masses and radii are measurable, so that Stokes' law can be checked and the coefficient of viscosity η of air computed. In the oil-drop experiment the same value of η is applied ($\eta = 1.82 \times 10^{-4}$ cm^{-1} g sec^{-1}), and Stokes' law is used for the computation of the (submicroscopic) radius r. Stokes' law can be well demonstrated by showing the fall of small steel spheres through glycerin.

After the determination of the radius r, the mass m of the drop follows as

$$m = \rho \times \tfrac{4}{3}\pi r^3$$

When Millikan's experiment is repeated over and over again with the same drop and the same electric field E, we notice that once in a while the upward velocity abruptly changes, indicating that the charge q on the drop has changed by picking up charge, positive or negative. In this process the mass of the drop remains unchanged, as is indicated by the unchanged downward velocity. We can even incite such a change of charge by irradiating the space between the condenser plates by X rays or rays from radium.

So far we have measured values of the charge q on an oil drop apart from any preconceived idea regarding the structure of electricity. This structure becomes directly evident in Millikan's results. He found that the charges on oil drops do not have all possible values within a continuous range, but only certain discrete values. For example, through a period of several minutes the drop may have a constant charge of 6.40×10^{-20} emu. Then it may change its charge, spontaneously or under the effect of X rays, to 8.00×10^{-20} emu. After a while it may go to 3.20×10^{-20}, later to 6.40×10^{-20} emu, i.e., exactly the same value the drop had at the beginning. Such values of charge, in any random order, recur not only for this one drop but also for all other drops. Millikan listed all the values of charge ever observed in the following table, which we limit to the five lowest values:

$$1.60 \times 10^{-20} \text{ emu}$$
$$3.20 \times 10^{-20} \text{ emu}$$
$$4.80 \times 10^{-20} \text{ emu}$$
$$6.40 \times 10^{-20} \text{ emu}$$
$$8.00 \times 10^{-20} \text{ emu}$$

From this table, or still better from Millikan's more extensive table, it is evident that the charges on small oil drops occur only in multiples of a smallest charge. The accurate value is

$$1.60207 \times 10^{-20} \text{ emu}$$

As this result is independent of the conditions of the experiment, in particular the sizes of the drops, Millikan drew the important conclusion that here a property of electricity is manifest: There is a fundamental charge that cannot be subdivided into smaller charges. This, presumably, is the charge e on the electron of which Thomson had measured the ratio e/m.

In our brief discussion we failed to do justice to the art of Millikan's experiment. As a matter of fact, only for relatively large drops did he find that the charges are multiples of the fundamental unit, while small drops show systematic deviations. These drops are so small that, under the microscope, their Brownian motion (Sec. 4.3) is observed as a random motion superimposed on their regular rise or fall. It would be absurd to assume that the structure of electricity depends on the size of the drop. Hence Millikan rather assumed that for the smallest droplets one of the laws on which his method is based becomes invalid. In particular he assumed that Stokes' law, which was tested only for larger spheres, would need a correction factor when applied to spheres so small that their size becomes comparable with the mean free path of the gaseous molecules. Therefore, he used his measurements of the smallest drops for the evaluation of two constants: the charge q on the drop and the correction factor for Stokes' law.

Later, Millikan's determination of the charge on the electron was confirmed and improved upon by an independent method, as will be discussed in the chapter on X rays (Sec. 14.1h).

When performing Millikan's oil-drop experiment in the laboratory, the student is impressed by the fact that the structure of electricity becomes evident from the data collected within a few hours. For this purpose the student needs only measure several different values of charge on the same drop. More difficult is the accurate evaluation of e which includes the correction to Stokes' law.

7.2. Masses of Atoms and Molecules. Now we know Millikan's value of the absolute charge e of the electron, Thomson's value of its specific charge e/m, and also the specific charges of ionized atoms, derived from electrolysis or positive-ray analysis. On this basis we compute the absolute masses of electrons and atoms with a high degree of accuracy. Also Avogadro's number N_0, the number of molecules per mole, follows from Eq. (6.3), based on Faraday's law $F = N_0 e$. The best numerical values known* are given in the following table; the last decimal place of each figure is uncertain. The masses of other atoms and of molecules are easily computed with the help of their atomic or molecular weights.

　　a. The Electron:

$$e = 1.60207 \times 10^{-20} \text{ emu}$$
$$e/m = 1.75888 \times 10^{7} \text{ emu/g}$$
$$m = 9.1085 \times 10^{-28} \text{ g}$$

---

* DuMont, J. W. M., and E. R. Cohen, *Revs. Mod. Phys.*, **25**, 691 (1953).

b. The Hydrogen Ion H^+:

$$e/m = 9.579 \times 10^3 \text{ emu/g}$$

c. The Neutral Hydrogen Atom:

$$m = 1.6733 \times 10^{-24} \text{ g}$$

d. Avogadro's Number:

$$N_0 = 6.0247 \times 10^{23} \text{ mole}^{-1}$$

The *sizes* of atoms and molecules can be given only with much lower accuracy, not because our method is inferior but because they are not so sharply defined as the *masses*. We shall consider this further in our discussion of atomic structure. Since the atoms are described as consisting of electric charges, they do not form sharply defined, smooth surfaces but are surrounded by electric fields. Various methods for the determination of the sizes lead to results that only approximately agree. The simplest argument is as follows: The density of a liquid ($=$ mass/volume) may be expressed in terms of molecular quantities as

$$\text{Density} = \frac{\text{mass of 1 molecule}}{\text{volume of 1 molecule}}$$

The volume of one molecule of water is found to be 29.9×10^{-24} cm^3. (Strictly speaking, this is the volume occupied by 1 molecule of liquid water.) The common result of all such determinations is that the diameters of atoms and the simpler molecules are a little larger than 10^{-8} cm.

Avogadro's number N_0 and the molecular diameters are needed for the computation of the mean free path l of gaseous molecules: $l = 1/(4\pi N r^2)$ [Eq. (5.1)]. Here N, the number of atoms per cubic centimeter, is easily computed since the molar volume is known to be 22.4 liters (Sec. 3.1). For nitrogen $2r$ is found to be 3.1×10^{-8} cm, and l under standard conditions is 6×10^{-6} cm.

How do molecular dimensions compare with what we can see through a microscope or weigh on a balance? The smallest length resolved under the optical microscope, 3×10^{-5} cm, comprises about 1,000 water molecules; hence molecular dimensions are far below the wavelength of light. But the electron microscope (Sec. 6.2c) is able to resolve lengths of the order of magnitude of the size of large molecules. The smallest mass we can weigh, about 10^{-9} g, would comprise approximately 10^{14} water molecules.

7.3. The Electron Volt. In Sec. 6.2b we discussed the acceleration of electrons (or, in rare cases, positive ions) emitted by a glowing filament. Now we know the charge e of these particles and apply the experiment mentioned to the definition of a new unit of energy commonly used in atomic physics. The kinetic energy W_k of particles of charge e that have fallen through a potential difference V is computed above [Eq. (6.8)] as $W_k = Ve$. The mass m does not enter into this equation. Hence the energy W_k is independent of the mass and is completely defined by the potential difference and the charge. Since in many modern experiments electrons and ions are observed that have been accelerated through a measured potential difference, it is convenient not to compute the energy of the particle in ergs but to introduce a new unit of energy, the "electron volt" (abbreviated ev). One electron volt is defined as the kinetic energy of any particle carrying the electronic charge e which has been accelerated through a potential difference of 1 volt. In equations correlating various electric and magnetic quantities and their energies, the absolute unit erg remains indispensable. The electron volt is only an abbreviation for an energy of 10^8 emu of potential difference $\times$ 1.602 $\times$ 10^{-20} emu of charge; hence 1 ev = 1.602 $\times$ 10^{-12} erg. Conventionally a "300-volt electron" means an electron that has been accelerated by a potential difference of 300 volts. Later, in nuclear physics, we shall use the units million electron volt (Mev) and billion electron volt (Bev).

The relation 1 ev = 1.602 $\times$ 10^{-12} erg makes it possible to apply the unit electron volt to any kind of energy which otherwise is measured in ergs. In particular, it is commonly applied to the kinetic energies of neutral particles, like neutral atoms or molecules (or "neutrons," which will be discussed in nuclear physics), although such particles do not receive their kinetic energies from electric fields acting on charges. For example, the average thermal kinetic energy of any atom or molecule at 0°C is 0.0353 ev.

The energy given to the electron in high vacuum by a potential difference is fully available when the electron hits the anode and its kinetic energy is there changed into heat. This is a method commonly used for baking out metal plates in high vacuum. The various energy exchanges will become clear by a comparison with familiar mechanical processes. Water stored in a reservoir at a high altitude above a valley represents potential energy. This energy is converted into heat by either one of two ways. Either the water is allowed to flow down to the valley through pipes so narrow that by friction all the potential energy changes into heat and no kinetic energy is formed, in a manner comparable with the flow of electricity through an ohmic resistance; or in a waterfall the potential energy is all changed into kinetic energy which is converted into heat when the water hits the ground, in a manner comparable to the heating of a metal in high vacuum by electron bombardment.

SUMMARY OF CHAPTER 7

In the oil-drop experiment Millikan measured the electric charge on submicroscopic oil drops by observing their velocity of fall through air under the effect of gravity and their velocity of rise against gravity under the effect of an electric field.   He measured the masses of the oil drops with the help of Stokes' law describing the velocity of fall of a spherical body through a viscous medium.   His outstanding result is that the charges on drops occur only as multiples of a smallest charge 1.602×10^{-20} emu.   As this charge is entirely independent of the special conditions of the experiment, he concluded that it is a fundamental property of electricity and is identical with the charge e on the electron.

On this basis and with the help of the results of the preceding chapters, the masses of electrons and atoms and Avogadro's number are computed.

A convenient unit of energy, the electron volt, is defined as the energy given to a particle carrying the charge of 1 electron when it is accelerated through a potential difference of 1 volt; 1 ev $= 1.602 \times 10^{-12}$ erg.

PROBLEMS

(Study Appendix 1, "Units.")

7.1. *Oil-drop experiment.*   In the oil-drop experiment a condenser is used with a plate separation of 2.50 mm.   A droplet is observed falling without electric field through a distance of 1.00 mm in 25.3 sec.   When a potential difference of 154.8 volts raises the same droplet, it travels a distance of 1.00 mm in 18.0 sec.   The density of the oil is given as $\rho = 0.920 \, \text{g/cm}^3$, the viscosity of air as $\eta = 1.82 \times 10^{-4} \, \text{cm}^{-1} \text{g sec}^{-1}$. How large is the electric charge on the droplet expressed in emu?

7.2. *Oil-drop experiment.*   How large an electric field E must you apply to lift the oil drop (mass m, charge q) with twice the velocity with which it is falling when the field is turned off?   Calculate the numerical value of E for a drop of mass $m = 3.26 \times 10^{-13}$ g and a charge of 3 electrons.

7.3. *Acceleration of electrons.*   Suppose that the negative plate of an evacuated parallel-plate condenser (plate distance d, potential difference V) emits electrons, leaving the plate with negligible initial velocity.

Calculate:

a. The distance x covered by a particle as a function of the time t;

b. Its velocity v as a function of t;

c. Its velocity v as a function of the distance x;

d. Its kinetic energy W_k as a function of x;

e. The velocity with which the particle strikes the positive plate;

f. The time required for crossing.

g. Introduce numerical values into the answers to (*e*) and (*f*): $V = 120$ volts; $d = 2.00$ cm.

HINT: Remember the laws of free fall.

7.4. *Kinetic energy of electrons and ions.*   Starting from the principle of conservation of energy, compute the velocities v and kinetic energies W_k (in ergs and ev) of the following particles, all accelerated by 110 volts: (*a*) an electron, (*b*) a singly charged H ion, (*c*) a single charged Na ion, (*d*) a doubly charged Ca ion.

7.5. *Thermal kinetic energy of molecules.*   For comparison with the result of the preceding problem, compute the velocity (in cm/sec) and the kinetic energy (in ergs and ev) of hydrogen molecules at room temperature (293° abs).   The density ρ of molecular hydrogen at room temperature and 1 atm pressure is 8.38×10^{-5} g/cm³. One atmosphere pressure is exerted by a mercury column of 76 cm height (density of mercury $= 13.55$ g/cm³).   Use Eq. (3.4).

7.6. *Comparison of units.* In a chemical reaction, *e.g.*, the combination of two H atoms forming an H_2 molecule, each molecule formed liberates a certain energy, which we may measure in the fundamental unit, the erg. Practically, the reaction is allowed to take place in a calorimeter, and the heat liberated measured in kilocalories per mole of gas. What is the factor of proportionality between this new unit and each of the other units, erg and electron volt? Two H atoms have an energy of combination of 4.45 ev. Express this energy in kcal/mole.

COMMENT: Apparently, there can be no relation between 1 ev (a unit of energy) and 1 kcal/mole (a unit of energy/mass). In this case, however, ev always means electron volts per molecule; correspondingly, here ergs always mean ergs per molecule.

7.7. *Force exerted by positive-ion current.* Cesium ions Cs^+ emitted from a glowing filament form an electric current of 10^{-10} amp. After being accelerated by a potential difference of 110.0 volts, they strike a target, giving off all their momentum (inelastic collisions; see Prob. 3.5). How large is the force on the target?

7.8. *Change of mass of mercury atoms.* In the electric discharge through mercury vapor, atoms are being excited to an energy of 4.9 ev (see Sec. 12.1). Express the increase in mass given to the mercury atom in terms of percentage of its original mass.

COMMENT: Notice that this increase is far below the observable limit.

7.9. *Gain of mass by dissociation.* When dissociating a hydrogen molecule H_2, we spend the energy of dissociation $D = 4.4$ ev. The two free atoms so produced contain this amount of energy more than the molecule. Hence, according to Einstein's principle, they have a larger mass. Compute this increase of mass. What percentage of its mass does each atom gain by the process described?

7.10. *Space charge.* (*a*) A beam of electrons of cross section A is traveling with uniform velocity v. The beam represents a current i. Calculate the number n of electrons per cm^3 in terms of A, v, and the electronic charge e. (*b*) Calculate the space charge (in coul/cm^3) for $A = 2.00\ cm^2$; $v = 10^9\ cm/sec$; $i = 10^{-3}$ amp.

7.11. *Heating of target.* Electrons emanating from a glowing cathode are accelerated by 20,000 volts and incident on a copper anode (mass 26.8 g). The electrons form a current of 10 milliamp. In order to judge whether you can operate this tube (say for the demonstration of X rays) without cooling the anode, calculate the time it will take for the target to reach a temperature of 200°C, starting from 20°C. Suppose that during the run the anode does not give off heat. Specific heat of copper = 0.094 cal/(g. degree).

7.12. *Raindrop falling.* A very small waterdrop is falling at the rate of 1.00 cm in 250 sec, through air under standard conditions. Calculate the radius of the drop.

7.13. *Number of molecules in drop.* Of how many molecules H_2O does the drop of the preceding problem consist?

7.14. *Avogadro's number.* Starting from Avogadro's number N_0 calculate the number of molecules contained in 1 cm^3 of a gas under standard conditions. Remember that this number, too, is a universal constant (Sec. 1.3). Use the molar volume (Sec. 3.1.).

7.15. *Volume of a molecule.* Calculate the volume and radius of an argon atom (identical with the argon molecule), using the same approximation as in Sec. 7.2. Given: density of liquid argon = 1.40 g/cm^3; atomic weight = 40.0.

7.16. *Space occupied by atoms of a gas.* A bulb contains argon under standard conditions. What fraction of the bulb is occupied by the argon atoms? (See Prob. 7.15.)

HINT: Consider the molar volume.

7.17. *Molecular collisions.* For argon gas under standard conditions, calculate (*a*) the mean free path; (*b*) the velocity u of the atoms; (*c*) the mean time between consecutive collisions; (*d*) the mean number of collisions suffered by 1 atom per second.

7.18. *High vacuum.* A pressure of 10^{-7} mm of mercury is considered to be "high vacuum." For this pressure and 0°C calculate the number per cm³ n of molecules.

7.19. *Velocity of electron in cylindrical tube (calculus problem).* Many radio tubes are built with cylindrical symmetry, a straight filament being mounted at the axis of a cylindrical anode (radii r_f and r_c, respectively). Compute the velocity v of an electron emitted from the filament in terms of the distance r and the charge per unit length q on the filament. Given: the electric field around an infinitely long, straight, uniformly charged wire: $E = 2c^2q/r$ (r = distance; q = charge per unit length).

HINT: Express the gain of kinetic energy W_k (as a function of r) = loss of potential energy $W_p = \int$ force $\times dr$.

7.20. *Self-energy.* Calculate the self-energy (energy equivalent of total mass) of (*a*) an electron; (*b*) a proton; (*c*) a uranium atom of atomic weight 238.

PART IV

QUANTUM STRUCTURE OF LIGHT

After discussing the atomic structure of matter and the electronic structure of electricity, we must next present the evidence for the *quantum structure of light*. Historically, the quantum theory had its origin in the explanation of black-body radiation. However, in order to avoid the mathematical treatment indispensable for this theory, we shall introduce the quantum structure of light on the basis of the photoelectric effect. We shall discuss first the experimental facts, next the unsuccessful attempt to explain them on the basis of the electromagnetic theory of light, and, finally, Einstein's quantum theory of light. Photochemistry and the Compton effect will supply supporting evidence. A brief report on wave mechanics will attempt to reconcile the conflict between the old and the new theories of light.

CHAPTER 8

PHOTOELECTRIC EFFECT AND THE QUANTUM OF LIGHT

8.1. Experimental Facts. Heinrich Hertz discovered that an electric spark starts more readily when the electrodes are exposed to ultraviolet light (1890). The underlying phenomenon is investigated by means of the apparatus shown in Fig. 8.1. In a highly evacuated quartz bulb the metal plate M is exposed to light, quartz being used because it transmits ultraviolet as well as visible light. Between this plate and another metal plate P which is shielded from the light, a potential difference V is

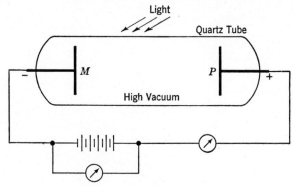

FIG. 8.1. Photoelectric effect.

applied which initially makes the plate P (called the "collector plate") positive with respect to the illuminated plate M. The light incident on the plate M causes an electric current to flow. The direction of the current indicates that light liberates from the metal *negatively* charged particles, which are then pulled to the collector plate P by the potential difference V.

For the further investigation of the nature of these particles, we apply the method of electric acceleration and magnetic deflection by which we tested the nature of the particles emanating from a glowing filament (Sec. 6.2b). We omit the construction of the apparatus and record only the result, that the specific charge of the liberated particles is the same as that characteristic of electrons, thereby proving that *light liberates electrons from a metal surface.*

The current-potential curve of the photoelectric cell of Fig. 8.1, for constant illumination, is given by Fig. 8.2. With increasing potential difference V the current I reaches a limiting value, called "saturation current," which is determined by the limited number of electrons per second liberated by the light.   For zero potential difference, *i.e.*, in the absence of an electric field acting between the plates, the current still flows in the same direction.   Thus the light provides not only a conductivity but in addition an electromotive force.   Even for small *negative* values of potential difference (retarding the electrons), the current flows *in the same direction* as for positive values. However, it diminishes for increasing negative values until, at a sharply defined potential difference of a few volts, the current goes down to zero. This value is called the "stopping potential" V_s.   (In the experiment of Fig. 8.2 the current I has already the full saturation value for zero potential difference.   In technical photoelectric cells, because of unfavorable geometrical conditions, this is not the case.)

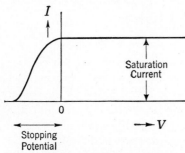

FIG. 8.2. Photoelectric current I plotted against the accelerating potential difference V for constant illumination.

When the photoelectric metal M is isolated (instead of being connected, as in the circuit of Fig. 8.2) and is initially on ground potential, the illumination liberates electrons and thus imparts to the metal a positive charge.   The process comes to an end when the surface has reached a positive potential high enough to prevent the further escape of electrons in spite of the illumination.

We understand the significance of the stopping potential by comparison with an experiment in mechanics.   While a stone *falling down* picks up kinetic energy at the expense of its potential energy, a stone *thrown upward* will rise until its initial kinetic energy is completely changed into potential energy; hence, if we know the maximum height reached, in other words the maximum potential energy, we can calculate the initial kinetic energy.   On the other hand, in the electrical experiment we calculate the kinetic energy *given to* a particle (charge e) by the potential difference V as $W_k = Ve$ [Eq. (6.8)].   Correspondingly, the value of the stopping potential V_s enables us to calculate the maximum kinetic energy W_m *taken away* by the electric field from the electrons which are liberated by light from the plate M.   The conservation of energy is expressed by

$$W_m = \tfrac{1}{2}\,mv_m{}^2 = eV_s$$

where W_m is the initial kinetic energy of the fastest electrons and v_m their velocity. The slope of the IV curve on the side of *retarding* potentials (left branch of Fig. 8.2) indicates that many electrons are able to overcome small retarding potential differences (less than the limit V_s), but that only a vanishing number of electrons is endowed with the maximum kinetic energy of liberation W_m measured by the stopping potential.

The exact shape of the sloping curve between the stopping potential and the saturation current is affected by the construction of the tube to such an extent that the detail is not worth discussing.

In the systematic study of the photoelectric effect we vary at will the light and the metal illuminated. In order to have well-defined conditions, we use monochromatic light described by its intensity and wave-

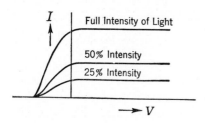

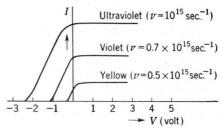

FIG. 8.3. Photoelectric current I plotted against the accelerating potential difference V for various intensities of illumination of the same metal.

FIG. 8.4. Photoelectric current I plotted against the accelerating potential difference V for three different frequencies of light incident on a potassium surface. The relative values of the currents I are irrelevant.

length* λ (or, instead, its frequency ν in the unit sec⁻¹). We measure the saturation current and the stopping potential as functions of these independent variables and so obtain results described as follows. Using the same metal and the same frequency of the light, but varying its *intensity*, we obtain a family of current-potential curves given in Fig. 8.3. They indicate that the stopping potential is independent of the light intensity and that the saturation current is proportional to the intensity.

For the understanding of the nature of light we are concerned with the measurement of the stopping potential V_s as a function of the frequency ν of the light. Again we observe the current-potential curves for, say, a sodium surface, this time varying the *frequency*, say, from $\nu = 10^{15}$ sec⁻¹ (ultraviolet) to $\nu = 0.7 \times 10^{15}$ (violet), $\nu = 0.5 \times 10^{15}$ (yellow), and, finally, $\nu = 0.4 \times 10^{15}$ (red). The curves (for each frequency a family, as in Fig. 8.3) are plotted in Fig. 8.4. Red light fails to

---

* The wavelength of light is conventionally expressed in angstrom units, abbreviated A; 1 A = 10^{-8} cm. However, in equations like $\nu = c/\lambda$ all quantities must be expressed in the same system of units. We shall use the cgs system.

produce any photoelectric effect. From these curves we derive the relation between the stopping potential V_s (which is uniquely determined by the frequency of light ν) and this frequency. On the diagram, for each value of ν we read the corresponding value of V_s and plot V_s against

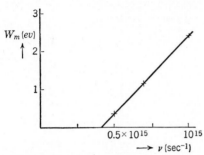

ν. We may as well plot the maximum kinetic energy W_m of the photoelectrons which is proportional to V_s. The resulting diagram (Fig. 8.5), thus derived from Fig. 8.4, shows a linear relation between these variables. We may express the same relationship by a linear equation between the maximum kinetic energy eV_s and ν

FIG. 8.5. Derived from Fig. 8.4. Maximum kinetic energy W_m of the photoelectrons from a potassium surface (measured by the stopping potential) as a function of the frequency ν of light.

$$eV_s = h\nu - \phi \qquad (8.1)$$

Here h and ϕ represent constants characteristic of the straight line, the numerical values of which may be computed from the measurements plotted in Fig. 8.4. The diagram and the equation indicate that the kinetic energy W_m becomes zero for a sharply defined frequency limit $\nu = \phi/h$. This is called the "threshold frequency" of the photoelectric effect; no effect whatever is observed for lower frequencies.

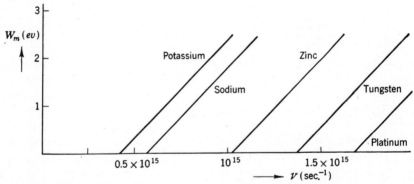

FIG. 8.6. Same as Fig. 8.5. Comparison of various metals.

In our final set of experiments we vary the *metal* exposed to light. Plotting the straight line just described for sodium, zinc, platinum, and wolfram (tungsten), we obtain another family of curves given in Fig. 8.6. We notice the fact that all these lines have the same slope but that their intersections with the ν axis, indicating the threshold frequencies, differ.

This same fact is expressed in terms of Eq. (8.1) by stating that h is a constant common to all metals; in other words a universal constant, while ϕ is a constant characteristic of the metal called "work function."

It is evident from Eq. (8.1) that ϕ and $h\nu$ both have the dimension of energy; hence h has the dimension of energy/frequency and is measured in erg seconds. The numerical values are as follows: $h = 6.6252 \times 10^{-27}$ erg sec; ϕ between 1.6×10^{-12} and 10×10^{-12} erg (or between 1 and 6 ev), depending upon the metal.

So far we have merely reported experiments and represented their results by diagrams and a simple equation. We summarize these results in so far as they are important for the theory. The maximum kinetic energy W_m of the photoelectrons is independent of the *intensity* of the light. It depends on the *frequency* of the light by the relation $W_m = h\nu - \phi$, where h is a universal constant and ϕ a constant characteristic of the metal.

8.2. Failure of the Electromagnetic Theory. To begin with, we try to explain the observed facts described in the preceding section on the basis of the electromagnetic theory of light which, at the end of the last century, seemed to be established beyond any doubt. Here we shall briefly review the background of this theory. The old controversy between the wave theory of light (Huygens, 1678) and the corpuscular theory (Newton, 1675) had been decided in favor of the wave theory by the work of Fresnel and Young (between 1800 and 1820). The main arguments in favor of the wave theory are given by the phenomena of interference and diffraction. The dark interference fringes, observed, for example, in Newton's rings, prove that light superimposed on light may produce darkness. This is a strong argument for the idea that light consists of a wave motion, because, by the superposition of two wave trains, standing waves may be produced that contain spots without any motion whatever. On the other hand, the corpuscular theory of light seems incompatible with the dark interference fringes because corpuscles of light superimposed on other corpuscles cannot produce darkness. Another argument for the wave nature of light is given by diffraction. A knife-edge placed in the path of parallel light does not cast an absolutely sharp shadow; some of the light enters the geometrical shadow and thus slightly deviates from rectilinear propagation. This is a well-known property of waves, in this case of very short length. Corpuscular rays, however, should not show diffraction.

These two arguments for the wave theory leave the nature of the light waves unknown. The nature of the waves was discovered much later by Maxwell (1865). He started from a mathematical investigation of electricity and magnetism which, to begin with, did not seem to be concerned with light. He represented the relations between electric and magnetic fields by a set of differential equations not to be discussed here. On the basis of this investigation he was able to predict the existence of *electromagnetic* waves with the following properties. In vacuum they should travel with a constant velocity, which Maxwell computed on the basis of electric and magnetic data to be 3×10^{10} cm/sec. At the surface of insulators (glass, water) they should be partly reflected, partly refracted with a certain change in their polarization. These properties— and additional properties theoretically predicted—agree so completely with the properties of light, as known from experiments, that the conclusion is inevitable that light consists of electromagnetic waves.

Maxwell's theoretical argument was strongly supported by the experiments of Hertz (1890). With electrical apparatus (wires, spark gaps, induction coils) Hertz produced an effect that was propagated by a wave motion from one loop of wire to another. The wave nature could be demonstrated by the production of standing waves. The order of magnitude of wavelengths was measured as decimeters. These electromagnetic waves could be reflected, refracted, and polarized in the same way as the electromagnetic waves predicted by Maxwell. Thus Hertz's experiments confirm Maxwell's theory. At the same time they make it plausible that light waves are electromagnetic waves that differ from those explored by Hertz only in their wavelengths.

It is a strange coincidence that, in the same experimental work that seemed firmly to establish the electromagnetic theory of light, Hertz discovered the photoelectric effect, which turned out to be incompatible with this theory and led to its profound modification. Is the electromagnetic theory of light capable of explaining the photoelectric effect? At the first glance it seems possible. In this theory electric and magnetic fields are attributed to the light waves, which may well exert forces on the electrons contained in the metal and so liberate them from the metal surface. However, on this basis we should predict that light of high intensity, *i.e.*, consisting of strong fields, would give high kinetic energy to the electrons liberated. This is not the case; on the contrary, the experiments show that the kinetic energy is independent of the light intensity. Furthermore, according to the theory we should expect that light of low frequency (infrared), if sufficiently intense, would be as effective as high-frequency light (ultraviolet). Again this prediction of the electromagnetic theory contradicts the experiments, which show that light of a frequency below a sharply defined threshold is entirely ineffective. So we are forced to conclude that the electromagnetic theory of light fails to explain the photoelectric effect.

This failure is further illustrated by the following estimate. The classical theory predicts a time lag between very weak illumination and the photoelectric effect because the energy of the light is expected to be uniformly distributed over the atoms of the surface so that each atom will need some time to accumulate the energy required for electron emission. As an example, in the illumination of a sodium surface by very weak violet light the energy available for photoelectric effect was estimated as 10^{-3} erg/cm^2 sec. If we arbitrarily assume that 10 surface layers of atoms (diameter of atom 3×10^{-8} cm) contribute to the effect, the time required by any one atom for the accumulation of the necessary energy is estimated as $1\frac{1}{2}$ years. The experiment, however, shows that even very weak light causes an instantaneous photoelectric effect. The vast discrepancy between theory and experiment shows that the energy of light cannot be uniformly distributed over the wave front. Hence a radically new hypothesis is needed.

8.3. Quantum Theory. In order to appreciate Einstein's quantum theory of the photoelectric effect, we must briefly survey the earlier development. Planck, in 1900, introduced the quantum theory in his discussion of the radiation emitted from a black body. This radiation, when analyzed by the spectroscope, covers the whole range of frequencies continuously. For any one temperature it is given by a curve as in Fig. 8.7. For various temperatures a family of curves results of which three examples are shown in the figure.

Although the details of Planck's quantum theory of black-body radiation cannot be treated on our introductory level, the fundamental importance of Planck's discovery justifies an extensive report. We consider a black body in thermal equilibrium and visualize it as consisting of very many molecules which, like small radio transmitters, emit and absorb radiation by their vibrations. The blackness of the body leads to the more detailed picture of very many vibrators with frequencies that cover the whole spectral range. Now incoming radiation of any frequency will soon hit a vibrator able to absorb it. The theory describes the processes of emission and absorption on the basis of the electromagnetic theory and, finally, accounts for the thermal equilibrium by applying the equipartition theorem to the vibrators, $i.e.$, the theorem we mentioned above when discussing specific heats (Sec. 4.2). This theorem states that, on the average, each vibrator carries the same kinetic energy $= \dfrac{3}{2} \dfrac{R}{N} T$. (Here we deal with the kinetic energy $of\ the\ vibration,$ while the translational energy of the same molecule has nothing to do with our argument.) This consistent application of the laws of physics to the theory of the black body leads to a catastrophic disagreement with observation. This $theory$ predicts that at high frequencies black-body radiation will be increasingly intense, approaching infinity. On the other hand, the $observations$ (Fig. 8.7) show that at high frequencies, $i.e.$, toward the ultraviolet or X-ray range, the radiation approaches zero.

In order to remove this striking discrepancy Planck introduced the hypothesis that the application of the equipartition theorem to vibrating molecules has certain limits. Planck invented the bold new concept that a molecule vibrating with its characteristic frequency ν can harbor energy only in quanta of the amounts 0 or $h\nu$ or $2h\nu$ or $3h\nu$, etc., where h is a new fundamental constant of physics, now universally called "Planck's constant." In other words, his hypothesis states that the energy of a molecule has a quantum structure. The consequences of this hypothesis are as follows: (1) For a vibrator of *low characteristic frequencies* the quanta $h\nu$ are so small that the molecule behaves approximately as if

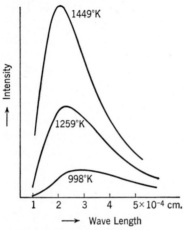

there were a continuous range of energy. Thus we understand why in the low-frequency range the old theory gave a good approximation to the observed black-body radiation. (2) On the other hand, *for high frequencies* the quanta $h\nu$ are large. Hence a molecule of large characteristic frequency ν can contain energy either zero or of the large amounts, $h\nu$, $2h\nu$, etc. Most thermal collisions, however, involve much smaller energies and, therefore, are ordinarily unable to impart any energy of vibration to the molecule. Hence molecules of excessively large vibrational fre-

FIG. 8.7. Black-body radiation.

quency ν fail to vibrate most of the time and play no part in the radiation of light. (For the same reason the vibration of molecules has only small effects on the specific heat; Sec. 4.2.) Their average energy computed on this basis turns out to be much smaller than $\frac{3}{2}kT$ and approaches zero for increasing characteristic frequency ν of the vibrating molecule. The lack of vibration of the molecules of high frequency explains the sloping down of the curves of Fig. 8.7 toward high frequencies. The mathematical discussion carried out by Planck resulted in a quantitative agreement of theory and experiment, provided that the newly introduced fundamental constant h is given the numerical value $h = 6.62 \times 10^{-27}$ erg sec. (We notice that this is the same figure that we found when representing certain straight lines to describe the photoelectric effect.)

Planck's new hypothesis is concerned with the energy content of molecules, not with the nature of light, since the theory does not imply that the energy of a quantum, after being emitted from a molecule, travels through space as a concentrated entity. Planck's hypothesis of the quantum structure of the energy stored in a molecule is not derived from any law of the older physics, now commonly called "classical physics," but is a fundamentally new idea introduced to interpret black-body radiation.　Planck's discovery proved to be the starting point of an overwhelmingly successful development, the *quantum theory* of atoms and molecules.

We shall not apply Planck's argument, but we had to mention it in order to point out the background of Einstein's theory of the photoelectric effect.　To explain this effect, which is essentially described by Eq. (8.1), Einstein (1905) introduces a fundamental change into our concept of the nature of light.　He assumes that the energy of light is not continuously distributed over the wave front, as the energy of water waves is, but *remains concentrated in packages of energy content hν* where ν is the frequency of light and h a new universal constant assumed to have a numerical value such that the theory agrees with the observations of the photoelectric effect.　Hence the individual packages, called *quanta of light* or *photons*, have a small energy content for light of low frequency and a large one for light of high frequency.　Furthermore, Einstein assumes that each package hν is so concentrated that it can transfer its whole energy content to 1 electron.　Applying the principle of conservation of energy to this transfer, Einstein postulates that the energy of the quantum hν when hitting the metal surface goes into two parts, one part being used for the liberation of 1 electron from the metal and the balance for kinetic energy:

$$1 \text{ photon} = h\nu = \phi + \text{kinetic energy of 1 electron}$$

This is essentially the same as the empirical Eq. (8.1).　Thus the theory predicts the observed fact that ϕ is a constant characteristic of the metal, while h is a universal constant which characterizes the property of light as consisting of energy quanta hν.　Here it becomes evident that the constant h, introduced above in the description of a very special phenomenon, the slope of certain straight lines concerned with the photoelectric effect, has a much more general importance in the theory of the quantum structure of light.　This transfer of the energy of light to the electrons does not by any means take place for all the quanta incident on the metal.　It is a fact that most metal surfaces are good reflectors of light.　Therefore, we must assume that only a small fraction of all quanta incident on the metal consume their energies by producing a photoelectric effect.

In this theory, high intensity of visible light is described as due not to very large quanta but, instead, to a very large number of quanta per second traveling as a light ray.　Thus light of high intensity is expected to liberate many electrons per second and so cause a relatively large photoelectric current without, however, giving to each electron a larger energy than low-intensity light of the same frequency does.　This agrees entirely with the observation.

The new theory seems to predict that light of frequency ν must give the same kinetic energy $h\nu - \phi$ to *any electron liberated*. This theoretical prediction seems to contradict the gradual sloping down of the current I toward increasing retarding potentials (Fig. 8.2). The shape of the curve indicates that the fraction of the electrons liberated *with the full value* of the theoretical kinetic energy is actually vanishingly small. How is the slope of this curve reconciled with the idea of the quantum theory? The outstanding argument is based on the well-known fact that light is not absorbed at the metal surface proper but is able to penetrate thin layers of metal. Therefore, the photoelectric effect, which is a special process of absorption of light, may well take place at a certain depth below the metal surface. In this case the liberated electron has to traverse several molecular layers before it escapes; on the way it may lose a part of the energy given to it by the quantum. Furthermore, the electron liberated from the surface with the full kinetic energy given by Eq. (8.1) can overcome the full stopping potential only if it happens to leave the metal plate in a direction perpendicular to the surface. Therefore, in agreement with observation, only a vanishingly small fraction of all photoelectrons is expected to reach the plate when the full theoretical stopping potential is approached.

Einstein's quantum theory of light is frequently called the "corpuscular theory of light." The word "corpuscular," however, overstates the case. The theory does not claim that the quanta of light have the same properties as, for example, atoms. Outstanding differences are as follows: The quantum of light always travels with the velocity 3×10^{10} cm/sec. Matter, however, is observed to travel with any lower velocity; the theory of relativity even claims that matter can never reach the velocity of light. Light is easily *absorbed*, e.g., by a black body, and its energy changed into heat; furthermore light is easily *created*, e.g., when heating a metal filament by an electric current. This comparison makes it evident that one must not visualize a light quantum as a small piece of matter shooting through space.

Our discussion of the quantum theory is based on the experimental investigation of the photoelectric effect in which the new constant h first appears as a constant describing the slopes of certain empirical lines. Actually, Einstein in 1905 postulated the quantum of light and established his fundamental equation of the photoelectric effect [Eq. (8.1)] long before the difficult experiments were performed. Eleven years later the theory was confirmed by Millikan's measurements and by his determination of Planck's constant h from the photoelectric effect. Only the simple principle of his apparatus is described by Fig. 8.1, while the actual apparatus, constructed for the preparation of clean metal surfaces, was so complicated that he called it a "machine shop in high vacuum."

It is striking how thoroughly the theory affects our judgment of the importance of one field or another. Strictly from the experimental point of view, the photoelectric effect seems to be a rather remote corner of physics with technical applications of limited significance. However, Einstein's theory makes it clear that the photoelectric effect gives evidence of the nature of light, one of the greatest problems of physics.

8.4. Applications of the Photoelectric Effect. The fact that the photoelectric current is proportional to the intensity of light makes the photoelectric cell a convenient and accurate photometer. For research purposes a modification, the "photomultiplier," is extensively used. In this instrument an additional effect is applied, "secondary electron emission." When a metal surface is bombarded with electrons accelerated by, say, 100 volts, the following two effects take place concurrently. The surface

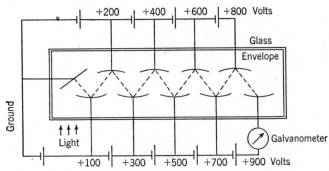

Fig. 8.8. Schematic diagram of photomultiplier.

may swallow the electrons and let them flow away as "conduction electrons" or the impinging electrons may knock out new electrons, called "secondary electrons," from the surface. Under favorable conditions of energies and materials, more electrons may leave the surface than are incident, so that a resulting current flows opposite to the incident electron current and is stronger than this current. (The principle of conservation of energy postulates that the combined kinetic energies of the secondary electrons are less than the kinetic energies of the incident electrons.) This effect is used to amplify an originally very weak photoelectric current. Figure 8.8 shows the arrangement of the instrument called a "photomultiplier." While the photoelectric surface P emits a very weak current, each secondary emitter (called "dynode") amplifies the current so that the over-all amplification may amount to 10^6.

The use of photoelectric cells is of great importance in television. Of numerous other applications only two typical ones may be mentioned. The "magic eye" opens doors to incoming persons. Light and dark cigars are sorted with the help of photoelectric currents indicating the light scattered by the cigars.

8.5. Supporting Evidence Given by Photochemistry. Simultaneously with the fundamental equation of the photoelectric effect, Einstein proposed the fundamental law of photochemistry as another foundation of the quantum theory of light.   In photochemistry chemical reactions produced by light are investigated.   In most cases the reaction progresses in several steps.   The absorption of light causes a primary reaction which is followed by secondary reactions of the atoms and radicals produced. Einstein's fundamental law is the consistent application of the idea of the light quantum.   It states: *Each quantum of light absorbed causes 1 molecule to react in the primary reaction.*

The relation of this statement to the observations will become clear when we consider an example.   It is observed that hydrogen iodide, HI, is decomposed by light into hydrogen, H_2, and iodine, I_2.   The "yield" of the reaction is defined as the number of HI molecules decomposed, divided by the number of quanta absorbed.   The yield has been measured as 2 molecules decomposed for each quantum absorbed, which seems twice the amount predicted by Einstein's fundamental law.   In order to explain this yield, secondary reactions are assumed as follows.   First each quantum $h\nu$ absorbed decomposes 1 molecule, schematically written

$$HI + h\nu \rightarrow H + I$$

(How dissociation by light shows up in a continuous absorption spectrum will be discussed in Sec. 12.4*b*.)   The free H atom so produced has such a strong affinity for another H atom that it decomposes a second HI molecule and so forms an H_2 molecule by the reaction

$$H + HI \rightarrow H_2 + I$$

However, the free I atoms produced by these two steps cannot decompose HI molecules; instead, each migrates through the gas until it meets another free I atom, with which it forms a molecule:

$$I + I \rightarrow I_2$$

This theoretical scheme explains the observed yield of 2 molecules per quantum since each photochemical decomposition of 1 molecule is automatically followed by one and only one additional decomposition.

The quantum theory of light makes understandable a fact that has been known for a long time.   Ultraviolet light is far more effective in producing chemical reactions than visible light; on the other hand, for most reactions infrared light is completely ineffective.   For example, the human skin feels red, and infrared, light only as producing *heat;* however, it is *chemically* affected by ultraviolet light.   The theory explains this fact by the idea that each chemical change in a molecule, *e.g.*, dissociation, requires a certain minimum energy to be supplied by the quantum. If the quantum has energy in excess of the minimum required, as may be the case for ultraviolet light, this excess goes into kinetic energy of the products. If, however, the energy of the quantum is insufficient, the process cannot take place. For example, the lowest frequency of light sufficient for the dissociation of HI molecules is about $\nu = 7.5 \times 10^{14}$ sec^{-1} ($\lambda = 4,000$ A). The energy of this quantum $h\nu$ follows as 5.0×10^{-12} erg, or 3.1 ev, or 72,000 cal/mole (see Sec. 7.3).

It is not safe to assume that this limit represents the energy of dissociation of the HI molecule, since it has been found that some molecules do not respond to certain ranges of frequency although the energy of the quantum would be sufficient to produce the chemical reaction. This is explained in detail in the theory of molecular spectra with which we are not concerned here. We shall discuss experimental evidence for it in Sec. 12.10. All we can safely conclude from the fact mentioned is that the energy of dissociation of HI is *equal to or smaller than* 5.0×10^{-12} erg.

Photochemical reactions play a part in living organisms. The process of visual excitation seems to be connected with a photochemical reaction in the retina. The quantum of light enters into the question: How many quanta are required to produce the faintest sensation of light? One quantum is not sufficient, but it seems that as few as five to seven quanta absorbed by the retina may produce a sensation. The light flash incident on the eye must contain more quanta since by no means all quanta incident on the eye reach the retina. The photochemical reaction of outstanding importance is "photosynthesis." This is the reaction responsible for the nutrition of plants. Red light enables the chlorophyll, a green dye contained in leaves, to break up CO_2 molecules contained in the air and build the C atoms into the structure of the plant. The number of quanta required to start photosynthesis reveals important features of the process (see Sec. 12.4).

Our examples make it clear that photochemical reactions give evidence supporting the quantum theory of light, although, because of the secondary reactions, the evidence is not so clear-cut as that based on the photoelectric effect.

8.6. Supporting Evidence Given by the Compton Effect. In our endeavor to find experimental tests of the quantum theory of light we must mention the Compton effect, although we shall be able to discuss it in detail only after investigating X-ray spectra (Sec. 14.3). We shall find evidence that X rays are essentially of the same nature as light, except that their wavelengths are 1,000 or 10,000 times smaller than those of visible light. We can measure the wavelengths or frequencies of X rays, observing diffraction by a ruled grating or, preferably, a crystal grating (Sec. 14.1f). Furthermore, for any frequency ν so determined, we can compute the energy of the quanta $h\nu$.

A. H. Compton (1923) discovered that X rays of a sharply defined frequency incident on material of low atomic weight, like carbon or paraffin, may suffer a change of frequency when scattered. While the spectrum of the scattered X rays still contains the original frequency, in addition X rays of smaller frequency are produced, the shift of frequency depending on the angle between incident and scattered rays. Compton also discovered that this shift of frequency can be predicted by a bold application of the quantum theory of light. He assumed that each quantum of X rays, as well as a moving body, may be characterized by its energy and its momentum. This enabled him to apply the laws of mechanical impacts, governing the collisions between billiard balls or between atoms, to the impacts of X-ray quanta on matter. We have learned already that atoms and molecules contain electrons in their structure (Sec. 6.2a). At the impact of an X-ray quantum on an electron contained in the carbon or paraffin a part of the energy of the incident quantum is transferred to the electron. The mathematical analysis of this process, to be discussed later, leads to the prediction that the X-ray quantum loses a part of its energy, hence the scattered X ray shows a *shift toward low frequencies* in good agreement with the observed shift. In addition, the magnitude of the *energy transferred to the electron* is theoretically predicted; it has been measured with a technique to be discussed later (Wilson's cloud chamber, Sec. 17.2), again in agreement with the theory. Thus the Compton effect supplies another confirmation of the quantum theory of light.

8.7. Brief Report on Wave Mechanics. The student is by no means asked to discard the "classical" electromagnetic wave theory of light, which is firmly founded on the observations of diffraction and interference, and instead to accept the more recent quantum theory. Einstein himself, when proposing the theory of light quanta in 1905, did not claim that it represents an absolute truth. He suggested it only as a tentative new principle that may lead to new discoveries. The discrepancy between the quantum theory (assuming energy quanta concentrated in space) and the electromagnetic theory (assuming waves whose energy is diluted proportional to the inverse square of the distance) is solved by "wave mechanics" (1925). We must postpone the discussion of wave mechanics because we are not prepared yet to study its experimental foundation, *i.e.*, electron diffraction. Therefore, we prefer first to discuss the structure of individual atoms. This arrangement will demonstrate how great and well-founded a progress in the understanding of atoms we can make without referring to wave mechanics, which, however, is indispensable on the advanced level. Here we insert only a brief report on wave mechanics.

The solution of the discrepancy came from the surprising discovery that a beam of *electrons*, as well as a beam of *light*, when incident on an exceedingly fine grating is subject to *diffraction*. We are forced to conclude that Newtonian mechanics breaks down in the description of the motion of the lightest particles. This failure of the old theory opens up the opportunity for a new hypothesis. In order to describe electron diffraction, we hypothetically *attribute waves to particles* (wavelength = h/momentum) and compute the diffraction pattern of these waves passing through the fine grating. Thus in this branch of mechanics we correlate the concepts of *particles and waves* as in optics we correlate *quanta and waves*. Hence the new discrepancy in the description of the lightest particles is analogous to the discrepancy we just discussed that is concerned with light. What part do we attribute to the waves? We shall first discuss the solution offered by wave mechanics in terms of *light*. To begin with, we must discard the naïve concept that quanta which do not collide with matter necessarily travel in straight lines. Instead wave mechanics predicts the motion of quanta by the following hypothesis: We must first compute the propagation of waves starting from the source of light as prescribed by the "classical" theory of light. However, it is assumed that these waves do not carry energy *uniformly distributed* over the wave front as water waves or sound waves do. Instead the energy is supposed to be *concentrated in quanta hν*. The waves have only the rather abstract function to prescribe the probability that quanta are traveling through one or another spot. Thus, for example, interference fringes behind a slit are understood as follows. The computation of waves leads to certain maxima and minima at definite positions in space, indicating that quanta are traveling through these positions with high or low probability, respectively, and so produce bright and dark fringes on a screen.

Wave mechanics applies the same basic idea to the description of the motion of the lightest particles. Again we introduce the hypothesis of waves, which here do not carry *mass* uniformly distributed but only describe the probability that particles are traveling through one or another spot. Heavier particles are associated with wavelengths so exceedingly short that diffraction is not noticeable. This last statement of wave mechanics agrees with Newton's first law, which predicts rectilinear motion of a body on which no force is acting.

The student may well anticipate the study of electron diffraction and wave mechanics (Chaps. 21 and 22), keeping in mind that the understanding of electron diffraction presupposes the study of X-ray diffraction (Sec. 14.1f).

SUMMARY OF CHAPTER 8

Here we finish our discussion of the structure of matter as consisting of atoms, of electricity as consisting of electrons, and of light or X rays as consisting of quanta.   Looking back, we compare the evidence on which these various statements are founded.

The *atomic structure of matter* is inferred from the vast array of the facts of chemistry.   The existence of atoms is confirmed by the positive-ray analysis in which atomic weights are found bearing the same proportions as those determined by chemical methods.

Very much simpler is the evidence of the *atomic structure of electricity*. The smallest electric charges accessible to measurements, those carried by tiny oil drops, have values represented by multiples of a certain charge.   As this charge is independent of all special conditions of the experiment, we are forced to conclude that it is a fundamental property of electricity.

Most involved, it seems to us, is the argument that leads to the *quantum structure of light*.   The fundamental law of the photoelectric effect correlates the maximum kinetic energy W_m given to the photoelectrons with the frequency ν of the light: $W_m = h\nu - \phi$.   This equation, which describes the observed facts, seems incompatible with the wave theory of light.   Einstein anticipated this equation long before the experiments were performed by assuming that light waves contain, instead of energy uniformly distributed over the wave front, quanta of energy $h\nu$ so concentrated that one incident quantum may liberate one electron if the quantum is large enough.   The principle of conservation of energy, when applied to the liberation of an electron by a quantum, leads to an equation identical with that describing the experiment.   In particular, Einstein's idea explains the threshold frequency characteristic of a metal by the minimum size of a quantum just able to supply the energy of liberation ϕ. Although the wave theory of light is well supported by interference and diffraction of light, the quantum theory of light seems indispensable for the explanation of the photoelectric effect.

As another application of the quantum theory of light Einstein discovered the fundamental law of photochemistry, which states that each quantum of light absorbed causes one molecule to react in the primary photochemical reaction.   The theory of the Compton effect (a wavelength shift observed in scattered X rays) supplies another confirmation of the quantum theory of light.   Wave theory and quantum theory of light, although apparently contradictory, are reconciled by wave mechanics.

PROBLEMS

8.1. *Determination of Planck's constant.*   An experiment on the photoelectric effect on potassium leads to the following data: Irradiations with yellow light from a sodium arc and ultraviolet light from a mercury arc (5,890 and 2,537 A) liberate electrons with the stopping potentials 0.36 and 3.14 volts, respectively.   Given the charge on the electron, derive (*a*) Planck's constant h; (*b*) the work function ϕ of potassium; (*c*) the long-wavelength limit of the photoelectric effect on potassium.

8.2. *Stopping potentials.* Light of the prominent mercury line 2537 A ejects from a metal surface electrons that have a stopping potential of 2.60 volts. Calculate the stopping potential of electrons ejected from the same metal by the other prominent mercury line 1849 A.

8.3. *Number of quanta required for heating.* Green light ($\lambda = 5,000 \times 10^{-8}$ cm) is completely absorbed by the mercury bulb of a thermometer. This bulb contains 2.00 g of mercury. How many quanta of light must be absorbed in order to heat the bulb 3.00°C? Neglect all losses of heat.

8.4. *Number of quanta received by one cm².* Suppose that a source of yellow light ($\lambda = 5,900$ A) has an intensity of 1 candlepower. This means that at a distance of 1 m from the source, the energy passing 1 cm² in 1 sec is 1.162×10^{-5} cal. How many light quanta are passing 1 cm² in 1 sec? (1 cal $= 4.18 \times 10^{7}$ ergs.)

8.5. *Number of quanta per second barely visible.* The human eye is barely able to see a star of sixth magnitude, equivalent to 10^{-8} candlepower at a distance of 1 m. How many quanta are passing per second through the pupil of the eye? (Diameter of pupil = 3 mm.) Assume the same λ as in Prob. 8.4 and the same conversion factor.

8.6. *Density of quanta.* (a) Light of frequency ν is traveling in a parallel beam of intensity I (in erg/cm² sec). Calculate the density in space n of quanta (= number/ cm³) in terms of I and ν. (b) Calculate the density n for barely visible yellow light as defined in Prob. 8.5.

8.7. *Yield of photoelectric effect.* Only a small fraction of all quanta incident on a metal surface liberate electrons. The probability for the individual quantum to do so is called the "photoelectric yield." Calculate the yield for the light defined in Prob. 8.4, assuming that on a sodium surface of 5.00 cm² it causes a saturation current of 2.31×10^{-8} amp.

PART V
ELECTRONIC STRUCTURE OF ATOMS

In the kinetic theory of gases we describe the individual atom as a body of a certain mass and size. In the next two parts we shall discuss the detailed structure of individual atoms. We shall start from Rutherford's observation of the scattering of alpha particles, which leads to the picture of an atom consisting of a small nucleus surrounded by electrons. Here we shall carry the exploration of the nuclei only so far as it is needed for the understanding of spectra and the periodic table of elements. The picture of the nuclear atom so arrived at justifies the subdivision of the further discussion into that of the *electronic* structure (Part V) and that of the *nuclear* structure (Part VI).

CHAPTER 9

NUCLEAR ATOM AS REVEALED BY ALPHA-RAY SCATTERING

9.1. Discovery of the Nuclear Atom. Rutherford and his collaborators, in 1911, investigated the scattering of alpha rays by thin metal foils. By this time alpha rays were known as one of the radiations emanating from radium and some other radioactive elements. For the present purpose it is sufficient to record some of their outstanding properties, which give evidence of their nature. Alpha rays, when hitting certain substances, for example zinc sulfide crystals, produce flashes of light called "scintillations." When a zinc sulfide screen is irradiated by rays from a weak radium sample, a well-rested eye using a magnifying lens resolves the light emitted from the screen into short localized flashes. These scintillations show that the alpha ray is emitted discontinuously and might be composed of a stream of particles. The student may see such flashes when viewing the luminous paint of a watch through a magnifying lens in a dark room; this paint contains a very weak radioactive material embedded in a fluorescent screen.

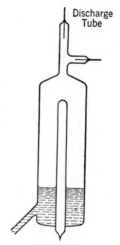

Discharge Tube

FIG. 9.1. Experiment showing the identity of alpha particles and helium nuclei.

Alpha rays have a *penetrating power* which enables them to pass through metal foils or thin glass walls. This is demonstrated by the observation that such thin foils do not prevent the alpha rays from causing the discharge of an electroscope.

The nature of the alpha rays becomes evident when they accumulate in a glass tube and are made to exhibit their optical spectrum. This experiment was performed by Rutherford in an apparatus shown in Fig. 9.1. A quantity of a radioactive gas (radon, see Sec. 17.4) was introduced into a very thin-walled glass tube. This was surrounded by a wider, highly evacuated glass tube which was connected with a small electric-discharge tube. For the spectroscopic investigation all gas that accumulated in the wider tube was compressed into the small discharge tube by the raising of a mercury level. After a few days the accumulated gases when excited by an electric discharge exhibited the spectrum of

99

helium.   A control experiment showed that helium gas could not have leaked through the thin-walled tube.   Rutherford concluded that the alpha rays are composed of particles which are essentially the same as helium atoms but which can penetrate the thin glass wall while helium atoms cannot.   This result immediately gives information about the mass of the alpha particle.   If we assume that the alpha particle has the same mass as the helium atom it resembles, the mass of the alpha particle is larger than the mass of hydrogen in the ratio of their atomic weights.   Hence the mass is $m = 6.64 \times 10^{-24}$ g.

What distinguishes the alpha particle from the helium atom?   Alpha particles are deflected by strong electric or magnetic fields in the direction characteristic of *positively* charged particles.   Their specific charge e/m and speed are measured by the method which J. J. Thomson applied to cathode rays, discussed in Sec. 6.2a.   Here, however, the ray does not originate in an electric discharge but is emitted from a radioactive substance which continuously ejects in any direction high-speed alpha rays from which a narrow pencil is selected by a diaphragm and subjected to the electric and magnetic fields.   The result is $e/m = 4.82 \times 10^3$ emu/g.   This figure combined with the mass m given above leads to a positive charge $e = 3.20 \times 10^{-20}$ emu.   This is just twice the well-known electronic charge (Sec. 7.1).   The speed v of the particles is characteristic of the specific radioactive element; *e.g.*, radium emits alpha particles of a speed $v = 1.519 \times 10^9$ cm/sec.

Here is an apparent discrepancy, since in the earlier experiment of Fig. 9.1 we found that the alpha particles collected in a glass tube emit the same spectrum as *neutral* helium atoms while in the deflection experiments they show up as *positively charged* particles.   This discrepancy forces us to assume that each alpha particle, while slowing down by collisions, picks up two electrons either from the glass wall or the mercury surface and so changes into a neutral atom.

We summarize the properties of alpha rays that were known before Rutherford's work on their scattering: The rays consist of individual particles which are identical with *doubly positively charged helium ions*. They are able to produce scintillations and to pass through metal foils.

Rutherford and his collaborators investigated the scattering of alpha particles by observing what happens to a beam of such particles when penetrating thin gold foil (Fig. 9.2).   Their apparatus was in principle constructed as follows.   Radium R, enclosed in a metal capsule, emits through a canal a narrow pencil of alpha rays which are incident on gold foil F.   The scattered particles are observed on a fluorescent screen S through a microscope M.   While the radium and the foil are mounted on a table, the screen with the microscope can swing around the foil and thus intercept the alpha particles scattered into any direction, forward as well as behind the foil.   The apparatus is evacuated (not indicated on the diagram) so that collisions of the alpha particles with air molecules are excluded.

Let us try to predict what happens.   A thin gold foil of 6×10^{-5} cm thickness is experimentally proved airtight and hence has no holes.   Each

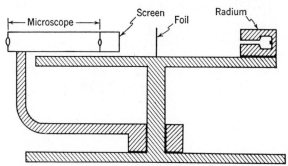

FIG. 9.2. The screen with the microscope swings around the gold foil and shows scintillations due to *alpha particles scattered in any direction*.   The apparatus is mounted in vacuum.

gold atom has a diameter (estimated by the methods discussed in Sec. 7.2) of 3×10^{-8} cm.   Therefore, the foil toward which we shoot alpha particles contains as many as 2,000 molecules lined up along its thickness. We may compare the gold foil with an array of billiard balls, closely packed on a large table, 2,000 balls thick, and represent the alpha particle by another, much lighter ball which we try to shoot through the thickness of 2,000 balls (Fig. 9.3).   We feel safe in predicting that we shall be unable to shoot this lighter ball through the vast array of billiard balls, or, by analogy, to shoot the alpha particles through the gold foil.

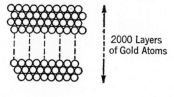

FIG. 9.3. Alpha particle incident on gold foil; atoms pictured as solid balls.

This plausible prediction turned out to be wrong.   Rutherford found that most alpha particles still produce scintillations at nearly the same spot as before the foil was introduced.   Hence they are hardly affected by the gold foil.   But a small percentage of the particles are deflected through considerable angles, some even by more than 90°, *i.e.*, turned back by the foil.   For each material the number of alpha particles scattered is proportional to the thickness of the foil provided this is small.

Rutherford explained these observations by introducing the important assumption that the mass of the gold atom is concentrated in a very small nucleus.   More in detail, his picture is as follows.   Since, in the electric discharge, electrons are knocked out of atoms, leaving positive ions, we infer that electrons occur in the *external* structure of atoms. Rutherford's new assumption is that the center of each atom is formed by a nucleus carrying a positive charge which keeps the electrons assembled. In the neutral atom the nuclear charge has to be as large as the total charge of all the surrounding electrons. The Coulomb force binding the electrons to the nucleus has the same mathematical form as the gravitational force, both being inverse-square laws. Hence, to a certain extent, Rutherford's atom is similar to the solar system; the electrons travel around the nucleus as the planets travel around the sun. Since the mass of the electrons is very small as compared to the mass of the atom Rutherford assumes that nearly the whole mass of the atom is concentrated in the nucleus. For the explanation of the high transmission of gold foil for alpha particles Rutherford assumes further that the nucleus is exceedingly small as compared to the whole atom.

To a limited extent Rutherford's idea of circulating electrons was anticipated by Ampère (1823) in a much earlier period when nothing was known of the structure of individual atoms. In order to explain the magnetism of iron, Ampère assumed that each atom contains a small circular current which may be oriented by an external magnetic field.

In applying Rutherford's picture of the atom to the passage of alpha particles through gold foil, we keep in mind the law of elastic collisions derived in mechanics (see Prob. 9.1). The results of this important problem will be applied to several other arguments. There it is proved that a light body that hits a heavy body simply bounces back or is deflected sideways without an appreciable transfer of kinetic energy. Everybody knows that a ball that hits the earth bounces back and changes only its direction, not its kinetic energy. In the opposite case of a heavy body striking a light object, the heavy body continues on its straight path with negligible loss of kinetic energy, while the light object is thrown aside. An example is given by the collision of a heavy truck with a pedestrian, in so far as we are allowed to treat this collision as elastic. After the collision, the truck continues its straight path.

On the basis of the theory of the nuclear atom, Rutherford's observation is understandable. As seen from the incoming ray, all the nuclei contained in the thin gold foil by no means appear to fill the whole surface area uniformly, but are only little specks which, like the stars in the sky, are very small as compared to their mutual distances. While most alpha particles shoot straight through the array of nuclei, a few approach close enough to a gold nucleus to be strongly deflected although without transferring any appreciable energy, the alpha particle being much lighter than the gold nucleus. The observed fact that the large deflections are rare (say one in several thousand) proves that they are due to single events, since several close approaches of one particle during its passage would be vanishingly rare.   More frequently the alpha particles collide with the numerous electrons contained in the gold.   Here the alpha particle is the much heavier body and shoots straight ahead, throwing the light electrons away from its path.   This prediction of two types of collision processes suffered by alpha particles, rare collisions with nuclei and frequent collisions with electrons, will be strikingly confirmed by observations with the cloud chamber to be described in Sec. 17.2.

In order to explain the free passage of the alpha particle through the spaces between the nuclei, the alpha particle itself must be assumed to be a very small body, not of the dimensions of an atom with its revolving electrons but as small as a nucleus.   This inference completes our picture of the alpha particle, which we found at first to be a helium atom that had lost 2 electrons.   Now, by its penetrating power, we recognize it as an atom stripped of *all* electrons.   We draw the conclusion, important for our later discussion of chemistry, that the alpha particle is a helium nucleus carrying two positive electronic charges.   This complicated argument will be confirmed by the spectrum emitted from helium ions (Sec. 10.6).   We shall further explore the properties of alpha particles in Secs. 16.3 and 17.2.

The effective size of the atom is entirely different in the kinetic theory of gases and in the case discussed here, the passage of alpha particles. In the kinetic theory we are dealing with mutual collisions between atoms or molecules; their *electronic* structures are responsible for their cross sections.   The alpha particle, however, is deflected not by electrons but only by nuclei.   Here the effective size of a gold atom is represented only by the small space in which the Coulomb field surrounding the nucleus is strong enough to produce a noticeable deflection of the alpha particle.

Considering the great complication of many modern experiments in nuclear physics that require a staff of experts and special buildings, it is striking how simple is the technique in Rutherford's experiment on the scattering of alpha particles.   An alpha emitter behind a gold foil, a fluorescent screen attached to a microscope that can be rotated in an airtight metal box—these are the essential parts required for an experiment that has led to one of the most important new ideas on atomic structure.

9.2. Charge of the Nucleus.   Rutherford and his collaborators developed the qualitative observations just discussed into a measurement of nuclear charges.   Suppose we compare two foils, silver and platinum, both with the same number of atoms per square centimeter of the foil. Then the alpha ray suffers *equal numbers of deflections* in both foils, but **the** nuclei with *larger nuclear charge*, producing larger Coulomb forces, cause *deflection through larger angles*.   Thus the number of particles scattered by a foil at various angles of deflection serves to determine the charges of the nuclei.   The theoretical treatment, which requires calculus, is given in Appendix 6.

Table 9.1 gives the nuclear charges (in multiples of the electronic charge) measured in this way by Chadwick for three elements.   They are compared with the atomic numbers of the elements.

The atomic number of an element, familiar to the chemist, is defined as follows: When writing all elements in the order of their atomic weights, we count the lightest element, hydrogen, as 1, the second lightest, helium, as 2, etc.   These numbers are called the "atomic numbers" of the elements.   Some minor adjustments of the numbers so defined will be mentioned in the chapter on the Periodic Table of Elements, Sec. 13.1.

Table 9.1.   *Atomic Numbers and Nuclear Charges*
(In multiples of the electronic charge)

Element	Atomic No.	Nuclear charge
Copper.............	29	29.3 ± 0.5
Silver..............	47	46.3 ± 0.8
Platinum...........	78	77.4 ± 0.8

The table shows the striking and simple result that, within the accuracy of the measurement, *the nuclear charge equals the atomic number*.   In our discussion of spectroscopy we shall find more evidence confirming this important relation.

9.3. Size of the Nucleus.   In addition to the vague result that the nucleus is very small as compared with the size of the atom, the scattering of alpha particles leads to an estimate of the size of the nucleus.   In most cases the theoretical picture of point charges mutually repelled by the Coulomb force adequately describes the observed scattering.   This picture leads to the simple theory of scattering (Appendix 6).   From the kinetic energy of the impinging alpha particle we can compute the distance of the closest possible approach, which takes place in a head-on collision (see Prob. 9.3).   The good agreement between theory and observation proves that the Coulomb law correctly describes the repulsive force down to this distance; hence it gives an upper limit for the size of the nucleus.   For uranium this has been determined to 3×10^{-12} cm, for copper 10^{-12} cm.

It has been found, however, that the agreement between theory and experiment, although good for the heavy elements, fails for the bombardment of light elements like aluminum by high-energy alpha particles. (Here the theory must be refined by taking into account the fact that the target nucleus recoils when hit by the alpha particle, as discussed in Prob. 9.3.)   In this case the approach of the alpha particle to the nucleus is extremely close, partly because of the high kinetic energy of the particle, partly because of the low charge of the light nucleus.   The deviation of the scattering from the theoretically predicted law forces us to assume that for this very close approach the repulsion is no longer correctly represented by our theory which is based on the Coulomb law but that these alpha particles penetrate so far that a bodily collision takes place.   The distance of approach, which is 0.6×10^{-12} cm for the aluminum nucleus, is then an estimate of the size of the nucleus.   When in a model the nucleus is given the diameter 1 cm, the whole atom has a diameter of about 400 m.

The present chapter gives us the preliminary knowledge of the nuclei that will be needed for the discussion of spectroscopy and the periodic table of elements.   The systematic discussion of nuclei will be continued in Part VI.

SUMMARY OF CHAPTER 9

The nature of alpha rays is inferred from the following observations. The rays produce short, localized scintillations on certain screens, indicating that they consist of individual particles, which are able to penetrate metal foils.   When collected in a small glass tube, they show by their optical spectrum that they are essentially the same as helium.   This gives the individual particle a mass of nearly 4 hydrogen atoms.   The measurement of e/m (combined with this mass) shows that each alpha particle carries the charge of 2 electrons but with a positive sign, in other words, that it is a doubly charged helium ion.

Rutherford discovered that alpha particles penetrate thin gold foils without an appreciable deflection except for a few particles that are scattered through large angles.   Rutherford explained this observation by the picture of the nuclear atom.   He assumed that the mass of the gold atom is concentrated in a small nucleus carrying a large positive charge, which attracts electrons and holds them in stable orbits around the nucleus just as the sun holds the planets in their paths by gravitation. At the same time he assumed that each alpha particle is a very small bullet, presumably itself a nucleus.   This last assumption, combined with the above result that the alpha particle carries two positive electronic charges, attributes to the helium nucleus the positive charge 2, giving the neutral helium atom 2 external electrons.

The deflections of alpha particles by films of various metals have been studied quantitatively.   In this way the nuclear charges of various atoms have been measured, with the result that the nuclear charge equals the atomic number.

The order of magnitude of the nuclear size is 10^{-12} cm.

PROBLEMS

9.1. *Elastic collisions I (head-on collisions).* Elastic collisions are of great importance in atomic physics. The concept describes, for example, collisions between gaseous atoms or collisions of electrons with atoms or of alpha particles with nuclei or, in
the theory of the Compton effect, of X-ray quanta with electrons. In the text we
shall repeatedly refer to the present problem.

Elastic collisions are collisions in which the kinetic energy present before the collision is completely conserved as kinetic energy. This is true, to a good approximation,
for collisions between billiard balls. After the collision, the bodies in general proceed
in different directions. We restrict ourselves to the special case of the head-on collision, *i.e.*, the case in which all motion before and after the collision takes place in the
same straight line.

Suppose that a body of the mass m_1 (velocity u_1) collides head on with a body of the
mass m_2, which, before the collision, is at rest (velocity $u_2 = 0$). Compute the velocities v_1 and v_2 after the collision on the basis of the laws of conservation of energy and
momentum. Write the result for three special cases: (1) $m_1 = m_2$, (2) m_1 negligible
compared with m_2, and (3) m_2 negligible as compared with m_1.

HINT: *a.* Write the principle of conservation of energy, stating that before and after
the collision the total kinetic energy is the same.

b. Write the law of conservation of momentum, making the corresponding statement for the linear momentum. Since the momentum of a body may be positive or
negative, you must define a direction as positive, *e.g.*, the direction of the velocity u_1.

c. Express the unknowns v_1 and v_2, in terms of the known quantities m_1, m_2, u_1.

d. Write this result for the three special cases mentioned above. (The quadratic
equation will give two solutions, one of which represents the case of m_1 continuing its
path without affecting the target m_2. This solution is ruled out since one body cannot penetrate another.)

9.2. *Elastic collisions II.* This is an example of an elastic collision in which we
drop the assumption of the head-on collision (Prob. 9.1). We simplify the problem
by assuming equal masses of the two bodies. The problem serves as a preparation for
the theory of the Compton effect (Sec. 14.3; see Fig. 14.23).

A projectile, *e.g.*, a billiard ball or an atom (velocity u_1), collides with a target of
equal mass which, before the collision, is at rest. The projectile bounces off at any
angle ϕ. (Let us define the angles which are counterclockwise to the direction of u_1,
like ϕ in the figure, as positive.) We arbitrarily consider those projectiles which
bounce off at a given angle ϕ. Compute the velocities v_1 and v_2 of both bodies and
the angle θ at which the target goes off. Finally introduce $\phi = 30°$.

HINT: As in the preceding problem, we write the equations expressing the conservation of energy and linear momentum. As the energy is a scalar quantity, its
conservation is described by one equation. The linear momentum, however, is a
vector, hence described by its three components. Since we are dealing with a process
taking place in a plane, only two components must be taken into account, the third
being zero.

a. Write the following equations: (1) the conservation of energy; (2) the conservation of the component of the momentum in the direction of the incoming projectile,
and (3) the same in the direction normal to the incoming projectile.

b. Evaluate the unknowns v_1, v_2, and θ as follows: (1) Rearrange Eqs. (2) and (3) so
that only the members containing θ are on the left sides. (2) Square and add the
equations; this yields an equation for $v_2{}^2$. (3) Use this equation combined with
Eq. (1) to eliminate $v_2{}^2$. This leaves an equation for v_1. (4) Express v_2 and $\sin \theta$ in
terms of the given quantities u_1 and ϕ. (5) Introduce $\phi = 30°$.

9.3. *Approach of alpha particle to nucleus.* Suppose that the fastest alpha particles occurring in nature (those emitted from thorium C'', energy 8.8 Mev) are scattered by uranium. Compute the distance of the closest possible approach, assuming that the force acting between the alpha particle and the uranium nucleus is given by the Coulomb repulsion. Equate the initial kinetic energy to the potential energy at the closest approach. See the review given in Sec. 10.3.

9.4. *Passing of alpha particles through gold foil.* Alpha particles are incident on gold foil of a thickness 6×10^{-5} cm. Calculate the fraction of the surface area of the foil that, as seen from the incoming alpha particles, is occupied by the gold nuclei. Given: density of gold 19.3; diameter of gold nucleus $= 3 \times 10^{-12}$ cm.

COMMENT: Deflection takes place not only by direct hit but also by a passage close to a nucleus.

CHAPTER 10

SPECTRUM OF THE HYDROGEN ATOM
AND BOHR'S THEORY

Rutherford's theory of the nuclear atom, further developed by Bohr, has led to a detailed explanation of atomic spectra, in particular the spectrum of the hydrogen atom. This is the subject of the present chapter. We shall start from the discussion of the spectrum observed and shall find that the electromagnetic theory of light fails to explain it. Next we shall discuss Bohr's theory of the hydrogen atom and its application to the helium ion. Finally, in order to judge the validity of Bohr's theory, we shall give a brief report of further comparisons between the advanced development of the theory and experiments.

10.1. Spectrum of Hydrogen Atoms. We begin the study of spectra with a brief historical outline of spectroscopy. Newton, in 1666, was the first to analyze white light into its spectral colors by observing the dispersion of sunlight passing through a prism. Later (around 1800) the spectrum was extended on both sides of the visible region into the ranges called "infrared" and "ultraviolet." Fraunhofer (1814) improved the observation of the solar spectrum and found many narrow, black lines on the bright, colored background. Kirchhoff and Bunsen (1859) discovered that any given spectral line defined by its wavelength (or frequency) is characteristic of a type of atom; *e.g.*, a prominent pair of yellow lines at 5,890 and 5,896 A, emitted from a bunsen burner or electric arc between carbon electrodes, indicates the presence of sodium atoms. Furthermore, they found that certain spectral lines observed in absorption, *i.e.*, as black lines on the background of a white spectrum, exactly coincide in wavelength with well-known emission lines. This is true for the yellow pair of lines just mentioned. Hence the absorption lines as well as the emission lines serve for the identification of sodium atoms. This discovery explained the dark lines observed by Fraunhofer in the solar spectrum. Kirchhoff and Bunsen interpreted them as absorption lines produced by the solar atmosphere on the white background emitted from the body of the sun. Since they were able to identify many of the Fraunhofer lines with spectral lines observed at the laboratory, *e.g.*, those of sodium, calcium, and iron, they accomplished the equivalent of a chemical analysis of the solar atmosphere. Since then almost all the lines observed in emission or absorption in the spectra of the sun and stars have been so identified.   This is the basis of astrophysics.   The progress that has been made in the study of the cosmos using this discovery would have seemed unthinkable before the time of Kirchhoff and Bunsen.

The analysis of atomic spectra began in 1885 when Balmer represented, by a simple formula, a series of spectral lines observed in an electric discharge through hydrogen.   In 1906 Lyman discovered a hydrogen series in the extreme ultraviolet related to the Balmer series.   The analysis of spectra, atomic and molecular, has been continued up to the present time. On the basis of Rutherford's discovery of the nuclear atom (1911), Bohr in 1913 introduced his theory explaining the hydrogen spectrum, which was the starting point of a vast development of atomic theory.

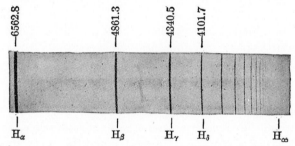

FIG. 10.1.   Balmer series of atomic hydrogen excited by an electric discharge (photographic negative). H_∞ marks the computed position of the series limit.   (*Courtesy of G. Herzberg and Dover Publications.   Reprinted from G. Herzberg, "Atomic Spectra and Atomic Structure,"* 1944.)

When an electric discharge is maintained in hydrogen, a very complicated spectrum is observed.   This spectrum is seen to consist of two parts: a well-ordered series of a few brilliant lines superimposed on a mess of very many weaker ones.   It is plausible to attribute the few bright lines to hydrogen *atoms* and the many background lines to hydrogen *molecules*, for the atoms, being simpler, might be expected to emit the simpler spectrum.   Although ordinary hydrogen gas consists of diatomic molecules, in the electric discharge one may well assume that the current dissociates some molecules into atoms.   This idea is confirmed by the fact that with increasing current the few brilliant lines gain in relative intensity, thus indicating increasing dissociation by the current.   We are interested only in the lines attributed to hydrogen atoms.   The visible part of the atomic spectrum consists of four lines, but a photographic investigation of the near ultraviolet region shows that these four are followed by many more lines, all converging toward a limit (Fig. 10.1). The first line of this series, called H_α, has a wavelength in vacuum of 6,562.80 A.   (Since experiments with gratings or interferometers yield measurements of *wavelengths*, it is conventional to use wavelengths for the description of experimental results; *frequencies* are more important for the theory.)

This is the series of lines, which Balmer represented by the simple formula

$$\nu = cR \left(\frac{1}{2^2} - \frac{1}{n^2} \right) \qquad n = 3, 4, 5, \ldots$$

Here ν is the frequency in $\sec^{-1}$; $c =$ velocity of light. (We introduce the factor c in order to represent the spectral lines by their *frequencies* in $\sec^{-1}$; without the factor c the formula would give *wave numbers =* reciprocal wavelengths in cm^{-1}.) For $n = 3$ the formula gives the first line, the conspicuous red line of the series, for $n = 4$ the second line, etc.; finally, as n approaches infinity, the convergence limit $\nu_c = cR/4$. R is a constant computed so that the formula represents the observed frequencies and is called the "Rydberg constant" after the distinguished Swedish spectroscopist. Its numerical value is

$$R = 109{,}677.58 \text{ cm}^{-1}$$

This figure gives evidence of the high accuracy of spectroscopic measurements.

In the extreme ultraviolet Lyman (1906) discovered a similar series with its first line at 1,215.7 A. He represented this series by the similar formula

$$\nu = cR \left(\frac{1}{1^2} - \frac{1}{n^2} \right) \qquad n = 2, 3, 4, \ldots$$

Here the constants c and R have the same significance as before. This series converges at the frequency $\nu_c = cR$. The theoretical significance of the Lyman series which becomes manifest in Bohr's theory justifies its designation as the prototype of all spectral series. Later Paschen found another similar series in the infrared represented by

$$\nu = cR \left(\frac{1}{3^2} - \frac{1}{n^2} \right) \qquad n = 4, 5, 6, \ldots$$

With improved experimental technique more such hydrogen series have been discovered in the infrared, but no other series are found in the ultraviolet at frequencies higher than those of the Lyman series.

All these series are represented by one comprehensive formula

$$\nu_{\text{obs}} = cR \left(\frac{1}{n''^2} - \frac{1}{n'^2} \right) \tag{10.1}$$

The subscript "obs" emphasizes that this formula describes observed frequencies which later will be compared with those resulting from the theory. The formula [Eq. (10.1)] gives the Lyman series when $n'' = 1$ and $n' = 2, 3, 4, \ldots$. Furthermore, it gives the Balmer series for $n'' = 2$ and $n' = 3, 4, 5, \ldots$. Several such series are schematically given by Fig. 10.2. Although our experimental knowledge of the infrared is limited, we infer that there are infinitely many such series, described by the same formula with larger integers n''. We shall call this the "Balmer formula."

In applying this formula, it is easy to change from the Lyman series to the Balmer series, $e.g.$, by exchanging $n'' = 1$ for $n'' = 2$. But the formula fails to say how difficult it is for the experimental physicist to observe the various series. The Balmer series is the one most easily found. Its visible lines may be seen with any spectroscope, and the higher lines in the near ultraviolet are photographed with a quartz spectrograph.

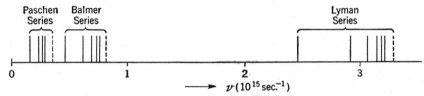

Fig. 10.2. First three series of atomic hydrogen. Broken lines indicate series limits. More infrared series appear at frequencies lower than those of the Paschen series.

The Lyman series, however, does not show up in the quartz spectrograph, in spite of the fact that quartz transmits ultraviolet light down to 2,000 A, a much shorter wavelength than the transmission limit of glass. Beyond this range three difficulties are encountered concurrently: (1) The quartz becomes opaque and must be replaced by one of the rare crystals like fluorite, which transmits light of still shorter wavelengths. (2) Ordinary photographic plates fail to respond, because the gelatin absorbs the light so strongly that it does not penetrate into the emulsion; special photographic plates must be prepared. (3) Since the air becomes opaque, the whole apparatus must be evacuated. Great progress has been made with fluorite vacuum spectrographs, but they fail to record the Lyman series because even fluorite crystals are opaque at the extremely short wavelength range of this series. For the range beyond that of fluorite, Lyman used a concave grating since this does not require any transparent substance and relies solely on the reflecting power of the metal on which the grating is ruled. In the extreme ultraviolet, this power, although weak, is still high enough. This explains the construction of Lyman's spectrograph (Fig. 10.3). A highly evacuated wide brass tube contains the grating, the plate of special type, and the slit; the electric discharge tube with hydrogen is cemented on in front of the slit.

Other difficulties are encountered in the investigation of the infrared spectrum. There a glass prism is opaque and must be replaced by a rock-salt prism or a grating. Photographic plates fail completely for reasons discussed in the section on photochemistry (Sec. 8.5). Instead, a bolometer or thermocouple records the incident radiation.

10.2. Failure of Electromagnetic Theory of Radiation. The electromagnetic theory of radiation (Sec. 8.2), based on the work of Maxwell and Hertz, has been so eminently successful that we must try to apply it to the spectrum just described. In this theory the atom is supposed to be similar to the antenna of a radio transmitter, although much smaller, of course, and radiating a much higher frequency. At first glance such a transmitter seems to emit light with some of the properties of the spectrum described. A transmitting antenna made of a straight piece of wire has a fundamental frequency of vibration and a series of harmonics of

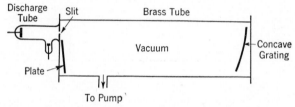

FIG. 10.3. Vacuum spectrograph (schematic diagram). The discharge tube is sealed to the wall of the spectrograph in front of the slit.

higher frequency, much like the characteristic frequencies of a violin string. But this series cannot be compared quantitatively to the series spectrum of hydrogen because the higher antenna harmonics are multiples of the fundamental frequency ν; i.e., their frequencies are 2ν, 3ν, 4ν, etc. Hence this series predicted by the electromagnetic theory fails to show the finite convergence limit characteristic of the hydrogen spectrum observed. Furthermore, the transmitter fails to show more than one such series, while the hydrogen atom exhibits many.

We may try to modify our theory by discarding the straight-wire picture and replacing it by Rutherford's nuclear atom, which, in the simplest case, would be 1 electron revolving about the nucleus. But here the electromagnetic theory leads to another difficulty. From the laws of planetary motion we know that the electron may revolve about the nucleus in circular or elliptic orbits. Suppose that energy is given to this system, e.g., in the discharge tube by the impact of a *free* electron, so that the *revolving* electron is thrown into a distant orbit, which we assume as circular for the sake of convenience. If the electron would stay there, it would have a well-defined frequency of revolution. But the electromagnetic theory tells us that the electron would perform differently from a planet. While the planet, as a *neutral* body, continues indefinitely on the same orbit, the electron, being a *charged* body, loses energy continuously by radiation at a rate predicted by the theory. This energy is radiated at the expense of the energy stored in the revolving motion. Thus the electron must gradually spiral in toward the nucleus and thereby increase its frequency of revolution. (The relation between the radius and the frequency of revolution is easily computed on the basis of elementary mechanics.) Since this process would go on continually, the spectrum would not consist of sharp lines but would be continuous. This prediction based on the electromagnetic theory contradicts the observed facts and makes the failure of this theory when applied to sharp spectral lines evident.

10.3. Review of Gravitational Motion. In Bohr's theory we shall study the simplest aspect of Rutherford's nuclear atom, the case of only 1 electron circling about a nucleus. In the present section we shall review some formulas of elementary mechanics that are applied in Bohr's theory. Since the Coulomb force keeping the electron to the nucleus has the same mathematical form as the law of gravitation, we take over the results of the theory of planetary motion, for simplicity restricting ourselves to circular orbits. In order to make the calculation applicable to more highly charged nuclei, we keep in mind that their charges are given by their atomic numbers Z as Ze (see Sec. 9.2).

Notation and Units:

m = mass of electron, g
e = charge on electron, emu
Ze = charge on nucleus, emu
r = radius of circular orbit, cm
ω = angular velocity, sec^{-1}

Hence we write

$v = r\omega$ = linear velocity, cm/sec
$I = mr^2$ = moment of inertia, g cm^2
$I\omega = mr^2\omega = mvr$ = angular momentum, g cm^2 sec^{-1}

The force of attraction is given by the Coulomb force

$$\text{Force} = c^2 \frac{Ze^2}{r^2}$$

The factor c^2 is due to the fact that throughout we apply the electromagnetic system of units (see App. 1). In circular motion a centripetal acceleration = v^2/r occurs. Hence this motion requires for its maintenance a centripetal force = mv^2/r. When we whirl a stone around on a string, this force is given by the tension of the string. In our case, the force is supplied by the Coulomb force. Therefore, the condition for the circular motion is

$$c^2 \frac{Ze^2}{r^2} = \frac{mv^2}{r} \quad \text{or} \quad c^2 \frac{Ze^2}{r} = mv^2 \qquad (10.2)$$

Since c, Z, e, and m are constants, this is an equation between two variables r and v which, as far as the present argument goes, may have values covering a *continuous range*.

Next we compute the total energy W, composed of kinetic energy W_k and potential energy W_p. The kinetic energy W_k is easily expressed as $W_k = mv^2/2 = c^2Ze^2/2r$. Finding the expression for the potential energy W_p is more difficult. The potential energy, or energy of position, of the electron with respect to the nucleus depends only on the relative distance r. We are interested only in the difference between the potential energies of two positions. We define this difference as the work required to lift the electron by a force counteracting the Coulomb attraction from the smaller radius r_1 to the larger radius r_2. For readers familiar with calculus the rigorous derivation is given as Prob. 10.14. An approximate derivation is as follows. If we restrict ourselves to a change of radius $r = r_2 - r_1$ very small as compared to each of these radii, the Coulomb force c^2Ze^2/r^2 may be treated as constant or, still better, may be expressed by writing the geometrical mean of the radii r_1 and r_2, that is, by replacing r^2 by $r_1 \times r_2$. So we obtain

$$\Delta W_p = c^2 \frac{Ze^2}{r_1 r_2} (r_2 - r_1) = c^2 Ze^2 \left(\frac{1}{r_1} - \frac{1}{r_2} \right)$$

When computing ΔW_p over a larger distance, we subdivide this distance into many small steps, apply the approximate formula to each step, and compute the total energy ΔW_p as the sum of these small contributions. Since all these intermediate values of $1/r$ cancel out, our final result

$$\Delta W_p = c^2 Ze^2 \left(\frac{1}{r_1} - \frac{1}{r_2} \right) \qquad (10.3)$$

is the same as derived above for each small step. By definition the energy ΔW_p is positive—i.e., we *impart potential energy* to the system— if $r_2 > r_1$. If instead we assume $r_2 < r_1$, the same equation applies, yielding a negative ΔW_p, hence stating that the system *loses potential energy* when the electron moves down from a large distance r_1 to a small distance r_2.

It will be convenient to define an arbitrary zero point of potential energy. Since we shall be interested only in differences of potential energy, we may define this energy as zero for any arbitrary radius r, except $r = 0$ because this would lead to infinitely large potential energies. We define $W_p = 0$ for $r_1 = \infty$ because this choice offers the convenience of shortening the equations. This definition, which necessarily makes $r_2 < r_1$, is admissible, since it leads to finite values of W_p, as is evident from Eq. (10.3), which, for $r_1 = \infty$, is written $\Delta W_p = -c^2 Z e^2 / r_2$. Now we call this energy difference W_p and may drop the subscript 2 because we have got rid of r_1. Hence

$$W_p = -c^2 \frac{Ze^2}{r}$$

The negative sign of the W_p has no physical significance since it is based on an arbitrary definition of the zero point. Similarly, within a laboratory room we may define $W_p = 0$ at the ceiling and so make all potential energies within the room negative. For any definition the essential property of W_p, its increase with increasing r, is preserved.

The total energy of the revolving eléctron becomes

$$W = W_k + W_p = c^2 Z e^2 \left(\frac{1}{2r} - \frac{1}{r} \right) = -c^2 \frac{Ze^2}{2r} \qquad (10.4)$$

Here again the negative sign has no physical significance since it is based on the arbitrary definition of the zero point of W_p.

10.4. Bohr's Theory. The hydrogen atom was the object of the first theoretical attack, because as the lightest of all atoms it is assumed to have the simplest structure. This is confirmed by the fact that its spectrum, described above, is by far the simplest of all atomic spectra ever observed. Bohr's *starting point* was Rutherford's theory of the nuclear atom, Planck's quantum theory ascribing to each vibrating atom a quantized energy content $nh\nu$ (see Sec. 8.3), and Einstein's theory attributing energy quanta $h\nu$ to light of frequency ν. Bohr's *aim* was to establish a theory from which he could derive the observed hydrogen spectrum as given by the Balmer formula

$$\nu_{\mathrm{obs}} = cR \left(\frac{1}{n''^2} - \frac{1}{n'^2} \right) \qquad (10.1)$$

As the simplest atom presumably contains only 1 revolving electron, its nucleus has a positive charge of the same value. This charge is experimentally confirmed by positive-ray analysis (Sec. 6.3), in which a great abundance of *singly* charged hydrogen atomic ions H^+, but no *doubly* charged ions H^{++}, are observed. In the preceding section we found that, for a revolving electron, the electromagnetic theory would predict a continuous spectrum, in contrast to the sharp-line spectrum actually observed. Bohr's first, far-reaching hypothesis states that the electromagnetic theory has to be discarded in the description of the radiation from atoms.   It is true that the electromagnetic theory is thoroughly confirmed by experiments in the macroscopic realm of physics, in particular for the radiation from antennas.   But this success does not force us to assume that the same theory will apply to processes in individual atoms, for atoms are so very much smaller than any of our laboratory tools that conditions are entirely different.

This is a general consideration that had been applied before in other fields of physics.   For example, Newton's mechanics had been confirmed by laboratory experiments and astronomical observations to such an extent that it was thought to represent an absolute truth.   Now we know that it is only an approximation which fails for velocities comparable to that of light.   Therefore, it is not unusual that an apparently well-established law of physics is changed under conditions that are vastly different from those under which the law was originally discovered.

This repudiation of the electromagnetic theory gave Bohr a wide field for new hypotheses to describe the radiation from the electron revolving about the nucleus.   We shall first discuss Bohr's general idea and next the mathematical development.

Einstein's quantum theory of light suggests the hypothesis that an atom, when emitting light of the frequency ν, loses by radiation the energy $h\nu$ by going down from a state endowed with energy W' to another with lower energy W''.   Under this assumption the sharp spectral lines observed indicate that the atom exists only in states of sharply defined energy content and emits a quantum $h\nu = W' - W''$ when going from an upper to a lower energy level.

How are these sharply defined energy levels to be predicted?   Planck's hypothesis, which was mentioned in the historical survey, fails to lead to the desired result.   It only suggests the guess that Planck's constant h somehow determines the energy levels.   A more specific suggestion is given by noticing that Planck's constant has the dimensions of an angular momentum (erg sec = cm²g sec⁻¹).   This coincidence may lead to the guess that the angular momentum of the revolving electron is proportional to a multiple of Planck's constant h.   Bohr found that the desired result is actually reached when the following quantum condition is introduced: The revolving electron exists only in "quantized" energy levels defined by the condition that its angular momentum = $nh/2\pi$ where n is any integer beginning with 1; n is called the "quantum number."   The factor $\frac{1}{2}\pi$ is justified partly by the success of the theory, partly by the desired transition from quantum theory to classical theory discussed below.   No claim is made that our argument leading to the fundamental hypothesis is conclusive.   The reasoning is intended only to show that it may be worthwhile to establish tentatively a proportionality between the angular momentum and Planck's constant.   The guess must be tested by comparing the mathematical conclusions with the observations described by Eq. (10.1). We restrict our treatment to circular orbits of the electron. The results of the more elaborate theory of elliptic orbits will be briefly reported in Sec. 10.7.

a. *Orbits Given by Classical Physics.* As discussed in the review of gravitational motion, classical physics supplies the condition: centripetal force = Coulomb force, or

$$mv^2r = c^2Ze^2$$

b. *Quantized Orbits.* From the continuum of orbits given by this equation, the quantum condition (angular momentum = $nh/2\pi$) selects certain sharply defined orbits

$$mvr = \frac{nh}{2\pi} \qquad n = 1, 2, 3, \ldots \qquad (10.5)$$

For any quantum number n the orbit is defined, because now we have two equations with the two unknowns r and v. These are easily evaluated in terms of n, and the constants e, Z, m, and h as follows:

$$r = n^2 \frac{h^2}{4\pi^2mc^2Ze^2} \qquad (10.6)$$

and

$$v = \frac{1}{n} \frac{2\pi c^2Ze^2}{h} \qquad (10.7)$$

Furthermore, the total energy W of the electron with respect to the nucleus is given by Eq. (10.4):

$$W = -\frac{c^2Ze^2}{2r} = -\frac{1}{n^2} \frac{2\pi^2c^4mZ^2e^4}{h^2} \qquad (10.8)$$

We shall distinguish W' and n' for the upper level from W'' and n'' for the lower level by single and double primes.

c. *Spectrum Theoretically Derived.* The frequencies of the spectral lines are theoretically derived by Einstein's equation $h\nu_{th} = W' - W''$, or

$$\nu_{th} = \frac{W' - W''}{h} = \frac{2\pi^2c^4mZ^2e^4}{h^3} \left(\frac{1}{n''^2} - \frac{1}{n'^2} \right) \qquad (10.9)$$

d. *Comparison with Observation.* We are satisfied that this equation for ν_{th} has the same mathematical form as Balmer's equation for ν_{obs} (Eq. 10.1), since the quotient in front of the bracket contains only constants. But beyond this general resemblance between the two equations, Bohr is able to predict the numerical value of the factor cR which is found experimentally in the Balmer formula. For the hydrogen atom Bohr assumes a nuclear charge of the same absolute value as the electronic charge e. The numerical value for e is taken from the oil-drop experiment, that for e/m from the cathode-ray experiment, and that for h from the photoelectric effect. In this way Bohr derives the numerical value of the factor cR

$$\frac{2\pi^2 c^4 m Z^2 e^4}{h^3} = 3 \times 10^{10} \times 109{,}700 \text{ sec}^{-1}$$

This compares with the factor of the Balmer formula which is derived from spectroscopic measurements:

$$cR = 3 \times 10^{10} \times 109{,}677 \text{ sec}^{-1}$$

The quantitative agreement is as good as the limited accuracy of the experiments permits. This is the first outstanding success of the theory.

We introduced Bohr's quantum condition with the idea of obtaining a simple theoretical basis from which the multitude of observed spectral lines may be predicted. There is an additional postulate which may well have guided Bohr in his discovery. While we admit that for atomic dimensions the laws derived from large-scale experiments do not apply, we should postulate that for increasing dimensions a transition is found between the new laws of quantum theory and the established laws of classical theory. Let us compare the predictions given by the two apparently widely different theories for very large values of r, hence very large values of n, and much smaller values of $(n' - n'')$ (say for $n' = 1{,}000$ and $n'' = 999$ or 998, etc.). Quantum theory leads to the following approximation based on Eq. (10.9) when we write n instead of n' or n'', except in the difference $n' - n''$:

$$\nu_{\text{th}} = \frac{2\pi^2 c^4 m Z^2 e^4}{h^3} \frac{(n'^2 - n''^2)}{n'^2 n''^2} \simeq \frac{4\pi^2 c^4 m Z^2 e^4}{h^3} \frac{(n' - n'')}{n^3}$$

On the other hand, classical physics predicts that the revolving electron emits light whose frequency is given by the frequency of revolution of the electron. This is computed using Eqs. (10.6) and (10.7):

$$\text{Time of 1 revolution} = \frac{\text{circumference}}{\text{velocity}} = \frac{2\pi r}{v}$$

hence

$$\text{Frequency} = \frac{1}{\text{time of 1 revolution}} = \frac{v}{2\pi r}$$
$$= \frac{4\pi^2 c^4 m Z^2 e^4}{h^3} \frac{1}{n^3}$$

This equation is somewhat marred by our limiting ourselves to circular orbits.   The more general result, which here can only be mentioned, states that for the elliptic orbit the electron emits a fundamental frequency, which is given by the last equations, and, in addition, "higher harmonics" of twice, three times, and four times this frequency, etc. This result of classical physics coincides with the result of the quantum theory given by the preceding equation.   Thus we see that Bohr's theory meets the postulate that in the limiting case of very large radii the frequencies predicted by the two theories, quantum and classical, become identical.

In spite of the great success of Bohr's theory, the student is not urged to accept it right away, as it certainly was not generally accepted at the time of its discovery in 1913.   One may judge that the success is dearly bought by discarding classical physics and replacing it by arbitrary assumptions; hence there is no mathematical way of saying whether these assumptions are necessary or may be replaced by something different.   In order to arrive at a judgment of Bohr's theory, throughout the following arguments we must keep in mind these questions: How do more detailed observations compare with the conclusions of Bohr's theory? How great is the fertility of Bohr's theory in stimulating new experiments?

The difficulty inherent in Bohr's theory is not of a mathematical nature.   But the student may find it difficult to "understand" the fundamental hypothesis.   Here we notice that the method of progress in the study of *theoretical physics* is in many cases different from that in the study of *mathematics*.   In mathematics we start from a proposition whose validity is well established and, by a strictly logical argument, find an as yet unknown result which is sure to be as correct as our proposition. On the other hand, in many theories of physics, to begin with we know what we want to find as the *final result* because this is supplied by the experiment, *e.g.*, the Balmer formula.   Next we try to invent a new hypothesis to serve as the starting point, *e.g.*, Bohr's hypothesis.   The student may be disappointed by the fact that the new hypothesis is by no means a revelation which immediately impresses him as a new truth. This difficulty is inherent in the quantum theory, since our feeling for processes in nature is based on daily experience well described by classical physics.   But we must not approach processes in atoms with the naïve expectation that we may feel what is bound to happen.   Here our only criterion for the validity of the hypothesis consists in the comparison of the theoretical prediction with the observed facts.   Thus in Bohr's theory we derive the frequencies of spectral lines from the fundamental hypothesis [Eq. (10.9)] and compare them with the observed frequencies given by the Balmer formula [Eq. (10.1)].   The agreement between the theory and the experiment gives reason to believe that the hypothesis is sound.

The theory is then further tested by investigating experimentally all possible further conclusions. If they agree with the observations, the theory stands confirmed. If a new experiment reveals a discrepancy the theory needs to be modified or, possibly, discarded. This process is still going on in modern quantum mechanics, in particular in its application to nuclear structure.

10.5. Conclusions. *a. Numerical Values of r and v.* The radius r of the orbit has its smallest value for $n = 1$. The state of the atom so described is called the "normal" state. This implies that all atoms are in this state unless they are brought to an *excited state* ($n > 1$), *e.g.*, in the electric discharge by the impact of free electrons. After a short lifetime the excited atoms emit radiation. For the normal state ($n = 1$) we compute the radius r from Eq. (10.6) and find $r_1 = 0.53 \times 10^{-8}$ cm. Here Bohr's theory, although primarily designed to give an account of the spectrum, unexpectedly predicts the diameter of the atom. The prediction is in satisfactory agreement with other evidence (Sec. 9.2) although the usual measurements are obviously concerned with hydrogen molecules instead of atoms.

Why does the electron revolving in the "normal" orbit just computed not fall into the nucleus to which it is attracted by the Coulomb force? All we can say is that normal atoms are observed to have a diameter of the order of magnitude 10^{-8} cm. Therefore, we select $n = 1$ as the smallest quantum number, excluding $n = 0$. We admit that this does not answer the question. All we can do is adjust the quantum hypothesis so that it fits the observed facts.

We computed the orbits as given by classical physics on the basis of the centripetal force expressed in terms of Newtonian mechanics. Are we right in disregarding the relativity correction? This is not obvious, for that electrons are able to attain velocities comparable to the velocity of light has been found in cathode-ray investigations. In order to judge our approximation, we must compute the linear velocities of the revolving electrons from Eq. (10.7). The highest velocity, occurring for $n = 1$, is computed in terms of the velocity of light c as $v_1/c = 7.29 \times 10^{-3}$. This leads to an exceedingly small relativity correction. [On the basis of Eq. (6.14), at this velocity the mass m is expressed in terms of the "rest mass" m_0 as $m = m_0 \times 1.000027$.] However, observations made with powerful spectrographs are so exceedingly accurate that a small relativity effect has been observed. This will be reported later in Sec. 10.7.

b. Energy-level Diagram. The energies of the various quantized orbits are computed as

$$W = -\frac{1}{n^2}\frac{2\pi^2 c^4 m Z^2 e^4}{h^2}$$

and plotted in Fig. 10.4.   The negative energies given by the equation
are plotted downward, starting from $W = 0$.   This "energy-level diagram" represents the theoretical idea that the electron may be lifted
upward from the lowest level, the normal state, to the higher levels, the
excited states, from which it spon-
taneously falls down and emits light.
A spectral line is attributed not to
the individual level but to a difference between any two levels, the
upper level being the *initial* level of
the emission process, the lower level
the *final* level.

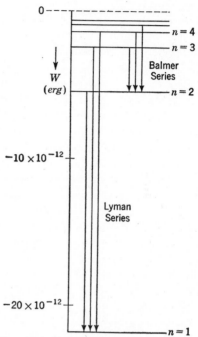

   The frequency of each spectral line
$\nu_{\text{th}} = (W' - W'')/h$ is proportional
to the difference between two energy
levels.   The *Lyman* series, characterized by the quantum number of
the lower level $n'' = 1$, is represented by all transitions (indicated
by arrows) ending at the normal
state of the atom.   The convergence
limit of this series is the highest frequency that can be emitted by a
transition between any two quantized hydrogen levels.   The *Balmer*
series, characterized by $n'' = 2$, is
due to all transitions ending at
$n'' = 2$; its very conspicuous red
line, which gives the red color to the
electric discharge through hydrogen,
is given by the transition from $n' = 3$

Fig. 10.4. Energy-level diagram of the
hydrogen atom.   The energy of the
level $n = \infty$ is arbitrarily counted as
zero.   The arrows indicate the first
three lines of the Lyman series and
those of the Balmer series.

to $n'' = 2$.   The transitions between the higher levels, from $n'' = 3$
upward, are responsible for the various infrared series.
   Comparing Bohr's theory with observation, the student must keep in
mind that the observation of one individual quantum process, say the
emission of one red quantum ($n = 3 \rightarrow n = 2$), is not possible.   What we
observe, visually or photographically, is the complete spectrum, *i.e.*, from
the point of view of the theory, the effect of very many quantum processes superimposed on one another.   A deficiency of Bohr's theory is as
follows.   An excited atom, say in the energy level $n = 4$, may go down
to the normal state ($n = 1$) in one process and thus emit its whole energy
as a quantum of the third line of the Lyman series.   Alternatively, the
excited atom may cascade down in any combination, *e.g.*, first from

$n = 4$ to $n = 2$ (emitting the second line of the Balmer series) and next to $n = 1$ (emitting the first line of the Lyman series). Bohr's theory fails to predict the relative probabilities of the various processes which determine the relative intensities of the various lines originating from the same level. For the higher levels of the atom there are many more different ways, more or less direct, for "cascading down" to the normal level. It is a limitation of the theory that only *frequencies*, not *intensities*, of spectral lines can be derived. This deficiency is remedied by wave mechanics (Chap. 22), which predicts intensities as well as frequencies.

The energy-level diagram effectively simplifies the description of the spectrum. Originally (Sec. 10.1) we described each series as an aggregate of infinitely many lines, and the whole spectrum as containing infinitely many such series. The same situation is much more simply described by the energy-level diagram which consists of only one aggregate of infinitely many levels from which all lines of all series are to be derived.

c. Energies of Excitation and Ionization. The energy-level diagram directly represents two important quantities characteristic of the atom, which will be discussed later in more detail: the *energies of excitation* and *ionization.* From the diagram we infer that the excitation of the hydrogen atom requires as a minimum the energy needed to lift the atom from the *normal* state $n = 1$ to the *lowest excited* state $n = 2$. This energy difference, called the "excitation energy," is computed from Bohr's theory as $W_2 - W_1 = 16.31 \times 10^{-12}$ erg $= 10.19$ ev. It may equally well be computed from the frequency of the first line of the Lyman series.

The other energy difference of outstanding importance is the one between the normal state ($n = 1$) and the convergence limit ($n = \infty$). For $n = \infty$, the revolving electron is lifted to an infinitely distant orbit, which is another way of saying that it is separated from the nucleus. Therefore, the energy difference described is the ionization energy of the atom. It is computed from the theory (or from the convergence limit of the Lyman series) as $W_\infty - W_1 = 21.76 \times 10^{-12}$ erg $= 13.58$ ev. Later we shall discuss another method, independent of the spectrum and Bohr's theory, for the measurement of these two characteristic energies (Sec. 12.1).

d. Combination Rule. It has been known for a long time that many combinations exist between the observed frequencies of the various lines emitted from the same atom. When we write the frequency of the first line of the Lyman series as L_1 and other frequencies of the Lyman series and Balmer series correspondingly, the empirical relation holds

$$L_1 + B_1 = L_2$$

This relation, called the "combination rule," and numerous similar ones follow directly from the energy-level diagram. Notice that you can add frequencies, or quantities directly proportional to frequencies (like energies or wave numbers), but it makes no sense to add wavelengths, because the justification of the combination rule lies in the energy-level diagram.

e. Bohr Magneton. According to Bohr's theory, each hydrogen atom represents a circular current, hence is equivalent to a small magnet. Let us compute the magnetic moments of the hydrogen atom in its various quantized orbits. We take for granted a result of electrodynamics which states that the magnetic moment is given by the relation

$$M = \text{area of orbit} \times \text{current (in emu)}$$

Since the current at the circumference is given by the charge e passing once during each time of revolution τ, we write current $= e/\tau = ev/2\pi r$ (see Sec. 10.4). Hence, introducing the quantum number n by Eqs. (10.6) and (10.7),

$$M = \pi r^2 \times \frac{ev}{2\pi r} = \frac{erv}{2} = n \frac{e}{m} \frac{h}{4\pi} \text{ (in emu)}$$

Hence all orbital magnetic moments of the hydrogen atom are multiples of a fundamental magnetic moment

$$\frac{e}{m} \frac{h}{4\pi} = 9.27 \times 10^{-21} \text{ emu}$$

This result is of importance in the theory of magnetism since other atoms and molecules have magnetic moments that can be expressed as multiples of the same value. The fundamental value of atomic magnetic moments here derived is called a "Bohr magneton." However, the word "magneton" does not imply that here we are dealing with a constant as fundamental as the electron. Our argument shows that the *magneton* is a derived constant, while the *electron* is one of the fundamental entities of physics which we cannot predict on the basis of other data.

10.6. Application to the Helium Ion. *a. Approximate Treatment.* Our program is to draw further conclusions from the theory and compare them with observed facts. The first success of Bohr's theory beyond the interpretation of the hydrogen spectrum was the application of the theory to the helium ion. Helium gas ordinarily emits a much more complicated spectrum than that of hydrogen atoms. However, under very violent conditions in an electric discharge, an additional spectrum appears with a simple structure closely resembling the hydrogen spectrum. The unusual conditions required for its excitation make it plausible to attribute this spectrum to *ionized* helium atoms He^+, while the complicated, more easily excited spectrum is attributed to *neutral* helium atoms.

In the visible range the helium-ion spectrum shows a series described by the formula

$$\nu_{obs} = 4cR \left(\frac{1}{4^2} - \frac{1}{n^2} \right) \qquad n = 5, 6, 7, \ldots$$

Here c = velocity of light as before and R is a constant very nearly identical with the Rydberg constant which enters into the Balmer formula for the hydrogen spectrum. For the time being we shall consider the two constants as identical and postpone the discussion of the slight difference between them. The last formula describes a helium series of which every second line (for $n = 6, 8, 10, \ldots$) coincides with a line of the Balmer series; but the helium series has additional lines (for $n = 5, 7, 9, \ldots$), one of them between any two successive lines of the

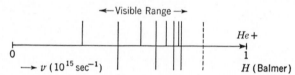

FIG. 10.5. Balmer series of hydrogen ($n'' = 2$) compared with series of ionized helium ($n'' = 4$). The small frequency difference between corresponding lines is not noticeable on the scale of the figure.

Balmer series (Fig. 10.5). In the ultraviolet and infrared, the helium ion has still other series described by similar formulas. All of them are given by the following comprehensive formula, which differs from the Balmer formula only by the factor 4:

$$\nu_{obs} = 4cR \left(\frac{1}{n''^2} - \frac{1}{n'^2} \right)$$

What prediction does Bohr's theory make regarding this spectrum? On the basis of an elaborate argument based on the investigation of alpha particles (their nuclear charge, specific charge, and scattering, Sec. 9.1) we attributed the nuclear charge +2 to helium, thus giving 2 external electrons to the neutral helium atom. This leaves only 1 external electron in the singly charged helium ion He$^+$, which we have assumed to be the carrier of the spectrum just described. As the presence of only 1 revolving electron is one of the essential assumptions of Bohr's theory, we should be able to predict the spectrum of the He$^+$ ion as well as that of the neutral H atom. Bohr's final equation contains the factor Z^2 (Z = atomic number). Hence for He$^+$ it predicts the factor 4, while the formula for the hydrogen spectrum carries only the factor 1.

This prediction agrees with the observed fact and thus strengthens our confidence in Bohr's theory.

This success of Bohr's theory extends further than merely to the spectrum of He$^+$. It has been found that the third element of the periodic table, lithium, when under violent excitation (by a spark discharge at low pressure and high voltage), emits a spectrum described by the formula $\nu_{obs} = 9cR(1/n''^2 - 1/n'^2)$, differing from the spectra treated above by the factor 9. Correspondingly, this spectrum is explained as emitted from a lithium atom that has lost all external electrons but one. The factor 9 requires the additional assumption that the lithium nucleus has the charge 3. Next for beryllium, the fourth element in the periodic table, an analogous spectrum has been observed differing only by the factor 16. Again the same idea applies with the additional special assumption that beryllium has the nuclear charge 4. The corresponding observations have been carried out for the next heavier elements in the periodic table up to oxygen. Thus the nuclear charges are experimentally determined for the next elements, namely, boron, carbon, nitrogen, and oxygen, as 5, 6, 7, and 8, respectively. These results give a strong confirmation of the general law: *the atomic number equals the nuclear charge* (measured in multiples of the electronic charge).

The first indication we found of this important law was based on entirely different experiments, the scattering of alpha particles (Sec. 9.2). There the evidence was derived from experiments with the *heavy* elements. Here, by applying Bohr's theory to the simplest spectra emitted by the *light* elements, the rule is corroborated. (This result is the justification for calling the nuclear charge Ze.)

b. Relative Motion of the Nucleus. We mentioned the observed fact that the numerical values of the Rydberg constant R that describe the spectra of He$^+$ and H, respectively, are nearly but not completely identical. This is another way of saying that, *e.g.*, the line $3 \to 2$ of the H atom (first line of the Balmer series) coincides very nearly but not exactly with a certain line of He$^+$ (the line $6 \to 4$; see Fig. 10.5). As a matter of fact, the wavelengths are 6562.8 A for the hydrogen line and 6560.1 A for the He$^+$ line. Correspondingly, the two values of the Rydberg constant are $R_H = 109,677.8$ cm^{-1} and $R_{He} = 109,722.4$ cm^{-1}.

Does the theory predict such a difference? The answer was given by Bohr, who pointed out that his original theory contained an approximation. He had assumed that the electron circles about the nucleus as a planet about the sun. On the basis of this simple assumption the *mass of the nucleus* does not enter into the final equation Eq. (10.9) since all that matters is that the mass of the nucleus is very large as compared to the electronic mass m. As a matter of fact, however, the planet and the sun both circle about the common center of mass. (This refinement follows from the principles of mechanics which require the common center of mass to remain at rest or move with a uniform velocity, hence not to revolve.) Seen from the center of mass, the two bodies must always be in opposite positions. Hence they revolve with the same *angular* velocity but with vastly different radii. The error introduced by our approximation (Secs. 10.3 and 10.4) is small because the center of mass very nearly coincides with the center of the nucleus. Bohr applied the same refinement of the theory to the motion of electron and nucleus. The details of this computation, which strictly follows Bohr's original theory, are relegated to a problem (Prob. 10.12). The result is

$$\nu_{\text{th}} = \frac{2\pi^2 c^4 Z^2 e^4}{h^3} \times \frac{mM}{m + M} \left(\frac{1}{n''^2} - \frac{1}{n'^2} \right)$$

where M = nuclear mass (in g). This equation contains the "reduced mass" $mM/(m + M)$ instead of the electronic mass m appearing in the approximate equation. Notice that for increasing M the new result approaches the old one. Bohr's new result *quantitatively* agrees with the experimental values of R.

The effect of the relative motion of the nucleus is noticeable in the spectrum of heavy hydrogen, called "deuterium." This is a rare form of hydrogen, which has the same nuclear charge as ordinary hydrogen but a nucleus twice as heavy. For deuterium Bohr's theory predicts all the same spectral lines as for ordinary hydrogen, except that all of them should be slightly shifted because the relative motion of the heavier nucleus is less noticeable. The wavelength shifts so predicted agree quantitatively with the observed spectrum. As a matter of fact, the predicted spectrum played a decisive part in Urey's discovery of heavy hydrogen (see Sec. 16.5).

This theory of the spectrum of He^+ constituted an amazing success for the Bohr theory. First, it predicted the approximate position of all He^+ series, interlocking with the hydrogen series, by the idea that the nuclear charge of helium is twice that of hydrogen. Next, it even predicted the value of the small difference between adjacent lines of He^+ and H by the relative motion of the nuclei. Finally it predicted the spectra of highly ionized lithium and heavier elements and led to the discovery of heavy hydrogen.

10.7. Report on Further Developments. We have witnessed two great successes of Bohr's theory, the theoretical derivation of the spectra of hydrogen atoms and those of the next heavier ions. It seems hardly possible that this agreement between observation and theoretical derivation is only accidental and that the processes in these atoms and ions are inconsistent with Bohr's hypothesis. In order to arrive at a more thorough evaluation of Bohr's theory, we shall give a report on the further comparison of experiment and theory. Since we shall deal with a development requiring a more advanced mathematical treatment, we shall report only results and omit the derivations.

Considering the great importance of Bohr's theory, Paschen measured the spectra of hydrogen atoms and helium ions with the highest precision, applying a large concave-grating spectrograph. His results were perplexing. He found that all lines, originally described as single, when photographed with high resolution show more or less elaborate fine structures. For example, all "lines" of the Balmer series are doublets; that means, each one of them consists of two lines very close together with nearly the same frequency difference between the components of each doublet. Much more complicated structures are seen upon close examination of all "lines" of ionized helium.

Sommerfeld succeeded in adapting Bohr's theory to this very complex observation. While our outline of Bohr's theory simplifies the problem

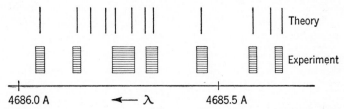

FIG. 10.6. Fine structure of the line 4,686 A of He^+, comparing theory and experiment. Intensities are not represented. The structure covers only about 0.8 A.

by considering *circular* orbits, Bohr, in his first paper, had already considered the more general case of *elliptic* orbits. They lead to exactly the same spectral lines as the circular orbits. However, Sommerfeld successfully generalized Bohr's quantum condition and took into account the theory of relativity. We have estimated (Sec. 10.5a) that the linear velocities of the electrons are so small, smaller than one-hundredth of the velocity of light, that this correction amounts to very little. But the "fine structure" splitting of the spectral lines into components is just such a small effect. On this basis Sommerfeld was able to predict the fine structure described, *i.e.*, the doublet structure of all Balmer lines of hydrogen and the very elaborate structures, different for each "line," of ionized helium. It is true that many of the components predicted by the theory are so close together that they cannot be resolved even by the most powerful spectrographs (Fig. 10.6). Furthermore, this theory predicts only the *frequencies*, not the *intensities*, of the various components. But within these limitations the very complex material supplied by experiments turned out to be theoretically predictable. This success confirms our belief in the Bohr and Sommerfeld theories of spectra. However, a small deviation between the modern, greatly refined theory

and the observations must be mentioned.   The red hydrogen line consists of components that are slightly closer together than predicted.
The discrepancy has recently been confirmed by experiments applying
the modern microwave technique.   This result leads to a refinement
of the fundamental assumptions (Lamb and Retherford, 1947).

The next successes of Bohr's theory are connected with the effects of
magnetic and electric fields on spectral lines.   When the source of light
is placed in a strong *magnetic* field, all spectral lines of hydrogen split
up into three components with mutual distances proportional to the magnetic field.   (Here we disregard the fine structure just discussed.)   This
is called the "Zeeman effect" after the discoverer.   Again, this effect has
been derived from Bohr's theory as generalized by Sommerfeld.   But we
do not dare list this success as a criterion confirming the *quantum* theory
of radiation as against the classical *electromagnetic* theory, because,
strangely enough, this effect has been quantitatively derived from the old
electromagnetic theory by H. A. Lorentz.   The situation is different in
the case of the *electric* field.   This, too, causes a splitting up of all spectral
lines of hydrogen but in much more complicated patterns, each original
line having its characteristic pattern.   This is called the "Stark effect."
From the quantum theory of Bohr and Sommerfeld all these elaborate
Stark patterns have been derived, while the classical electromagnetic
theory completely fails.

We summarize the successes of Bohr's theory and Sommerfeld's generalization by listing the observations that are predicted by the theory:

The line spectrum of hydrogen atoms

The diameter of the hydrogen atom

The line spectra of helium ions and certain ions of the next heavier
elements

The small wavelength shift explained by the relative motion of the
nucleus and the center of mass

The fine structure of all lines explained by the elliptic orbit treated with
the relativity correction

The Zeeman effect

The Stark effect

One cannot doubt that the theory represents a great step forward
toward the truth.   But we must recognize that its validity is limited.   It
fails to predict the spectra of atoms with more than 1 electron, like the
neutral helium atom.   Here the application of Bohr's theory has not led
to an agreement with the experiments.

SUMMARY OF CHAPTER 10

The spectrum emitted from atomic hydrogen is described by the
Balmer formula $\nu_{obs} = cR(1/n''^2 - 1/n'^2)$ where c = velocity of light, R

an empirical constant, $n'' = 1$ for the Lyman series, 2 for the Balmer series, etc., and n' an integer larger than n''.

This spectrum is theoretically derived by Bohr on the basis of the following hypotheses: The hydrogen atom consists of a stationary nucleus carrying a positive charge and only 1 revolving electron. From classical physics the idea is taken that the centripetal force is given by the Coulomb force. From the continuum of orbits so described, quantized orbits are selected by the quantum condition: angular momentum $= nh/2\pi$. The frequencies of spectral lines are derived from the equation: $h\nu_{th} = W' - W''$ where W' and W'' are energies of quantized orbits. These hypotheses lead to the theoretical formula

$$\nu_{th} = \frac{2\pi^2 c^4 m Z^2 e^4}{h^3} \left(\frac{1}{n''^2} - \frac{1}{n'^2} \right)$$

which quantitatively agrees with the formula describing the observation.

Bohr's theory predicts the diameter of the hydrogen atom in its normal state to 1.06×10^{-8}, which is in satisfactory agreement with observations.

The energy-level diagram greatly simplifies the description of the spectrum. It gives evidence of the energies of excitation and ionization and the combination rule.

The spectrum of He$^+$ is approximately described by a formula differing from the Balmer formula by only the factor 4. This is predicted by Bohr's theory by considering the nuclear charge 2 of helium. Similarly, the spectra of Li^{++} and Be^{+++} and heavier ions are predicted by attributing nuclear charges 3 to Li, 4 to Be, etc. This result confirms the rule: atomic number = nuclear charge (in multiples of e). A very small difference between the two Rydberg constants, observed for H and He$^+$, is predicted in agreement with observation, by taking into account the relative motion of the nucleus about the center of mass.

PROBLEMS

10.1. *Series formula.* (a) Applying the empirical series formula, calculate the wavelengths of the first two lines of the Paschen series ($n'' = 3$). (b) Calculate the convergence limits of the infrared series $n'' = 3$, 4, and 5. Use a slide rule.

10.2. *Combination rule.* Check the combination rule for the first two lines of the Balmer series (Fig. 10.1) and the first line of the Paschen series. Use a slide rule.

10.3. *Energy content of hydrogen atom.* Calculate the total energy W, the potential energy W_p, and the kinetic energy W_k of the electron revolving about the hydrogen nucleus for the quantum numbers $n = 1, 2, 10$, and ∞ (all in ev).

10.4. *Scale of energy-level diagram.* Write a scale of electron volts on the diagram of Fig. 10.4, beginning with zero at $n = 1$. Read the energy of excitation from the diagram.

10.5. *Spectral range of hydrogen spectrum.* Calculate the energies of the quanta (in ergs) that limit the visible range of light (4,000 to 8,000 A). On a slip of paper draw two arrows representing these quanta in the scale of Fig. 10.4. Identify the spectral lines emitted by hydrogen atoms as to whether they are in the visible or ultraviolet or infrared range, respectively.

10.6. *Excitation by heat.* Compute the temperature of atomic-hydrogen gas at which the *average* kinetic energy of the atoms would be sufficient to excite H atoms to their first excited level ($n = 2$). Why is thermal radiation observed at much lower temperatures?

10.7. *Frequency of revolution.* Calculate the frequency of revolution f of the electron circling about a nucleus of charge Ze in terms of the quantum number n and the fundamental constants.

10.8. *Relation between frequency ν of light and frequency f of revolution.* Prove that the frequency of light theoretically predicted by Bohr's theory is nearly the same as the frequency of revolution (see Prob. 10.7) in the case of very large quantum numbers n and a change of quantum number $n' - n'' = 1$.

HINT: Keep in mind that approximately $n' + n'' = 2n$ and $n'^2 \times n''^2 = n^4$.

COMMENT: This relation was of great importance for Bohr's discovery and the further development of his theory.

10.9. *Spectrum of* He⁺. Compare the spectrum of He⁺ with that of H as follows: (a) Compute the frequencies of the first lines of the series $n'' = 1$ for both H and He⁺. (b) Compute the first four lines of the He⁺ series $n'' = 2$ and compare them with the first lines of the Lyman series ($n'' = 1$) of H. (c) Do the same for the He⁺ series $n'' = 4$ as compared with the Balmer series $n'' = 2$. Make a schematic diagram of the four first series of He⁺ and the first two series of H (extending Fig. 10.5). Throughout assume the same value of the Rydberg constant R.

10.10. *Effect of gravitational force.* In Bohr's theory we assumed that the electron and the proton are kept together by the Coulomb force. In addition, there is the gravitational force. Compute how large this is as compared to the Coulomb force.

10.11. *Velocity of escape from the earth.* A meteor (mass m) with a negligible initial velocity falls from an infinitely large distance to the surface of the earth. Disregarding air friction, compute the velocity v with which it strikes the earth (radius $R = 6.37 \times 10^8$ cm; mass $M = 6.00 \times 10^{27}$ g; the force outside the earth is the same as if its total mass were concentrated at its center). A mass m thrown upward with a smaller velocity will fall back but when thrown upward with a larger velocity will leave the earth. Notice that the velocity of escape is independent of the mass m of the escaping body and, therefore, the same for rockets and atoms. Compare the velocity of escape v with the average thermal velocity of hydrogen atoms at 2000°K. The result explains why no hydrogen is found in the upper atmosphere.

10.12. *Relative motion of the nucleus (difficult problem).* In this problem the student is asked to introduce a more refined mechanical picture, taking into account the relative motion of the nucleus, into Bohr's theory of the emission of light from hydrogen atoms (Sec. 10.4). In any orbit, the electron and the nucleus circle about their common center of gravity, always keeping in opposite directions as seen from this center. Hence, the theory will be simplified by introducing their common angular velocity into the expressions for the centripetal forces and angular momenta.

Additional notation:

M = mass of nucleus
R = radius of orbit of nucleus
V = linear velocity of nucleus
ω = angular velocity

HINT: a. State the fundamental equations: Eq. (1) states that centripetal force of electron = Coulomb force = $Ze^2/(r + R)^2$; Eq. (2) states the same for the nucleus;

Eq. (3) states that the total angular momentum of the system of both particles $= \mu r^2 \omega + MR^2 \omega = nh/2\pi$. This system of three equations contains the three unknowns r, R, and ω.

b. Equations (1) and (2) furnish the well-known condition for the center of gravity. This serves for eliminating R. What is left is a pair of equations with the unknowns r and ω.

c. From this pair eliminate ω. Thus one equation is obtained for r in terms of n and the fundamental constants.

d. ω and $v = \omega r$ are expressed in terms of n and the fundamental constants. (It is advantageous to introduce v instead of ω for the simplest expression of the kinetic energy W_k.)

e. The total energy $W = W_k + W_p$ is expressed in terms of r, v, R, and V.

f. Since under (c) and (d) we derived only the expressions for r and v, we must replace R and V by r and v in the expression for the total energy W.

g. The last step, the computation of the frequency ν_{th}, is the same as in Bohr's theory. Introduce the "reduced mass" $\mu M/(\mu + M)$ of the system.

h. Compute the ratio of the Rydberg constants for hydrogen and ionized helium R_H/R_{He} on the basis of the atomic weights: 5.48×10^{-4} for the electron, 1.008 for hydrogen, and 4.00 for helium. Compare your result with the empirical data given in Sec. 10.6*b*. You will be able to use your slide rule when you introduce approximations, that is, $A/(A + \alpha) = 1/(1 + \alpha/A) = 1 - \alpha/A$ for α small as compared with A.

10.13. *Spectrum of heavy hydrogen.* Using the result of the preceding problem, calculate the wavelength difference between the red Balmer lines emitted by hydrogen, H, and "heavy hydrogen," called deuterium, D, which differs from ordinary hydrogen only by its larger atomic weight $= 2.01$, hence larger nuclear mass M (see Sec. 16.5).

HINT: Express the wavelength difference $\lambda_H - \lambda_D$ in terms of λ_H and the constants.

COMMENT: Heavy hydrogen was discovered by the displaced Balmer line here computed.

10.14. *Potential energy of gravitational force (calculus method, to Sec. 10.3).* On the basis of Newton's law of gravitation compute the work required to increase the separation of the masses m and M from r_1 to r_2, in particular from r_1 to ∞.

HINT: (*a*) Subdivide the distance $r_2 - r_1$ into elements Δr so small that within each element the force $F = GmM/r^2$ is approximately constant. Express the element of work ΔW required to carry m over this distance Δr. (*b*) Express the total work required to carry m from r_1 to r_2 as the sum of all these elements. (*c*) While these are approximations, the total work is rigorously expressed by going to the limit for $\Delta r \to 0$, *i.e.*, by replacing the sum by the integral. Evaluate this definite integral between the limits r_1 and r_2. (*d*) Express the total work for the special case $r_2 = \infty$.

CHAPTER 11

MORE COMPLICATED SPECTRA

11.1. Spectra of Heavier Atoms. *a. Energy-level Diagram.* The spectra of the heavier atoms have led to detailed information on atomic structure which culminated in the interpretation of the periodic table of elements. The greater complexity of these spectra is due to the presence of several electrons. The spectra of the various elements belonging to the same chemical group, like the alkalies or the halogens, are closely related, the alkalies exhibiting the simplest spectra. As typical of these spectra we shall describe the sodium spectrum (Fig. 11.1). At first glance the numerous lines seem to be arranged at random; no orderly series are obvious. Closer inspection, however, shows that certain lines of strikingly high intensity belong together as a series, called the "principal series," which converges like any hydrogen series. Among the

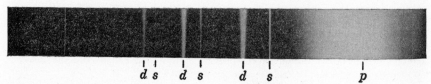

FIG. 11.1. Visible part of line spectrum of sodium in the electric arc (photographic positive). The only member of the principal series *p* is strongly overexposed. Note the distinction between the diffuse series *d* and the sharp series *s*.

weaker lines those of very sharp appearance and those of more diffuse character form separate series.

When interpreting the more complicated atomic spectra, we have not the satisfaction of studying a simple hypothesis from which we derive the spectrum as we did derive the hydrogen spectrum from Bohr's hypothesis. Instead we proceed as follows. We accept Bohr's idea that each spectral line is due to the transition between two energy levels, the frequency of the line to be computed from the relation $h\nu = W' - W''$. In the ideal theory each energy level should be predicted as representing the energy required to raise 1 electron to the excited level. Since, for the case of several electrons, we are unable to *predict* the energies of the levels, all we can do is *invent* levels such that the observed spectra can be derived from the energy-level diagram by applying the above equation. Each atom has its characteristic levels.

132

We shall describe the energy-level diagram of sodium. While our diagram for hydrogen (Fig. 10.4) contains only one column of levels, that for sodium contains several. Within the same diagram all columns of levels converge toward the same limit. The levels of the first vertical column are called "S levels," those of the second column "P levels," and those of the third "D levels." These letters are taken from the descriptive names (sharp, principal, diffuse) attached to the observed series (Fig. 11.2).

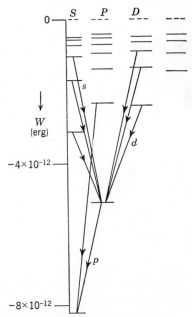

This diagram needs the following instruction how to correlate any observed spectral line with an energy difference between two levels. Not all possible transitions between any two energy levels lead to spectral lines. Only combinations of two levels that *belong to adjacent vertical columns are* "*allowed,*" *i.e.*, allow the computation of an observed spectral line. This rule, which is as empirical as the energy levels themselves, is called a "selection rule." We shall illustrate it by pointing out how the various series are represented in the diagram. First we notice that the normal state of the atom, *i.e.*, the state of lowest energy (see Sec. 10.5b), belongs to the column of the S levels (left vertical column). Which levels can go

FIG. 11.2. Energy-level diagram of the sodium atom; p = principal series; s = sharp series; d = diffuse series. The smallest frequency of the principal series belongs to the prominent yellow line.

down to the normal level by emission of a spectral line? Only the P levels can do it, because they represent the only adjacent vertical column. (The selection rule "forbids" the higher S levels or the D levels to combine with the lowest S level.) The series due to the transition of any P level to the lowest S level is called "*principal series*" because of its prominent intensity. Its first line is the intense yellow line which makes the light from sodium lamps yellow. Which levels can go down to the lowest P level by emission of a spectral line? Since the P levels have neighbors on both sides, we must consider the transitions from the right and left separately. Any higher S level going down to the lowest P level emits a line of the *sharp series;* any D level doing the same emits a line of the *diffuse series*. The diagram shows that, in agreement with the observation, the sharp and the diffuse series converge toward the same limit, which is given by the difference from the common convergence limit of all levels and the lowest P level.   The three series just discussed, principal, sharp, and diffuse, are only examples.   One may go through similar arguments, considering all "allowed" combinations between higher levels.   Furthermore, there are more columns containing only higher levels.   But between the higher levels all energy differences are smaller, hence all wavelengths longer, which places these series into the *infrared* region and makes them, for technical reasons, less easily observable.   Only the series which have the lowest S or the lowest P level as the final state are to be found in the *visible* or *ultraviolet*.   Only these series are indicated on the diagram.   The selection rule restricts only the transitions taking place with emission of light or, as we shall see later, with absorption of light; it does not restrict the excitation by electron impact.

This diagram fulfills the same purpose as that of hydrogen: A large number of spectral lines are described in the most economical way.   One may wonder whether the diagram of Fig. 11.2 describes the energies of the atom before and after emission uniquely, or whether it might be replaced by a different arrangement that would also yield the correct wavelengths for the emitted lines.   Actually it is much better founded than the argument just presented may seem to indicate.   Only an example will be given of the additional evidence.   With a spectrograph of higher resolving power it is observed that each line described above actually consists of a pair of closely adjacent components.   For example, the yellow line of sodium has two such components differing in frequency by 51.54×10^{10} sec^{-1}, which is only about 1/1,000 of the frequency of the line.   This indicates that we must supplement our energy-level diagram (Fig. 11.2) by assuming that either the upper or the lower level of the yellow line consists of two closely adjacent sublevels.   The question of which level is double is solved by exploring other spectral lines which are connected with one or the other of these levels.   The diagram shows that all lines of the sharp and diffuse series have the lowest P level as their *final* state which is identical with the *initial* state of the yellow line. Actually observation reveals exactly the same fine structure for all lines of these two series, *i.e.*, all are narrow doublets with the same frequency difference.   This observation proves that the doublet structure, first discovered for the yellow spectral line, is located in the lowest P level, not the lowest S level.   This is an example of an argument which corroborates an energy-level diagram such as that of sodium.

The spectra of other alkali atoms are strictly analogous so that for any line of sodium one can point out the corresponding line of any other alkali.   The elements of the other groups of the periodic table have

different, in most cases vastly more complicated, spectra.   As an example
we reproduce a small section of the iron spectrum, which illustrates how
difficult a problem its analysis may be (Fig. 11.3).

When we put the emitting source in a strong magnetic field, we find
that each spectral line is split up into several components with small frequency differences which are proportional to the field strength.   This

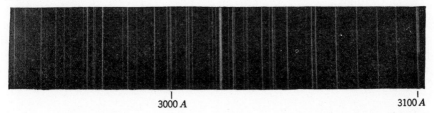

3000 A   3100 A

FIG. 11.3. Small section of iron spectrum from electric arc (photographic positive).

phenomenon is called the "Zeeman effect."   For most lines, the patterns
so obtained are more complicated than the group of three components
into which the hydrogen lines split.   An example is given in Fig. 11.4.
Even for the powerful fields of large electromagnets, these patterns are
so narrow that their investigation requires spectrographs of high resolving
power.

FIG. 11.4. Zeeman effects in lines of the zinc spectrum (photographic positive).   (a)
Without magnetic field; (b) with magnetic field.   (*Courtesy of J. B. Green.*)

The Zeeman effect contributes to the exploration of the sun.   Hale
(1908) discovered that at a sunspot spectral absorption lines show the
splitting characteristic for the Zeeman effect.   This observation led to
the measurement of the magnetic fields of the sunspots, which are of the
order of magnitude 3,000 oersteds and of an extension in space several
times the volume of the earth.

b. Displacement Law.   In our discussion of Bohr's theory we found
that the spectra of neutral hydrogen and ionized helium contain closely
related series.   The frequencies of the helium lines are four times larger

than those of the corresponding hydrogen lines because of the nuclear charge of helium, which is twice as large as that of hydrogen.

This is a special case of the spectroscopic displacement law, discovered by Sommerfeld. This law is based on the general rule that the nuclear charge equals the atomic number. (This rule we derived from alpha-ray scattering and confirmed by applying Bohr's theory to the lightest atoms.) The element magnesium, for example, has 12 external electrons, one more than its predecessor in the periodic table, sodium. Consequently, the singly charged magnesium ion Mg^+ has only 11 external electrons, just as many as neutral Na. This relation explains why Mg^+ and Na have spectra of the same type. Just as with H and He^+, the lines of Na and Mg^+ can individually be correlated, although the lines of the magnesium ion, because of the higher charge of the magnesium nucleus, are located at higher frequencies. This example leads to the displacement law: Any singly charged ion has the same type of spectrum as the neutral atom of the preceding element in the periodic table but shifted to higher frequencies.

One can extend this law to ions that have lost several electrons. We have studied the simplest case, comparing H, He^+, Li^{++}, etc., all spectra being described by Bohr's theory. Correspondingly the spectra of Na, Mg^+, Al^{++}, etc., are all of the simple, easily identified type of an alkali spectrum; but the spectra of the higher ions are increasingly shifted to the extreme ultraviolet (to high frequencies). Hence their investigation requires the difficult technique of the vacuum spectrograph. Such a group of atoms and ions, which all have the same number of external electrons but differ by their nuclear charges, is called an "isoelectronic sequence."

These experimental results described by the spectroscopic displacement law confirm the rule stating that the atomic number equals the nuclear charge, because this rule is needed to explain that any singly charged ion has the same number of external electrons as the neutral atom preceding it in the periodic table.

c. Energies of Excitation and Ionization. One can derive the *excitation* energy and *ionization* energy of an atom from its energy-level diagram, following the argument applied to hydrogen (Sec. 10.5c). For example, the theory predicts that the first line of the principal series (the yellow line of sodium, $\lambda = 5{,}896$ A; $\nu = 5.083 \times 10^{14}$ sec^{-1}) is excited only if the energy $h\nu = 3.36 \times 10^{-12}$ erg $= 2.10$ ev is imparted to sodium atoms in the normal state. Furthermore, the convergence limit of the energy-level diagram is interpreted as the energy (above the lowest, normal level) which, when absorbed by an electron in the normal state, will allow the electron to escape from the atom, hence represents the energy of ionization. The height of this convergence limit above the normal state of the atom is computed from the observed (or extrapolated) convergence limit of the principal series, *i.e.*, 2,412 A. The computation of $h\nu$ leads to an energy of ionization of 8.22×10^{-12} erg = 5.14 ev. (The unit electron volt should not obscure the fact that our computation of the energies is based on spectroscopic observations; see Sec. 12.1.)

d. Metastable Levels. The selection rule mentioned above states that emission of light takes place only by transitions between levels that belong to adjacent vertical columns. This leads to a curious prediction in the case of certain exceptional energy-level diagrams in which the location of the levels is somewhat different from the arrangement for sodium atoms. For example, in the energy-level diagram of Fig. 11.5 it happens that the third vertical column has its lowest level a little below those of both adjacent columns. In the electric discharge, all possible levels may be excited by impacts or reached, after the excitation process, by emission of light. Thus some atoms finally arrive at the lowest D level. Here, although they contain energy stored up, the atoms are "forbidden" to radiate by the selection rule, because the adjacent vertical columns have no levels with lower energy. This situation gives to these levels much longer lives than the ordinary excited atoms have. These special levels are called "metastable" in

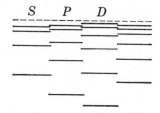

Fig. 11.5. Schematic energy-level diagram containing a metastable level (the lowest D level).

contrast to the common unstable levels and the one and only stable level, the normal state of the atom. The analysis of the line spectrum furnishes the metastable levels with the same accuracy as all other levels because they show up as *final* levels in the emission of certain spectral lines whose initial levels are known.

As good a picture of a metastable level as mechanics has to offer is given by a rock placed high up on a slope, resting in a shallow hole from which it may easily be pushed out. While any other position on the slope is *unstable* and the position at the bottom of the valley is *stable*, the hole gives some *inferior stability* to a position high above the stable state.

The prediction of metastable levels presented here on the basis of the diagram Fig. 11.5 is only a special case. The complete treatment of atomic spectra describes the fine structure levels with additional quantum numbers which necessitate more selection rules and present other chances of metastable levels. Such levels occur in mercury, helium, oxygen, and other atoms. We shall come back to them in the discussion of absorption spectra and impacts of the second kind (Secs. 12.4 and 12.10).

Metastable levels play a part in certain photochemical reactions in which, in the first place, light incident on a mixture of gases excites an atom, *e.g.*, a mercury atom. Since the excited state of the atom so produced after a very short lifetime (see Sec. 12.11) radiates its energy, this is not available for an energy-consuming chemical reaction. The situation is different, however, if by a collision the excited atom is promptly transferred into a metastable level which lives much longer and hence has a much better chance of utilizing its energy for a chemical reaction. Many photochemical reactions caused by metastable mercury atoms have been found.

It is an overstatement that the selection rule (Sec. 11.1*a*) completely prohibits transitions between levels that do not belong to adjacent vertical groups. It is better to say that such transitions, called "forbidden," have a much smaller probability than the "allowed" transitions, say, smaller by the factor 1/1,000,000. Hence in sodium (Fig. 11.2) the transition combined with radiation from the lowest D level *to the lowest S level* is not absolutely impossible; however, the spectral line so produced is in practice much too weak for observation because the competing "allowed" transition from the lowest D level *to the lowest P level* is much more probable. The situation is different for the metastable level (Fig. 11.5). Since here there is no "allowed" transition in competition with the "forbidden" transition, this may take place, although after a lifetime of the excited level possibly a million times longer than that of an unstable level. The consequences of this prolonged life are different in laboratory experiments and in very low-pressure atmospheres. For example, in an electric discharge a metastable level, exposed to numerous collisions with the walls or electrons or ions, hardly ever reaches the old age that would lead to its natural death by the "forbidden" radiation. Thus this radiation is hardly ever observed in laboratory experiments. However, the situation is different in the high layers of our atmosphere or in the solar corona. Here no walls are present as in the discharge tube, and the density of the gas is only about 10^{-15} of our atmosphere at sea level. Therefore, collisions are much rarer and the chances of survival of metastable atoms so much greater that intense spectral lines due to transitions from metastable levels are observed. The spectra of bright-line nebulae show lines which, decades ago, were attributed to a mysterious element called "nebulium." At present, we are sure that there is no place for more elements in the periodic table, as will be discussed in the section on X rays (Sec. 14.2*b*). Now these nebulium lines are attributed to forbidden transitions in ionized oxygen and nitrogen atoms. Lines in the solar corona have been explained as forbidden lines in highly ionized iron, nickel, and calcium atoms.

e. Report on Further Developments. In the further development of our knowledge of atomic spectra, experiment and theory are closely interlinked.   Omitting the mathematical background, we shall illustrate the advanced argument by discussing the simplest example, the spectrum of an alkali atom, say sodium.

The spectra of the alkali atoms (Figs. 11.1 and 11.2) occupy an intermediate position between the simple hydrogen spectrum and the other much more complex atomic spectra.   An alkali atom is assumed to consist of a nucleus surrounded by "shells" of electrons, which remain in their very stable positions, and one particular electron, called the "series electron," which can readily be excited.   When returning to a position of lower energy, the series electron is responsible for the radiation emitted. (This structure will be discussed further in the chapter on the periodic table, Chap. 13.)   When the series electron is in a large circular orbit around the nucleus and the other electrons, which lie in more closely packed shells, it is affected by the nucleus and the other electrons as if all their charges were concentrated at the nucleus.   Thus, in the case of sodium, the nucleus has a charge of $+11$, but this is masked by shells of altogether 10 electrons, so that the series electron is influenced by a charge of only $+1$ at the nucleus.   This picture explains the fact that in any alkali atom the high-energy levels have nearly the same relative positions as in the hydrogen atom.   On the other hand, the *lower* energy levels differ from those of the hydrogen atom, since here the series electron closely approaches the shells of the more stable electrons or may even penetrate into them.

It has been mentioned above that most spectral lines of an alkali atom show a narrow doublet structure (Sec. 11.1a) which is attributed to the doublet structure of certain energy levels.   This fact, combined with similar observations on other spectra, is explained by a new hypothesis which is of great importance for spectroscopy as well as for nuclear physics.   It is assumed that each electron, in addition to its *orbital* motion considered by Bohr, performs a *spin* motion about its own axis (Goudsmit and Uhlenbeck, 1925).   This is analogous to the spin of the earth about its own axis which is combined with its revolution about the sun.   Quantum theory restricts the spin of the electron by a quantum condition which is adjusted so that the conclusions agree to the observed facts.   This condition is strikingly simple: The angular momentum of the spin is $\frac{1}{2}h/2\pi$ (without a variable quantum number).

In order to correlate this spin with the orbital motion, we must go back to an older result derived from Sommerfeld's general quantum conditions. This theory predicts that, when the atom is subjected to an external magnetic field, the orbits take up discrete orientations (described by a new quantum number) with respect to the direction of the field.   This is called "space quantization."   We apply the same idea to the theory of the electron *spin* which is subjected not to an *external* magnetic field but to that caused by the *orbital* motion of the electron.   Here space quantization predicts that the spin is either parallel or antiparallel to this field. For the same orbital motion these two orientations of the spin represent energies which differ only slightly and are responsible for the splitting of the energy level belonging to the orbit into a close pair and thus, taking into account certain new selection rules, for the doublet structure observed.

At the same time the hypothesis of the electron spin helps to explain the complicated Zeeman patterns of the spectral lines which are observed when the source of light is placed in a magnetic field.   Here we must first compute the *total* angular momentum (the vector sum of the spin and orbital momenta).   Space quantization predicts that, in the external magnetic field, the total angular momentum assumes certain distinct orientations whose energy contents differ slightly.   Instead of the simple transition which, in the absence of a magnetic field, would produce one spectral line, a group of slightly modified transitions takes place which are responsible for the delicate structure of the Zeeman effect.

Having discussed the angular momentum of the electron spin, we refrain from discussing the special hypothesis concerned with its magnetic moment.   Furthermore, we omit the discussion of the spectra of the elements more complicated than the alkalis which are supposed to have not one but several "series electrons" whose mutual relations are consistently described by similar assumptions.   On the basis of the same guiding ideas, derived largely from space quantization, a vast material of atomic spectra has been interpreted.   This kind of work is still far from finished.   In particular many heavy elements show very complicated spectra which have not been analyzed yet.

A new fundamental hypothesis is needed for the interpretation of an exceedingly narrow "hyperfine structure" which, in spectrographs of the very highest resolving power, is found in many spectral lines.   The hyperfine structure is consistently explained by attributing angular momenta and magnetic moments to the *nuclei* and assuming similar rules for their orientations with respect to the *total electronic* angular momentum.   This is one of the few connecting links between spectroscopy and nuclear physics.   The exploration of the hyperfine structure of spectral lines has led to the determination of many nuclear angular momenta and the magnetic moments associated with them.   They have been confirmed by entirely different experiments (see Sec. 16.7) and thus strengthen our confidence in the basic ideas of spectroscopic theory.

f. Quantitative Spectral Analysis.   It has been known for a long time that in an electric discharge the relative intensities of the spectra of several gases in a mixture fail to indicate their relative concentrations. The reason is that there are other factors affecting the intensities, partly inherent in the atomic structure as probabilities of transition, partly depending on the velocity distribution of the electrons in the discharge. The many unknown factors involved prevented *quantitative* spectroscopic analysis for a long time.

Only in the last two decades has progress been made. This success is directly based on experience and is independent of atomic theory. Suppose that in the manufacturing process of steel we want to test the concentration of manganese in iron. To begin with, for the purpose of calibration, we prepare a set of mixtures of iron with small percentages of manganese, say, 0.3, 0.4, 0.5, etc., per cent. The spectra of these samples, excited by an electric spark, are photographed, and the relative intensities of some representative lines of iron and manganese are measured. Next, a sample with an unknown concentration of manganese is

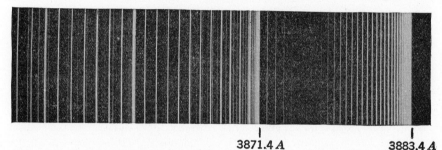

3871.4 A   3883.4 A

Fig. 11.6. Part of a molecular spectrum (CN), photographed with a diffraction grating.

investigated in the same way, and by comparison with the set of calibration spectra the concentration of manganese is determined. This method of testing, although of limited application, has practical importance because it is more rapid than many chemical tests. In particular it is suitable for the detection of small impurities.

11.2. Molecular Spectra. A typical molecular spectrum is given by Fig. 11.6. It is more complicated than an atomic spectrum by the appearance of broad bands. For this reason molecular spectra are frequently called "band spectra" as contrasting to "line spectra" emitted by atoms. In most cases these bands can be resolved into individual sharp lines, which by their crowded arrangement give the impression of bands. Typical of most bands are the sharp and intense edges. Superficially, they look very much like series converging to limits. But this impression is misleading, since in some cases the lines near the edge can be completely resolved and in other cases the law describing the individual lines is so well known that there is no question about the fact that the edge represents only a finite number of lines crowded together in a peculiar arrangement.

Only a brief report of the theory of band spectra will be given. These spectra, which for decades defied analysis, were interpreted soon after the discovery of the Bohr theory. Here both vibration and rotation of the atoms constituting the molecule occur and must be taken into account in addition to the electronic excitation. For both these motions, quantum theory predicts quantized energy levels.

As a striking example for the fertility of Bohr's quantum condition (Eq. 10.5) we discuss its bearing on molecular rotation. While in the *hydrogen atom* the radius of revolution r depends on the velocity, we describe the *diatomic molecule* as a rigid body characterized by a constant moment of inertia I. This picture leads to a simple prediction of the quantized rotational energy levels as follows. Bohr's quantum condition reads

$$\text{Angular momentum} = I\omega = \frac{Jh}{2\pi}$$

where the rotational quantum number J is any integer. As this equation contains only one variable, ω, we express the energy which, for the rigid molecule, is only kinetic energy of rotation as

$$W = \frac{I\omega^2}{2} = \frac{J^2}{I}\frac{h^2}{8\pi^2}$$

This result is confirmed by the analysis of molecular spectra. In our discussion of specific heats of gases (Sec. 4.2) we stated that molecular hydrogen, H_2, has particularly large rotational energy levels. The last equation is the theoretical basis for this statement, since H_2 is the molecule endowed with the smallest moment of inertia I.

The energy levels of the *rotation* have a very narrow spacing of the order of hundredths of an electron volt. Quantum transitions between such levels lead to radiation in the *extreme infrared*. The energy levels of *vibration* have a wider spacing of the order of tenths of an electron volt. Quantum transitions between vibrational levels produce a radiation in the *near infrared*. (Ordinarily a change of a *vibrational* quantum is accompanied by a simultaneous change of a *rotational* quantum. The various combinations lead to the "vibration-rotation bands" in the near infrared.) Finally, a quantum change of the *electronic* state of the molecule, which causes *visible* or *ultraviolet* radiation, ordinarily takes place with simultaneous changes of vibration and rotation. These combinations are responsible for the complicated band spectrum of Fig. 11.6.

A whole band system, covering many hundred angstrom units, may be due to one definite change of electronic orbit, hence correspond to one single line in an atomic spectrum. In the molecule the simultaneous changes of *vibration* and *electronic energy* cause the *coarse structure;* this means that any one *single band* with its sharp edge is due to a simultaneous change of electronic orbit, one well-defined change of vibration, and all possible changes of rotation. Finally, any *one single sharp line* within this band is attributed to a well-defined change of *rotation*.

Fine structures of the individual rotational lines belonging to a band are interpreted by the electron spin (see Sec. 11.1e), which proves as important in the interpretation of molecular spectra as in atomic spectra.

Recent new discoveries in spectroscopy are due to the extensive development of *microwave techniques* during the Second World War. Developed for the purpose of radar, microwave transmitters of great constancy make possible the investigation of important new absorption spectra of molecules in the range between the extreme infrared and radio wave lengths.

The interpretation of molecular spectra may well be listed among the great successes of the quantum theory. The analysis of these spectra led to a better understanding of molecular structure. Molecular spectroscopy is a wide field in which no border line exists between physics and chemistry.

SUMMARY OF CHAPTER 11

As an example of *a spectrum of an atom heavier than hydrogen*, the spectrum of sodium is described on the basis of its energy-level diagram. This contains levels arranged in several vertical columns. The selection rule states that transitions connected with emission or absorption of light take place only between levels that belong to adjacent vertical columns. Such transitions lead to the various series: principal, sharp, and diffuse. The spectra of other alkali atoms are strictly analogous.

The *Zeeman effect* of most lines is more complicated than the pattern of three Zeeman components shown by the hydrogen lines.

The *displacement law* states that any singly charged ion exhibits the same type of spectrum as the neutral atom of the element preceding it in the periodic table, but shifted to higher frequencies. This law confirms the rule: atomic number = nuclear charge.

The analysis of the spectrum and its description by the energy-level diagram lead to the prediction of the *energies of excitation and ionization*.

An atom in a *metastable level* is in an energy state such that the selection rule allows it only a small chance of radiating light and falling to a lower energy state. Thus it has a lifetime much longer than atoms in ordinary excited levels have. In the conventional light sources of the laboratory, atoms in metastable levels ordinarily have no chance at all of emitting light because, during their extended lifetimes in such levels, they are lifted out of the levels by collisions. Nevertheless they may have a chance of radiating light at the very low pressures that prevail in nebulae, the solar corona, and the upper atmosphere of the earth.

Bohr's theory does not quantitatively predict the energy levels of more complicated atoms. However, with the additional hypothesis of the electron spin, the theory gives account of the various series constituting an atomic spectrum, in particular of the fine structure of the lines and their splitting in a magnetic field (Zeeman effect). Finally, the hyperfine structure of spectral lines is interpreted by attributing a spin to the nucleus of the emitting atom.

Quantitative spectral analysis is possible only in special cases on the basis of a calibration.

Molecular spectra (band spectra) are interpreted as due to simultaneous changes of electronic energy, vibration, and rotation of molecules.

CHAPTER 12

FUNDAMENTAL PROCESSES

In the present chapter the various processes by which atoms and molecules may *receive* or *give away* energy will be interpreted on the basis of the quantum theory. We shall first consider collision processes, next the emission and absorption of light, then chemical processes involving excited atoms, and finally collisions of the second kind, which will take us back to chemistry. As a general point of view, we shall keep in mind our continued search for additional tests of the theory. For many processes we shall find illustrative cases in nature.

12.1. Excitation and Ionization by Controlled Electron Impact. We derived the excitation energy and ionization energy of atoms from the energy-level diagram, which is constructed solely on the basis of *spectroscopic* observations (Sec. 11.1*a*). In the present section we shall supplement the evidence (1) by a combination of *spectroscopic* and *electrical* observations and (2) by a purely *electrical* experiment. In any case we shall try to find an answer to the question: What happens to electrons which pass through a gas or vapor on their way from a glowing cathode to an anode?

By way of preparation we must find out what happens to electrons if all their collisions with atoms are governed by the laws of *elastic* collisions. These are general considerations that we shall apply later to the various collisions suffered by corpuscular rays in nuclear physics. The electrons emanate from the glowing metal with thermal velocities, which are negligible compared with those imparted by an electric field acting between cathode and anode. In any elastic collision between a fast electron and a slow atom, because of the vast difference of the masses, the electron keeps practically all its kinetic energy but changes its direction (see Prob. 9.2). If the electron coming straight from the filament bounces exactly backward, it is *decelerated* by the same potential difference which, before the collision, had *accelerated* it. It behaves the same way as a rubber ball dropped from a certain height and bounced back from the floor. If, instead, the electron bounces off at an angle with the field, the same is true for the forward or backward component of its velocity. Therefore, at any distance from the cathode all electrons have the same kinetic energy, only the *directions of their velocities* may have been changed by collisions. This applies in general to electrons that are deflected in any

direction *by elastic collisions* with atoms.   Unless the number of intervening collisions is excessive, the electrons when reaching the anode have
nearly the kinetic energy given by the potential difference between the
cathode and the anode; their velocities are altered by the effect of collisions but are directed preferentially parallel to the electric field.

The same is true for balls falling down under the effect of gravity.   If a ball bounces
back elastically from the floor, it rises until it reaches its original position, being
gradually decelerated.   At any horizontal level its kinetic energy when rising is the
same as it was at the same level when falling.   The same is true when it bounces off
in any direction after an elastic collision with a heavy obstacle.   This follows from
the principle of conservation of energy.

Franck and Hertz (1914) excited the 2,537 A line of mercury atoms by
controlled electron impact.   This first line of the principal series of

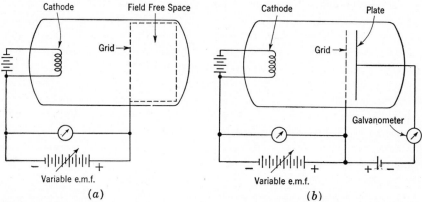

Fig. 12.1. Excitation of atoms by controlled electron impact (Franck and Hertz).
(*a*) Electrical and spectroscopic observation combined; (*b*) electrical observation
only.

mercury is probably the most photographed spectral line, as it is used in
many investigations in physics as well as photochemistry (see Sec. 12.10).
From the observed wavelength the energy difference between the initial
and final levels giving rise to the λ 2,537 line is computed to be 4.88 ev
(Sec. 11.1*c*).   The experiment is performed in low-pressure mercury
vapor, through which electrons from a glowing cathode travel.   The
electrons are accelerated toward a grid, beyond which they shoot into a
field-free space and hence keep the velocity they had when passing
through the grid (Fig. 12.1*a*).   At low values of the accelerating voltage
the vapor remains dark, but, when the voltage is increased to a certain
sharply defined value, the single line λ 2,537 suddenly appears, unaccom-
panied by any other radiation.   The critical voltage is found to be equal
to the excitation energy (4.88 ev) of the initial state for emission of
λ 2,537, within the experimental error.   If the impinging electrons are

given higher kinetic energy than required for the excitation of the quantized energy level, the same excitation takes place. In this case the electrons, after delivering the quantized energy to the atoms, retain the remainder of the energy. If the electrons are endowed with sufficient energy, they may excite the atoms to a higher quantized level.

In the other experiment to be discussed, first performed by Franck and Hertz (1914), the fate of the impinging electrons is traced by electrical experiments only. One uses a three-electrode tube containing a glowing cathode (preferably an equipotential cathode), a metal grid at a distance of a few centimeters from the cathode, and a plate right behind the grid (Fig. 12.1*b*). Again the electrons emanating from the cathode are accelerated by a *variable* potential difference to the grid. Those passing through the meshes of the grid have to overcome a small, *constant retarding* potential difference of, say, $\frac{1}{2}$ volt in order to reach the plate. A galvanometer reads the plate current. Other electrons flow through the metal of the grid and so form the other branch of the total current. The tube contains a gas or vapor, like mercury vapor, at a pressure so low that between the cathode and the grid the electrons suffer many collisions, but only a few or no collisions over the short distance between the grid and the plate.

On the basis of the considerations given above, we can predict what will happen if the collisions between electrons and atoms are *elastic*. Electrons when accelerated by one or several volts and passing through the meshes of the grid should easily overcome the small retarding voltage and reach the plate. If so, they are registered by the galvanometer.

Franck and Hertz measured the *plate current* as a function of the *accelerating potential difference* between the cathode and the grid. They found curves like those of Fig. 12.2, characterized by a succession of equally spaced maxima. For mercury vapor, for example, the distance between peaks is always 4.88 volts, irrespective of any detail of the apparatus. The authors explained the shape of the curves as follows: At low potential differences the current is limited by the space charge (Sec. 15.1), which is not materially affected by the presence of the vapor. This explains the first gradual increase of the current. Above a sharply defined energy limit, 4.88 ev in the case of mercury, the mercury atoms take away the kinetic energy from the electrons in collisions and so obtain their energy of excitation. These collisions are *inelastic* since kinetic energy is changed into another type of energy. If electrons reach the grid with a kinetic energy of 4.88 ev and are there robbed of this energy by mercury atoms, they are unable to overcome the retarding voltage; hence the *plate current drops*. At further increasing accelerating voltage the layer in which this energy loss occurs is shifted to a position closer to the cathode. Now the electrons, after suffering one energy loss, have a chance to recover and reach the grid with an appreciable energy, which enables them to overcome the small retarding voltage. This explains the second increase of the current. At a definite higher voltage the electrons already suffer this first loss near the middle of the distance, pick up just another 4.88 ev when they reach the grid, and there suffer a second loss of the same size. Hence the plate current drops again and

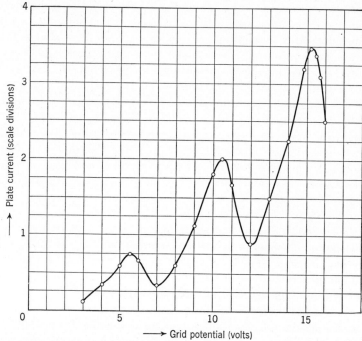

FIG. 12.2. Excitation potential of mercury vapor measured by controlled electron impact (students' laboratory experiment).

so forms the second maximum. This process continues for higher voltages. (We are not concerned with the fact that the whole curve may be shifted along the V axis depending upon the surface properties of the metals, described as "contact potential difference.") The difference between successive maxima is always 4.88 volts. The outstanding result is that here the excitation energy of atoms, e.g., 4.88 ev for mercury, is measured by a purely electrical method.

What bearing has the experiment of Franck and Hertz on the theory of radiation from atoms? Everybody knows that a very soft touch with the hammer excites a bell to a very low-intensity vibration. The experiment just presented, however, gives evidence that nothing of the kind happens when the electron hits the atom. At low energy the collisions are elastic and fail to give *any* energy of excitation to the atom. Only above a sharply defined limit, characteristic of the atom, is the atom able to receive energy in an inelastic collision. Then the full, quantized energy of excitation is transferred. The value so measured agrees with the value derived from the spectrum. Hence the experiment gives a strong confirmation of the fundamental idea of the quantum theory as opposed to the classical theory of radiation.

We apply this result to another determination of Planck's constant h as follows. The energy of excitation, *e.g.*, of sodium vapor, is measured spectroscopically by measuring the frequency ν of the first line of the principal series. Next the same energy characteristic of sodium vapor is measured by a voltmeter and expressed as eV. In the equation $h\nu = eV$, Planck's constant h is the only unknown and hence can be computed. The resulting value of h agrees with those obtained by other methods.

In more detailed experimental investigations it has been found that the chance for a transfer of excitation energy to the atom depends strongly on the excess energy of the impinging electron. Electrons with an energy slightly exceeding the minimum value have the highest probability; with a further increase of kinetic energy, this probability is strongly decreased.

Measurements of this kind have been carried out for all elements available as gases or vapors. For many years, while the technique of the vacuum spectrograph was not yet fully developed, these experiments gave the only available evidence of the excitation energies of the rare gases, the spectra of which were not completely accessible.

In nearly the same apparatus Franck and Hertz measured the *ionizing* potentials of gases and vapors. For this measurement the retarding potential between grid and plate is made much larger, perhaps as large as 20 volts. This potential keeps electrons away from the plate throughout the experiment. Furthermore, the pressure of the gas or vapor is reduced to so low a value that the mean free path is much longer and the electrons have a good chance of picking up higher kinetic energy without losing it to the *excitation* of atoms. For this arrangement the IV curve looks entirely differ-

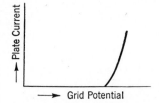

Fig. 12.3. Ionization potential measured by controlled electron impact.

ent (Fig. 12.3). The current is zero up to a certain limit and then suddenly increases. The galvanometer is deflected in the direction opposite to that of the other experiment. Franck and Hertz explained this curve as follows: The electrons are able to produce ionization only after reaching the ionization energy. The positive ions so produced near the grid are subjected to the field between the grid and the plate, pulled to the plate, and so registered by the galvanometer. (A correction must be applied for the contact-potential difference mentioned above.) The results of these *electrical* measurements agree with those obtained *spectroscopically* from the convergence limits of the series (Sec. 11.1*c*).

12.2. Electric Discharges through Gases. *a. Processes in the Electric Discharge.* Everybody has seen several types of electric discharge through gases. We have mentioned the low-pressure discharge (Secs. 6.2 and 10.1). Other examples are the arc, the spark, and discharges due to photoelectric effect, X rays, or radioactive rays. These various types may be classified into self-maintained and non-self-maintained discharges. These conventional designations, however, overstate the case. No discharge can be completely self-maintained, since in any case energy must be supplied. The distinction means only that the carriers of electricity are generated either by processes inherent in the discharge or by an outside agent like light.

It is easy to understand the *non-self-maintained* gas discharge. Here light or heat liberates electrons from metal surfaces; alternatively X rays or radioactive rays generate in the gas the electrons and positive ions that carry the current. In any case the carriers are generated by some outside agent, which must continue to act as long as the discharge runs. The intensity of the electric current depends on this agent. Therefore, we employ such non-self-maintained discharges for measuring the intensity of X rays or radioactive rays. An example is the X-ray dosimeter (see Sec. 14.1*d*).

It is less easy to understand the *self-maintained* gas discharge. Well-known examples are the neon sign, the electric arc, and lightning. Here the discharge itself generates the carriers of electricity by processes that we want to analyze. There are three types of self-maintained gas discharges: the spark, the arc, and the low-pressure discharge. We shall describe the low-pressure discharge in some detail because of the importance of the cathode ray and positive ray, both of which are parts of this discharge.

All gases at atmospheric pressure are good insulators unless the applied voltage is so high that a spark discharge occurs. At reduced pressure, say, of a few centimeters of mercury, a potential difference of a few thousand volts readily starts a discharge. The conductivity of the gas has a maximum at about 1 mm pressure. The phenomena we are interested in are most clearly exhibited at a pressure of a few hundredths of a millimeter. Figure 12.4 shows the discharge at this low pressure. The difference between the parts near the two electrodes is striking. Near the negative electrode, the cathode, there is a dark space, called the "Crookes dark space," a few centimeters long. This part of the discharge is rather sharply limited, on one side by the cathode (or rather by a thin luminous layer covering the cathode), on the other side by another luminous layer stretching farther into the discharge. The length of the Crookes dark space increases with decreasing gas pressure and, within a certain range, can be used conveniently for measuring pressures of gases. Its length is of the same order of magnitude as the mean free path of the gaseous molecules (Sec. 5.1). We are less concerned with the so-called "positive" column, which extends toward the positive electrode and in many cases shows another dark space followed by brilliant striations.

In order to explore the potential distribution along the discharge, we introduce into the tube several probes made of short metal wires sealed through the glass wall, with all but the tips covered with glass. An electrostatic voltmeter between the cathode and any probe measures the potential difference between these two spots. (A thorough investigation

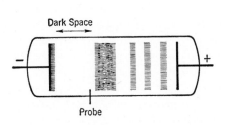

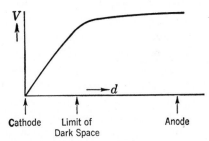

FIG. 12.4. Electric discharge through a gas at low pressure.

FIG. 12.5. Potential distribution along discharge. V = potential difference against cathode; d = distance from cathode.

shows that the probe method is subject to errors of several volts, but they are negligible as compared with the effect we shall describe.) The potential distribution over the length of the discharge tube is given in Fig. 12.5. It is evident that the potential is by no means uniformly distributed, as it would be along a conducting wire of uniform cross section. It shows by far the largest gradient, indicating a strong electric field, near the cathode, while along the rest of the discharge the gradient is small. The large potential drop near the cathode is called the "cathode drop." It can well be demonstrated in the lecture room.

The processes in the discharge responsible for the observations described are by no means fully understood. We shall discuss only the most important ones responsible for the conductivity and the various effects of the cathode drop.

At atmospheric pressure all gases are good, although not complete, insulators. Their very small conductivity, not easily measured, is presumably due to the ionizing effect of radioactive rays and cosmic rays, which are present everywhere. When a few free electrons resulting from this all-pervading ionization are accelerated sufficiently by an electric field, they are able to ionize atoms or molecules by impact. The free electrons produced in this way go through the same process. This "electron avalanche" is the primary agent maintaining conductivity all along the discharge. It operates better at low pressure, because a long mean free path reduces the danger of many small energy losses suffered by the free electrons in collisions that would prevent them from picking up the large kinetic energy required for ionization. Ionization by electron impact was assumed by Townsend (1899) to be responsible for the conductivity of gases before measurements of the ionization energies of the various gases were carried out.

We shall not explain the cathode drop and the striations, partly because it is not essential for our purpose, partly because no fully satisfactory explanations are known. Let us accept as a fact the high potential drop near the cathode, demonstrated by the probe method, and find out what part it plays in the discharge. We have mentioned the ionization processes creating free electrons and positive ions. Why did we concentrate on the effect of *electrons* in explaining the ionization and disregard the *positive ions?* In the weak field of the positive column the positive ions do not have a good chance to pick up energy because the ions have about the same mass as the atoms or molecules of the gas. Hence the kinetic energy that an *ion* picks up in the electric field is readily given off in a few collisions with atoms or molecules and dissipated into heat. The *electron*, however, has the advantage of keeping its kinetic energy when suffering collisions because of its very small mass (see Sec. 9.1 and Prob. 9.1). Unless the electron loses energy through the relatively rare process of excitation or ionization, it will accumulate kinetic energy as it accelerates in the electric field.

However, the kinetic energy of a positive ion is large when it is accelerated in the very high potential drop that extends from the cathode for about one mean free path. The field is so concentrated that it may give to the ion a kinetic energy of several thousand electron volts, without energy loss in intervening collisions. Endowed with this energy, the positive ion hits the metal of the cathode. It has been found out by special experiments that such impacts of ions on a metal surface liberate electrons. One impinging ion may well free several electrons. The electrons liberated from the cathode by its bombardment with positive ions supply more carriers of electricity, which help conduct the current.

The processes in the *electric spark* are essentially the same, although modified by the much shorter mean free path at atmospheric pressure. In the *electric arc* the bombardment of the cathode with positive ions is so violent that the cathode is heated to several thousand degrees centigrade and so becomes a copious thermal emitter of electrons. This process, most conspicuous in the glowing cathode of the carbon arc, is responsible for the large current carried by the arc.

b. Cathode Rays and Positive Rays. The processes near the cathode of the low-pressure discharge just described explain the production of the cathode ray and the positive ray. Electrons liberated from the cathode are exposed to the strong electric field in the cathode drop, which endows them with high kinetic energy. This process enables the electrons to shoot straight away from the cathode and form a cathode ray. In the low-pressure discharge (Fig. 6.1) one can distinguish two groups of electrons: those belonging to the cathode ray endowed with kinetic energies of thousands of electron volts, and those which may have energies up to 20 or 30 ev due to ionization of gaseous atoms by electron impact.

This origin of the cathode ray explains a strange feature of the electric discharge evident in Fig. 6.1. One might expect that electrons coming from the cathode would be pulled to the anode by the electric field. Actually, however, these electrons forming the cathode ray shoot away from the cathode in a straight direction, irrespective of the position of the anode. This is due to the concentrated potential drop in front of the cathode. If the total potential difference applied between cathode and anode is 10,000 volts, possibly 9,700 volts of this amount will be concentrated right in front of the cathode, accelerating the electrons in the direction of the field, away from the cathode. The remaining weak potential drop of 300 volts is distributed over a considerable distance and fails to deviate the cathode ray noticeably.

A positive ray or canal ray is observed when a canal is drilled through the metal of the cathode (Sec. 6.3). It consists of the positive ions just described as hitting the cathode. Those which happen to pass through the canal form the positive ray observed behind the cathode.

We summarize the effects of the concentrated potential drop in front of the cathode as follows: (1) It accelerates positive ions toward the cathode without intervening collisions to so high an energy that they knock electrons out of the cathode; those positive ions which shoot through a canal drilled through the cathode form the positive ray. (2) The same concentrated potential drop accelerates the electrons liberated from the cathode to so high a velocity that they form the cathode ray shooting away from the cathode.

c. The *aurora* (*northern lights*) is a special kind of electric discharge through air of low pressure at an altitude of 100 km or more. The aurora is excited by an ionized cloud which is ejected from the sun in a violent eruption. About 24 hr after the observation of such an eruption, which shows up as a brilliant flare near a sunspot, the aurora occurs. The ionized cloud needs this time to travel from the sun to the earth. The greenish color of most auroras is due to a forbidden transition (Sec. 11.1*d*) within O atoms. In the exceedingly low pressure of the upper atmosphere the metastable O atoms suffer very rare collisions and, therefore, have a better chance than in a discharge tube of radiating their energy in the "forbidden" transition.

Other effects of the approach of the ionized cloud from the sun are a "magnetic storm" (strong irregularities of the earth's magnetic field) and "radio fade-out" which is caused by an ionized layer in our atmosphere. The origin of these phenomena, which regularly occur jointly with the aurora, is by no means clearly understood. Radio fade-out, which seriously interrupts radio communication, is of military importance and explains the interest of the Armed Forces in sunspots whose motion on the solar disk allows us to predict the events described.

12.3. Excitation and Ionization by High Temperature. So far we have discussed excitation by impact of electrons and positive ions. Now we come to excitation by impacts between neutral bodies. It is well known that a solid body emits light when heated to a high enough temperature. This fact, demonstrated by every incandescent light bulb, is true for gases, too. The flame of the bunsen burner is not a clear-cut demonstration, because there one cannot readily distinguish the effects of heat and chemical reactions. But gases and vapors in high-temperature ovens emit their characteristic spectra in the absence of electric currents or

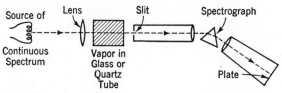

Fig. 12.6. Investigation of an absorption spectrum. The vapor removes light of certain frequencies from the otherwise continuous spectrum.

chemical reactions. This proves that thermal collisions between atoms or molecules may produce excitation. It is true that at the highest temperatures available in the laboratory (a few thousand degrees centigrade) the *average* energy of mutual collisions is only of the order of magnitude $\frac{1}{3}$ ev, which is much too small for the excitation of visible radiation. But at this temperature the occasional collisions of much higher energy are sufficiently numerous to produce light. Ionization, which may be considered as a special kind of excitation, occurs as well.

12.4. Absorption Spectra. Our foremost interest in absorption spectra is based on the evidence they give of atomic structure and processes in gases. (The word "gases" will include vapors since their distinction is of no importance spectroscopically.) Furthermore, absorption of light will give us a good chance of comparing the spectra of gases, liquids, and solids.

a. Sharp-line Absorption Spectra of Gases. For the simplest investigation of absorption spectra (Fig. 12.6) we focus on the slit of a spectrograph the light from a source emitting a continuous spectrum. Somewhere between the source and the slit we place the absorbing gas. This may be contained in a tube closed by glass windows or, for observations in the ultraviolet, quartz windows. For a demonstration experiment, the absorber may be a bunsen burner in which a small piece of metallic sodium is evaporated; a glowing filament (or the crater of the arc) provides the continuous background on which the absorption spectrum of sodium shows up as a black line in the yellow region.

We mentioned before (Sec. 10.1) the fact, discovered by Bunsen and Kirchhoff, that the *absorption* spectrum contains lines observed also in the *emission* spectrum. The demonstration experiment described gives the new evidence that the absorption spectrum contains only a selection from the emission lines. For example, the *absorption* spectrum of sodium vapor shows exclusively the principal series and no trace of the sharp or diffuse series (Fig. 12.7). The absorption spectrum of atomic hydrogen (investigated by a more elaborate technique than that of Fig. 12.6) shows only the Lyman series. In general, only those series show up in absorption which are connected with the normal state of the atom.

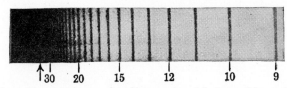

FIG. 12.7. Absorption spectrum of sodium vapor (photographic positive). Notice the continuous absorption beyond the limit of the absorption-line series; limit indicated by arrow. (*Courtesy of G. R. Harrison.*)

Bohr's theory interprets the difference between emission and absorption spectra as follows. For the *emission* of a quantum $h\nu$, the initial energy level for this specific quantum must be excited, say, by electron impact. For the *absorption* process, however, the atom receives energy from the incident light and thus is lifted from a lower to a higher level. In the experiment of Fig. 12.6 the incident light has a continuous spectrum, hence contains quanta of all energies. These quanta are incident, say, on sodium vapor whose atoms are practically all in the normal state. Only quanta of the proper size which are equal to the energy steps that raise the sodium atoms *from the normal state* to a higher state are absorbed by atoms and so excite them. Thus the light passing through the vapor loses only such quanta as are able to excite the *normal state* of the sodium atom. Hence only the spectral lines of the principal series of sodium are absorbed.

The hydrogen atom is able to absorb all lines of the Lyman series ($n'' = 1$) but, ordinarily, not the lines of the Balmer series ($n'' = 2$) because a quantum of red light, of the frequency of the first line of the Balmer series, does not meet any atom prepared to absorb it, *i.e.*, an atom residing in the excited level $n = 2$. In the difficult analysis of complicated spectra the absorption experiment is a helpful tool because it indicates which spectral lines are connected with the normal state.

Certain observations that are exceptions to the rule just discussed actually confirm the underlying idea. In the atmosphere of the sun atomic hydrogen does absorb the lines of the Balmer series, although this series is not connected with the normal state of the hydrogen atom. This exception is explained by the high temperature of the sun, which exceeds the temperatures available in the laboratory. As a result of this temperature, a small percentage of all hydrogen atoms (four or five out of every thousand million) are always to be found in the first excited level and so are able to absorb the lines of the Balmer series.

Our argument may seem inconsistent for the following reason: When we observe the absorption of white light by sodium vapor, the first line of the principal series, the well-known yellow line, is strongly absorbed. This process continually creates sodium atoms in the first excited level, which, in turn, is expected to act as the initial level for the absorption of the sharp and diffuse series. Why are not these series noticeable in the absorption spectrum? They fail to show up because of the exceedingly short lifetime of the excited state. It is true that many sodium atoms per second are raised to the excited level, but they radiate after so very short a lifetime that no appreciable population of atoms in the excited state is built up. Here we can only vaguely argue that the lifetime of the excited level is exceedingly short. Later (Sec. 12.11) we shall discuss a measurement of the lifetime which leads to a value of about 10^{-8} sec. The processes by which the lives of the excited levels are terminated, radiation or impacts of the second kind, will be demonstrated later (Secs. 12.6 and 12.10).

The comparison of the absorption spectrum with the energy-level diagram (Fig. 11.2) shows that the selection rule applies to absorption as well as to emission of light. Transitions take place only between levels that belong to adjacent vertical columns of the diagram. For example, the normal state of the atom, which belongs to the first vertical column, forms absorption lines only with the levels of the second column and not the levels of the first or third column.

The sharp absorption lines show that excitation of an atom *by light* occurs only if the frequency of the light exactly *equals* the value characteristic for the atom. In the case of excitation *by electron impact*, however, the kinetic energy of the electron must *equal* or *exceed* the energy required by the atom.

b. Continuous Absorption Spectra of Gases; Ionosphere. The absorption spectrum of sodium vapor shows *continuous* absorption beyond the convergence limit of the line series, in striking contrast to the good transparency between the sharp absorption lines. (Figure 12.7 shows *darkness* beyond the series limit in contrast to the *light* between the lines.) This continuous absorption indicates that the sodium atom may receive energy from quanta carrying more energy than that required for the liberation of an electron. It is a plausible assumption that the excess energy goes into kinetic energy of the liberated electron. The *continuous* character of this spectrum is due to the fact that the kinetic energy imparted to the electrons covers a *continuous* range.

This continuous absorption spectrum gradually falls off beyond the series limit, indicating that the ionization process by light takes place with highest probability for light just beyond this limit. For higher frequencies this probability gradually decreases. This is of importance in explaining the transparency of all matter observed at much higher frequencies, discussed under X-ray absorption spectra (Sec. 14.2*d*).

Our argument describes a process that is closely related to the photoelectric effect (Chap. 8), the only difference being that here the electron is liberated from a *free atom*, while in the conventional photoelectric effect it comes out of a *metal surface*. Sodium vapor illuminated by light of wavelengths shorter than the convergence limit of the principal series (2,412 A) should become conducting since it is being ionized. This observation has actually been made (although with experimental difficulties with which we are not concerned) and represents another confirmation of the quantum theory; the theory predicts the photoelectric effect on free atoms and even the value of their "work function" (see Sec. 8.3). Molecules as well as free atoms may be ionized by light of sufficiently high frequency. Most gases, however, have ionization energies much higher than sodium, which served as our example. Therefore, in most gases only extreme ultraviolet light, which is not easily accessible in the laboratory, can cause ionization.

Ionization by light of gaseous atoms and molecules is of vital importance for radio communication. In the early history of radio it seemed safe to predict that communication half around the earth would not be possible. Unexpectedly, however, it turned out that radio waves follow the surface of the earth. This is explained by the existence of ionized layers of gases at great heights in the upper atmosphere, which reflect radio waves back to the earth. Radio waves, after being emitted from an antenna nearly tangentially to the surface of the earth, soon hit an ionized layer at nearly grazing incidence, are reflected back to the earth, there reflected back to the "ionosphere," and so on (Fig. 12.8). The alternating reflections keep the radio waves enclosed within a spherical shell and enable them to follow the surface of the earth over long distances. In order to measure the height of the ionosphere, radio signals are sent vertically upward; the time interval between the transmission of the signal and the arrival of the radio echo from the ionosphere layer is measured.   Thus several discrete ionized layers at heights of one hundred and several hundred kilometers have been found.

What is the origin of these layers?   The answer is given by the fact that at sunrise the density of atmospheric ions promptly increases and at sunset promptly decreases.   (This applies to the lowest regular layer in about 100 km altitude.)   The reverse effects are observed at the beginning and end of a solar eclipse.   These observations prove that the

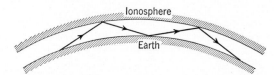

Fig. 12.8. Effect of the ionosphere on radio propagation.

ionization is due to *light emitted from the sun*.   This is just the process discovered in the laboratory experiment by the continuous absorption spectrum of sodium vapor beyond the series limit.   But in the upper atmosphere *extreme ultraviolet* light is required because the ionization energies of the atmospheric gases are high, between 12 and 16 ev.   For long-distance radio transmission it is an unexpected stroke of luck that nature provides a mirror at high altitude which forces radio waves to propagate along the curved surface of the earth.

Similar continuous absorption spectra are observed when light in the visible or near ultraviolet range is absorbed by *molecules*.   But this absorption is not associated with ionization, for the latter requires higher

Fig. 12.9. Absorption spectrum of iodine vapor (diatomic molecules). A row of sharp edges converging toward a limit, each edge consisting of an accumulation of sharp lines. Continuous absorption spectrum beyond the convergence limit.

energy.   For example, the absorption spectrum of molecular iodine, I_2, schematically given in Fig. 12.9, shows a range of continuous absorption at wavelengths below 4,995 A.   The energy range of this spectrum (2.48 ev and higher) is much too low for producing *ionization*.   This spectrum is connected with a convergence limit of bands explained by changes in energy of *vibration* of the molecule (see Sec. 11.2).   The limiting case of increasing vibration is presumably the *dissociation* of the molecule into neutral atoms.   The continuous spectrum beyond this limit results from the absorption of light quanta which impart some kinetic energy, in addition to the dissociation energy, to the free atoms produced.   These two effects of light, dissociation of a molecule and ionization, have in common the *continuous* character of the absorption spectrum which gives evidence of the *continuous* range of kinetic energy imparted to the products.   Only in this respect are molecular *dissociation* continua quite analogous to *ionization* continua.   Dissociation processes manifested by these continuous absorption spectra are important in originating photochemical reactions, because the free atoms or radicals produced by light are chemically active and cause secondary reactions (see Secs. 8.5, 12.9, and 12.10).

   c. Comparison of Gases, Liquids, and Solids.   Absorption of light gives the best chance for a comparison of the spectra of gases, liquids, and solids.   The absorption spectra of *gases* are distinguished by sharp lines (Fig. 12.7).   When light of a continuous spectrum, like that emitted from glowing carbon, traverses a *liquid or solid*, absorption takes place in broad, diffuse spectral ranges.   (Figure 12.10 shows the transmitted light as white and the absorption ranges, characteristic for the absorbing substance, as black.)   This fact is explained by the structure of liquids and solids.   They consist of atoms and molecules all in close contact with neighbors which affect all quantum transitions.   Only in the gaseous state can the transitions take place without any disturbance and so reveal the sharply defined energy levels characteristic of single atoms or molecules.   This distinction makes the spectra of gases most important to our knowledge of atomic structure.

   The absorption spectra of innumerable liquids and solids have been recorded.   Figure 12.10 shows the absorption spectra of cyanine (a dye used for making photographic plates green- and yellow-sensitive; see Sec. 12.10) and chlorophyll.   Chlorophyll absorbs reddish orange and blue light, the remaining green light being responsible for the reflected green color of leaves.   The absorption spectrum of chlorophyll has a very great importance, in particular the red band evident in the figure.   By this absorption band, chlorophyll acts as the receiver of sunlight and so stores up the greatest part of the energy that maintains all organic life and all human activity.   We can only briefly describe the process, called "photosynthesis," through which this storage of energy is accomplished.   The growth of plants requires the assimilation of the carbon which is contained in the air as carbon dioxide.   For this process energy is required to break up the structure of the carbon dioxide molecule.   This energy is supplied by the chlorophyll in the excited level to which it is lifted by the absorption of sunlight.   The details of this complex photochemical reaction by which ultimately carbon is built into the structure of the plant are not yet fully understood.

   The vast importance of this process is evident when we consider that all food consists of plants or else of meat from animals which, in turn, live on plants.   So ultimately all our food depends upon energy received from the sun by the chlorophyll.   The same is true for the greatest part of all energy consumed by industry, because our deposits of coal and oil origi-

Blue   Green   Yellow   Red

FIG. 12.10. Absorption spectra of liquids (photographic positive). (a) Cyanine, a dye used for sensitizing photographic plates; (b) chlorophyll.

FIG. 12.11. Solar spectrum (photographic negative); absorption lines largely due to the solar atmosphere.

nate from decaying organic matter and so represent energy of sunlight stored through millions of years. At present we are consuming this vast store of energy at a rate far exceeding the rate of replacement. This lack of balance confronts the human race with the problem of finding other, less exhaustible sources of energy. We shall come back to this problem in the discussion of nuclear energy.

12.5. Application to Astrophysics. The modern science of astrophysics is based entirely on spectroscopy and very largely on the quantum theoretical interpretation of spectra. The starting point was the interpretation by Kirchhoff and Bunsen (1860) of the black lines discovered by Fraunhofer (1817) in the solar spectrum (Fig. 12.11) as absorption lines of elements well known on the surface of the earth. Most of these lines are absorbed by the solar atmosphere, a few others by the atmosphere of the earth. These lines give evidence of the chemical constitution of the solar atmosphere. At present 61 of the known, stable chemical elements have been identified.

The quantum theory enters when the effect of the temperature on a stellar atmosphere is considered. At low temperature molecules like CN or OH can exist. With increasing temperatures (1) molecules dissociate, (2) an increasing fraction of the atoms are excited or even ionized. For a given chemical constitution, quantum theory permits the theoretical prediction of this effect of the temperature. So a scale for the intensities of various spectra of neutral atoms and ions can be theoretically computed as a function of the temperature under the assumption of a uniform chemical composition. The observed spectra of stars have been compared with this theoretical scale. Here it proved important that the spectra of ions can be identified as discussed in Sec. 11.1*b*. The unexpected result is that almost all observed spectra of stars fit into the theoretical scale. This agreement leads to the surprisingly simple conclusion that the great majority of all stars contain the same elements in about the same relative abundance as the sun. The same observations lead to the measurement of stellar temperatures.

12.6. Fluorescence. When sodium vapor is illuminated with yellow light, sodium atoms are raised to an excited state. We may ask what happens to the energy thus absorbed and find the answer in the demonstration experiment sketched in Fig. 12.12. Since the experiment, when performed with sodium vapor, requires heating of the glass bulb, it is more conveniently performed with iodine vapor, which happens to have the proper vapor pressure at room temperature (see Appendix 2). Intense white light is focused by a lens of large aperture on the glass bulb containing iodine vapor. The light *passing through* shows, by its violet tinge, the loss of green light absorbed by the vapor. In the bulb, *seen from any side*, the greenish bundle of light defined by the lens is clearly visible.   The experiment shows that the *light absorbed is reradiated in any direction*.   This radiation is called "fluorescence."

This explanation of *fluorescence* leads to a certain difficulty in the understanding of *absorption* of light.   Since here the light energy absorbed is immediately reradiated, apparently it does not disappear as light—contrary to the observation of the loss of intensity of the light passing through.   This apparent discrepancy is understood when we consider that the fluorescence dissipates the light toward *any direction in space*, as is evident from the experiment just described.   Only a very small fraction of the incident intensity is reradiated toward the same direction in which the incident radiation is traveling.   This consideration explains the appreciable loss suffered by the incident radiation.   (An additional reason, which is effective only at considerable pressure, will be discussed in Sec. 12.10.)

More detailed information is obtained by the investigation of the spectrum.   If sodium vapor is excited by the yellow sodium line (first line of

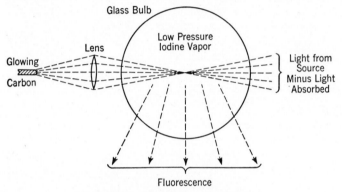

Fig. 12.12.   Fluorescence experiment.

the principal series), the fluorescence shows only *the same line*.   Although, in general, line spectra deviate vastly from the rules given by classical physics, here is an observation which is analogous to that made with any harmonic vibrator.   For example, a tuning fork when excited by sound of its "resonant frequency" picks up vibrational energy and reemits sound of *the same frequency*.   Because of this analogy the yellow spectral line of sodium is called the "resonance line."   In another experiment the exciting source supplies light exclusively of the *second* line of the principal series (in Fig. 11.2 represented by the *second* vertical arrow of the *p* group).   This light raises the energy of the atom from the normal state to the second lowest level of the *p* group.   In this case the fluorescence contains all emission lines originating directly or indirectly *from the level so excited*.   Hence it contains the same line that served for excitation and, in addition, all lines produced by cascading down from the same initial level over all possible routes to the normal level, making a detour over an S level or D level.   Any one transition obeys the selection rule.

All transitions involved in these detours are represented by shorter arrows than the exciting line, and hence represent lines of longer wavelengths. All spectral lines that would originate from higher excited levels are absent. The observation is in complete agreement with the prediction which is based on the energy-level diagram.

This observation represents a special case of Stokes' law (1853), which states that fluorescence contains light of the same frequency as the exciting light or lower frequency. This empirical law is immediately understood on the basis of the energy-level diagram and the principle of conservation of energy.

Even some inconspicuous exceptions to Stokes' law are understood. Some molecules have energy levels of vibration so low that even at room temperature a certain fraction of the molecules contain some vibrational energy. If one of these vibrating molecules absorbs a light quantum, the molecule contains a little more energy than that given by the quantum and so has the alternative of emitting light either of the *same* frequency as the exciting light or of a little *higher* frequency. Such a spectral line of higher frequency is called an "anti-Stokes" line. It violates Stokes' law only by the little energy content due to thermal motion, *i.e.*, at room temperature, an amount of the order of $\frac{1}{30}$ ev (see the anti-Stokes lines photographed in the Raman effect, Fig. 12.13).

On the basis of Stokes' law we understand that *ultraviolet* light may produce fluorescence in the *visible* range. This can well be demonstrated when the ultraviolet light from an intense carbon arc is isolated by a filter and incident, for example, on a glass bulb containing kerosene. The invisible light produces visible fluorescence. In recent years this conversion of ultraviolet into visible radiation turned out to be of importance for the construction of powerful lamps. It so happens that most gases or vapors (atomic and molecular hydrogen, mercury vapor, the rare gases) have their most intense spectral lines, caused by the transitions between normal and lowest excited states, in the ultraviolet. Therefore, a gas discharge like the mercury arc, although bright enough in the visible, wastes the greatest part of its energy as ultraviolet radiation. There are two ways of preventing this waste. One way is to use a discharge through sodium vapor, which is exceptional in that it has its most intense line in the yellow. The sodium arc, however, has the disadvantage that its pure yellow light gives a disagreeable impression. The other way consists of converting the intense ultraviolet light, emitted, for example, by mercury vapor, into visible light. This is done by fluorescence of thin crystalline layers covering the inside glass surfaces of fluorescent lamps. This arrangement has the advantage that, by the proper choice of fluorescent material, various colors can be produced; in particular, the intensity distribution of sunlight can be approximated.

Fluorescence is predominant in planetary nebulae.   These are extended masses of very low density that are intensely illuminated by a central star. The star, because of its very high temperature, emits ultraviolet radiation up to high frequencies with great intensity.   This radiation excites hydrogen atoms to high energy levels from which they may cascade down and, in certain steps, emit visible radiation.

Some fluorescent materials show an afterglow lasting several seconds or even minutes.   This is called "phosphorescence."   It occurs only in complex molecules in which the absorption of light produces a nearly stable, but not quite stable, rearrangement storing up energy.   When, after a while, the molecule goes back to a lower level, light is emitted.

In summarizing we may say that the absorption of light and fluorescence fit well into the picture of the atom given by Bohr.

12.7. Raman Effect.   We overstated the case by saying that, for example, sodium vapor is *completely* transparent for any wavelength between the lines of the absorption series (Fig. 12.7).   There is another, much less conspicuous effect that takes place for any frequency of light passing through a gas, removes some energy from the incident beam, and thus causes some, although very weak, absorption.   This effect is scattering of light.   Everybody knows that the blue sky is due to the scattering of sunlight in the atmosphere.   Observations at high altitude show that this process occurs even in a dust-free atmosphere, hence is due to the molecules of the air.   Scattering is stronger in liquids and solids because of their larger density.   The scattered light shows largely the same spectrum as the incident light.   For example, sunlight when scattered in the atmosphere shows the sharp "Fraunhofer lines" as well as direct sunlight does.   In terms of the quantum theory this most common type of scattering is interpreted by the rebound of quanta from molecules.

We are concerned with a different type of scattering, called "Raman effect," which is still weaker than the ordinary scattering just mentioned. Raman (1928) discovered the theoretically important, although inconspicuous, fact that there is a scattering process *which causes a change of frequency characteristic for the scattering substance.*   The experimental arrangement is similar to the one that serves for the demonstration of fluorescence (Fig. 12.12).   But here the source of light, *e.g.*, the mercury arc, emits spectral lines *which do not coincide* with absorption lines of the scattering material.   The bulb is filled, say, with liquid carbon tetrachloride, CCl_4.   The light scattered sidewise is analyzed by a spectrograph.   Figure 12.13 shows that in the scattered light each intense spectral line is surrounded by a pattern of weak lines characteristic for the scattering substance.   This is the Raman effect.

The new Raman lines are only slightly shifted with respect to the incident line; in other words, the changes of frequency that occur by the scattering process are small as compared to the frequency of the incident line.   The Raman effect is explained in terms of the quantum theory as follows: Considering first the lines shifted to *low* frequencies, we assume that a scattering molecule, *e.g.*, CCl_4, retains a small part of the energy of an incident light quantum $h\nu$ and thus is excited to a certain energy level. [Such low energy levels of molecules are, in most cases, due to excitation not of *electrons* but of mechanical *vibrations* of the constituent atoms with respect to each other (Sec. 11.2)].   In the same process the molecule scatters the balance of the incident quantum.   Thus the scattered quantum is smaller, but only a little smaller, than the incident quantum,

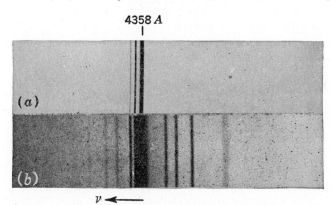

4358 *A*

(a)

(b)

$\nu \longleftarrow$

Fig. 12.13. Raman effect (photographic negative).   (*a*) Spectrum of mercury arc; (*b*) the same when scattered by CCl_4.   Note the symmetry in position but not in intensity.   The arrow shows the frequency difference corresponding to the average energy of thermal collision.   Wavelengths are given in Prob. 12.5.

and the frequency difference observed gives evidence of a characteristic vibrational transition of the scattering molecule.   In a five-atomic molecule like CCl_4 various modes of vibration are evident by the various frequency shifts observed in the Raman spectrum.

So far we have explained only the shift of lines toward *lower* frequencies.   Figure 12.13 shows that other, less intense lines are shifted to *higher* frequencies and so apparently violate the principle of conservation of energy.   They are explained by the same argument as the anti-Stokes lines observed in fluorescence.   At room temperature, a certain fraction of all molecules are endowed with small amounts of vibrational energy. If such a vibrating molecule is hit by the incident quantum, it may throw its energy into the scattering process and so scatter a larger quantum, which is a line of higher frequency.   Therefore, this shift to higher frequencies is limited to the small range due to thermal energies.   The intensity distribution evident in Fig. 12.13 agrees well with this explanation. The intense mercury line at 4,358 A is surrounded by a pattern symmetrical in position (on the frequency scale) but not in intensity. On the high-frequency side, the distant lines are very weak; at increasing temperature, they would gain intensity. Incidentally, the figure shows that Raman scattering is rare as compared with the scattering of the unshifted line. This is evident from the fact that, in order to bring out the Raman lines, the unshifted scattered line had to be overexposed.

The Raman effect differs from fluorescence (Fig. 12.12) as follows: In fluorescence the frequency of the incident light *coincides with an absorption frequency* of the fluorescent gas and produces excited levels which, after a short lifetime, emit a quantum. On the other hand, the incident light causing Raman effect *bears no frequency relation* to a characteristic frequency of the scattering molecule. This only retains a small part of the incident quantum so that the *frequency difference* between the incident and the scattered light is characteristic of a vibrational transition of the scattering molecule. This feature of the Raman effect, giving evidence of the characteristic vibrations of molecules, makes it an important tool for the investigation of molecular structure.

12.8. Chemical Process Producing Light. We mentioned that we cannot easily decide whether the light emitted from a bunsen burner is due to the high temperature or to a chemical process. In other cases, there is no doubt that a chemical process is producing light. This is true for the green light emitted from the firefly, presumably due to an oxidation process. A similar process is responsible for the glow of yellow phosphorus exposed to air. This property of phosphorus explains its name, which means "carrier of light." Light produced by a chemical process, called "chemiluminescence," is not of great importance. (The word "phosphorescence" may mean this property of phosphorus, although, conventionally, it means the afterglow observed in some cases of fluorescence; see Sec. 12.6.)

The light emitted by the *night sky*, called the *airglow*, is a special case of chemiluminescence. This light, which has nothing to do with the light from the stars, is so weak that most people are not even aware of its existence. During the daytime, sunlight dissociates the O_2 and N_2 molecules of the upper atomosphere. The free atoms so produced recombine slowly and continue to do so through the night. This chemical process leads to excited energy levels which radiate. The airglow, although a very inconspicuous phenomenon, is of considerable importance for our knowledge of the processes occurring in the upper atmosphere.

12.9. Light Producing a Chemical Process. Differing from chemiluminescence, the chemical processes produced by light, investigated in *photochemistry*, are most important. Such processes were discussed in Sec. 8.5 in presenting an argument for the quantum theory of light. They are listed here in order to make our survey of methods of observation complete.   In all cases the primary photochemical reaction, *i.e.*, the immediate effect of the light absorbed, is described by Einstein's fundamental law of photochemistry, one of the foundations of the quantum theory of light.   Frequently, however, the complexity of the secondary reactions masks the simple primary reaction.

12.10. Impacts of the Second Kind.   A new type of process, which is not predicted by the theory but fits well into it, is evident in the demonstration experiment on fluorescence, *e.g.*, of iodine vapor (Fig. 12.12), when we admit a foreign gas of atmospheric pressure to the iodine vapor of low pressure (0.2 mm) contained in the bulb.   The bright fluorescence observed without the foreign gas disappears completely.   Which of the two processes responsible for fluorescence (absorption of light and reemission) is prevented by the foreign gas?   The *absorption* is not disturbed, as is evident from the violet color of the light passing straight through; this may be confirmed by observing the absorption spectrum.   Hence we must assume that in the presence of the gas the molecules excited by light dispose of their excitation energy without radiating it.   This leads to the assumption of a new process in which excited atoms or molecules, when colliding during their lifetimes, may *give away* their energy of excitation without radiating it.   Such processes are called "impacts of the second kind," contrasting with "impacts of the first kind" in which excitation is *produced* at the expense of kinetic energy.

What happens to the energy given away?   The various answers to this question have been explored in detail by Franck and his collaborators. The answer is obvious in the simplest case.   Mercury vapor when excited by light of its "resonance line" 2,537 A shows fluorescence radiation.   (Only, because of its location in the ultraviolet range, it cannot be demonstrated so easily as fluorescence radiation of iodine vapor.)   This radiation is quenched by 1 atm of a rare gas, helium or argon.   Because of the chemical inertia of the gas, no chemical reaction can occur, and the only assumption left is that, by the collision, the energy of excitation is changed into *kinetic energy* of the partners.

Next Franck investigated whether excitation energy may be transferred during the collision into *excitation energy* of the colliding atom. Again fluorescence radiation of mercury vapor is excited by light of the wavelength 2,537 A.   Since the gas added must have a lower excitation energy than mercury in order to make a transfer of energy possible, sodium vapor is chosen as the added gas.   It reduces the intensity of the mercury fluorescence and adds a new effect: sodium lines appear in the fluorescence radiation.   In a control experiment it is checked that sodium vapor in the absence of mercury, illuminated by the same light, shows no fluorescence whatever.   Hence we must assume that mercury atoms, excited by light, when colliding during their lifetime with sodium atoms, may transfer their energy of excitation to the sodium atoms.

This interpretation is corroborated by the spectroscopic analysis. The mercury atom excited by light of 2,537 A contains an energy of 4.88 ev. The sodium spectrum excited in the experiment described is not so complete as when excited in the electric discharge. Here only those spectral lines are observed which originate from energy levels of sodium requiring 4.88 ev or less for their excitation. This completely agrees with the theoretical prediction. Thus the experiment proves that excitation energy may be transferred in collisions from one to another atom.

The next problem Franck solved was whether excitation energy may be transferred into *chemical energy*. For this investigation a chemical process had to be chosen which requires less than the 4.88 ev available in the excited mercury atom. The dissociation of hydrogen molecules requiring 4.45 ev meets this requirement. Hence hydrogen is added to the mercury vapor and the mixture exposed to light of the wavelength 2,537 A. As expected, atomic hydrogen is so generated. (Its production is tested by the reduction of copper oxide.) A control experiment shows that in the absence of the mercury vapor the same light fails to produce any reaction. This combination of experiments proves that light quanta of sufficient energy content, although not directly accepted by the hydrogen molecules, may be accepted by mercury atoms and their energy transferred in collisions to hydrogen molecules. This is called a "sensitized photochemical reaction," meaning that the hydrogen, although originally insensitive to the light, can be made sensitive by the addition of mercury vapor.

This reaction has technical interest in that it helps to explain a process that had been known for many years, the sensitization of photographic plates. Ordinary photographic plates (see Sec. 15.3) are sensitive only to blue light or light of higher frequency. That is why they are conveniently developed in red light. We conclude that red light does not dissociate silver bromide, AgBr. However, the plates can be sensitized for red light by bathing them in a dye like cyanine which absorbs red (see its absorption spectrum in Fig. 12.10). It is plausible to explain this sensitization by the same process discovered by Franck in the mixture of mercury vapor and hydrogen. Here it is assumed that the dye molecules when absorbing red light are brought to an excited level, which may transfer its energy and so dissociate a neighboring silver bromide molecule.

To begin with, one may guess that red light has no effect on the nonsensitized photographic plate because the quanta are too small to dissociate the AgBr molecules. The experiment described shows that this guess is wrong because the same quanta when accepted by the dye are able to blacken the plate. Here we are forced to assume that the absorption of light by molecules, *e.g.*, AgBr, is limited by properties of the molecule other than the energy required for a certain process. This is explained in the theory of molecular spectra. On the other hand, there is no prospect of extending the sensitization far into the infrared because we are sure that the quanta of far infrared radiation are too small to produce dissociation of AgBr. No absorbing dye can circumvent the principle of conservation of energy.

This example illustrates the general rule: The wavelength range effective in producing a photochemical reaction must meet two requirements: (1) it must have quanta large enough to initiate the reaction, and (2) it must be absorbed by the molecules to be affected.

Summarizing impacts of the second kind, we may say that an atom or molecule when colliding during the lifetime of an excited state may change its energy into kinetic energy, energy of excitation, or chemical energy.

12.11. Lifetime of Excited State. On several occasions while discussing absorption spectra and impacts of the second kind, we introduced the lifetime of an excited state of an atom. This places us under an obligation to describe the elaborate measurement of the lifetime performed by Wien in a canal-ray experiment. In the discussion of electric discharges we described the canal ray (or positive ray) as consisting of positive ions accelerated toward the cathode by the concentrated potential difference in front of the cathode and shooting through a canal drilled through the metal.

According to this explanation it is surprising that the canal ray contains neutral as well as positively charged atoms, as is evident when we try to deflect the ray by an electric field; only a part is deflected, while another part shoots in a straight line indicating neutral particles. In order to explain this and similar experiments, we are forced to assume that the particles, originally positively charged, readily exchange their charges in collisions, becoming neutral and going back again to their charged status, possibly even becoming negatively charged. This change of charge is consistent with the fact that we observe the lines of the Balmer series, although belonging to neutral hydrogen atoms, as a part of the spectrum of the canal ray.

Wien built his canal-ray tube (Fig. 12.14) such that the discharge proper operating at a pressure of a few thousandths of a millimeter communicated with the canal-ray chamber behind the cathode only through the narrow canal drilled through the cathode. This enabled him to maintain high vacuum in the *canal-ray chamber* by the permanent operation of a high-speed pump, while the pressure in the *discharge chamber* was kept at the value which is most favorable for producing positive rays. Under this condition, the canal ray does not become completely invisible, although, because of the high vacuum, the atoms constituting the ray do not suffer collisions. Instead the canal ray gradually fades away after leaving the cathode. Its light disappears within a few centimeters' distance. The experiment is unique in that light is emitted from spots at which no excitation takes place. Therefore, we must assume that the atoms, which are excited in the electric discharge, *i.e.*, before shooting through the canal, do not radiate instantaneously but carry their excitation energy from the discharge chamber through the canal into the canal-ray chamber. At any spot the intensity of the light gives evidence of the concentration of excited atoms. The intensity is higher near the cathode. Its decay away from the cathode shows the loss of excited atoms with increasing time.

A quantitative determination of the average lifetime is based on the combination of two successive measurements: (1) the linear velocity of

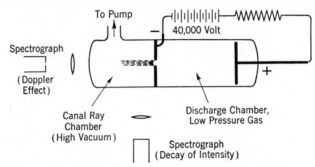

Fig. 12.14. Measurement of the lifetimes of excited states by the observation of the decay of the light emitted from a canal ray. Note the different functions of the two spectrographs. The light emitted from the discharge proper is about the same as in Fig. 12.4.

the ray and (2) the decay of the intensity along the ray. In the first experiment, for the determination of the linear velocity, the Doppler effect is recorded by a spectrograph photographing the light that is emitted from the ray "end on." Since the atoms are shooting toward the observer, he receives more vibrations per second than the atom emits per second, so that the spectrograph records all spectral lines as shifted toward higher frequencies. This shift, *e.g.*, for the red hydrogen line ($\nu = 0.457 \times 10^{15}$ sec^{-1}), is measured as $\Delta\nu = 0.15 \times 10^{13}$ sec^{-1}. The well-known formula for the Doppler effect leads to a velocity of the atoms $= 10^8$ cm/sec. In other words, the excited atoms at a distance of 1 cm from the cathode are 10^{-8} sec older than the atoms at the cathode itself, the atoms at a distance of 2 cm are 2×10^{-8} sec older, etc. Thus the linear extension of the ray is used as a time scale.

In the second experiment, a spectrograph, viewing the canal ray *sidewise*, records the intensity of the ray as a function of the distance from the cathode. The result is a decay of intensity following an exponential function $I = I_0 e^{-\lambda x}$ (x = distance from cathode, I_0 = intensity near cathode, I = intensity at distance x; λ = empirical factor). The "decay constant" λ is measured, for example, as 1 cm^{-1}. This means that the intensity decays *along each centimeter* to the fraction $1/e$ of its initial value. Since in the first measurement we found the time required to cover 1 cm as 10^{-8} sec, we may say, instead, that the intensity decays *during* 10^{-8} *sec* to the fraction $1/e$ of its initial value. This is a result of the same type as obtained in the observation of radioactive decay. It may seem confusing to call it a lifetime, because we do not observe birth and death of an individual excited atom. We only follow the rate at which a certain population of excited atoms gradually dies out. The properties of the exponential decay permit the computation of an average lifetime of excited atoms. The order of magnitude of the lifetimes of many atoms in their excited states is 10^{-8} sec. For various reasons, this ingenious method furnishes results of only low accuracy.

The very short lifetimes of excited levels here measured explain the fact that no appreciable population of excited atoms or molecules accumulates in electric discharges or fluorescent gases (see Sec. 12.6). At any moment the great majority of all atoms and molecules reside in their normal states except for the very low energy levels that may be reached by thermal collisions.

SUMMARY OF CHAPTER 12

1. In the excitation or ionization by controlled electron impact the limiting kinetic energy of the impinging electron, which is just able to produce excitation or ionization of a certain atom, is measured (method of Franck and Hertz).

2. Electric discharges through gases are classified into non-self-maintained and self-maintained discharges. In the non-self-maintained discharge, the conductivity of the gas is caused by an external agent like X rays or radioactive rays or a hot metal emitting electrons. The self-maintained discharge (arc, spark, low-pressure discharge) starts by a few stray electrons, which are present everywhere. Further carriers of electricity are generated in the gas by electron impact and at the cathode by liberation of electrons due to positive-ion impact.

The cathode ray consists of the electrons liberated from the cathode of the low-pressure discharge by the process just mentioned and accelerated by the high potential difference located in front of the cathode. The positive ray (canal ray) consists of positive ions accelerated by the same potential difference, shooting through a canal drilled through the cathode.

3. At sufficiently high temperature, excitation and ionization are produced by thermal collisions.

4. An absorption spectrum of a monatomic gas contains only those spectral lines which are connected with the normal state of the atom. A

Table 12.1. *Fundamental Processes by Which Atoms or Molecules Receive or Give Away Energy of Excitation*

A. Processes by which energy is received

Excitation energy is received from	Experiment	Result of experiment
1. Electron impact ("impact of first kind")	a. Electric discharge b. Controlled electron impact	Complete spectrum is excited Energy levels excited only up to limit, given by W_k of impinging electrons
2. Thermal impact (another example of "impact of first kind")	Gas burner, oven	At temperatures available at laboratory, preference for low excited energy levels, but no sharp limit
3. Light	a. Absorption spectrum observed Exceptional observation: Absorption spectrum observed at highest temperature (solar atmosphere) b. Fluorescence spectrum observed, mainly at low pressure c. Chemical change due to light is observed d. Scattered light may change frequency (Raman effect)	All possible transitions connected with normal level; i.e., principal series Some excited levels contribute absorption spectrum; absorption of Balmer series in solar atmosphere At low pressure the light energy absorbed is re-emitted (demonstration with iodine vapor) Example: Decomposition of AgBr in photographic plate Scattering molecule may keep part of incident quantum
4. Chemical energy	Glow of yellow phosphorus; firefly	
5. Transfer from an excited atom ("impact of second kind")	Mixture Hg + Na illuminated by mercury arc, which fails to excite Na directly but does excite Hg	Fluorescence radiation contains Na spectrum; the excitation is limited by the energy 4.88 ev indicating energy transfer from excited Hg to Na in collisions

B. Processes by which energy is given away

Excitation energy given away into	Experiment	Result of experiment
1. Light	Any electric-discharge or fluorescence or high-temperature experiment	Each excited atom has an intrinsic probability of radiation after very short lifetime of excited state

Table 12.1 (*Continued*)

Excitation energy given away into	Experiment	Result of experiment
2. Transfer to other atoms colliding during lifetime of excited state	*a.* Fluorescence quenched by addition of foreign gas (demonstration of iodine with 1 atm air)	Excitation energy transferred into *kinetic energy* (heat produced)
	b. Mixture Hg + Na; (A 5 of this table)	Hg transfers its excitation energy into *excitation energy* of Na
	c. Mixture Hg + H_2, illuminated with mercury arc, exciting the Hg	H atoms produced; Hg transfers its excitation energy into *chemical energy* (dissociation of H_2)

continuous range of absorption starting from the convergence limit of the absorption series, extending toward higher frequencies, indicates ionization of gaseous atoms, *i.e.*, photoelectric effect in the gas. By this process extreme ultraviolet light from the sun ionizes the upper atmosphere of the earth.

Gases show sharp-line absorption spectra (apart from the continuous ranges just mentioned), liquids and solids more or less diffuse absorption spectra. Of outstanding importance is the absorption spectrum of chlorophyll. The absorption of red sunlight enables the chlorophyll to break up the CO_2 molecules contained in the air and assimilate the carbon atoms. Animal life and industrial activity are maintained almost exclusively by energy ultimately received from the sun by this process.

5. Astrophysics is based largely on the investigation of emission and absorption spectra and their interpretation by quantum theory.

6. In fluorescence, atoms or molecules that have just been excited by absorption of light reradiate light (mostly of the same or lower frequency) in any direction.

7. Light of a sharply defined frequency, when scattered from molecules of a solid, liquid, or gas, shows shifted spectral lines in addition to the incident spectral line (Raman effect). This is explained by the ability of the molecule to keep a small part of the energy of each incident quantum (shift to low frequencies) or add some of its own vibrational or rotational energy to the quantum (small shift to high frequencies). The Raman effect is an important tool in the investigation of molecular vibrations.

8. Some chemical processes produce light (oxidation of phosphorus, airglow).

9. The production of chemical processes by light is the basis of photochemistry.

10. An excited atom or molecule when colliding during its lifetime may give away its energy of excitation as kinetic energy, energy of excitation of the other particle, or chemical energy (impacts of the second kind). An example for the last process is given by the sensitization of a photographic plate for yellow or red light.

11. The lifetime of the excited state of atoms has been measured in a canal-ray experiment as about 10^{-8} sec.

PROBLEMS

12.1. *Ionization energy.* The principal series of potassium converges at 2,870 A. Compute the energy of ionization of potassium atoms in ev.

12.2. *Lowest excitation energy.* Before the extreme ultraviolet was explored by the vacuum spectrograph, Franck and Hertz measured the excitation potentials of neon and argon as 16.6 and 11.5 volts, respectively. Compute the wavelengths of the corresponding spectral lines. Years later these lines were observed.

12.3. *Relation between wavelength and energy.* The wavelength of a spectral line (in A) times the energy difference between the levels (in ev) is a constant. Compute its numerical value. This constant facilitates calculations, *e.g.*, those of the preceding problems.

12.4. *Ionization of upper atmosphere.* By controlled electron impact the ionization potential of molecular oxygen is measured to 12.2 ev. Calculate the maximum wavelength that must be represented in the solar radiation to ionize molecular oxygen.

12.5. *Raman effect.* Light from a mercury arc of the wavelength 4359 A when scattered by CCl_4 shows Raman lines at the wavelengths 4,400 and 4,419 A on the long-wavelength side and 4,318 and 4,301 on the short-wavelength side (Fig. 12.13). Calculate the characteristic vibrational energy levels (in erg and ev) of the CCl_4 molecule.

12.6. *Lifetime of excited state.* Wien measured the intensity I of a certain spectral line emitted by his canal ray and decaying along the ray. I is represented by the equation $I = I_0 e^{-\lambda x}$ where $\lambda = 0.40$ cm^{-1} (notation as in Sec. 12.11). Next, using the Doppler effect, he measured the velocity of the radiating atoms as 5.0×10^7 cm/sec. After how long a *time interval* does the intensity of the radiation go down to $1/e$ of the original value?

12.7. *Inelastic collisions; excitation by positive-ion impact.* A collision in which a part of the kinetic energy is changed to another type of energy is called "inelastic." This applies to excitation of atoms by impact. The lowest excitation energy of neutral helium atoms, determined by the analysis of the spectrum or the method of controlled *electron impact* (Sec. 12.1), is $W = 19.75$ ev. *Helium ions*, He$^+$, however, of this kinetic energy, when impinging on neutral helium atoms which are at rest before the impact, fail to cause excitation because a considerable fraction of their kinetic energy must be distributed as kinetic energy between the two particles in order to satisfy the law of conservation of linear momentum. This law requires that the common center of gravity continue its path irrespective of the collision. Hence, a helium ion He$^+$ must be endowed with a considerable amount of excess energy in order to be able to transfer the energy W of excitation to a neutral helium atom. Suppose that a fast helium ion (mass M, velocity u_1) collides head on with a neutral helium atom which, before the collision, is at rest. By the impact the electronic system of the neutral helium atom is given the energy of excitation W. Compute the velocities of the ion (v_1) and the neutral atom (v_2) after the collision on the basis of the laws of conservation of energy and momentum. From your final equations for v_1

and v_2 find the lowest kinetic energy the impinging helium ion must possess in order to be able to give the electronic excitation W to the neutral helium atom.

HINT: *a.* State the laws of conservation of energy and momentum as you did in Prob. 9.1. But here the *energy* equation is changed since in the final state the additional energy W appears. The *momentum* equation, however, remains unchanged, since excitation consumes *energy* but does not affect the *linear momentum*. The equations are simplified by the assumption of equal masses of bullet and target.

b. Solve for the final velocities v_1 and v_2 as unknowns.

c. The quadratic equations so obtained have real solutions only for values of the initial kinetic energy above a certain limit. This is the lowest kinetic energy the helium ion must possess in order to be effective. Compute this limit.

12.8. *Recombination of electrons and positive ions (calculus problem).* A monatomic gas is partly ionized, *e.g.*, by ultraviolet light. After we turn off this light, the electrons and positive ions are uniformly distributed over the volume and gradually vanish by recombination, forming neutral atoms. At any moment there are equal numbers per cubic centimeter, n, of electrons and positive ions. The initial number is called n_0. Assume that the number dn vanishing during the time interval dt is proportional to dt and to both the number of electrons and that of ions, hence proportional to n^2. The coefficient of proportionality, called α, is a characteristic constant of this process. Calculate n as a function of n_0, α, and the time t.

12.9. *Light passing through an absorbing body (calculus problem).* This problem is important for its method. The same method will be applied to radioactive decay (Prob. 17.18). It has been observed that light of incident intensity I_0, when passing through a *thin* absorbing layer (thickness Δl), suffers a loss of intensity ΔI, which is approximately proportional to the thickness Δl and the incident intensity I_0. The factor of proportionality μ, called "absorption coefficient," is characteristic of the material. (It may depend strongly on the wavelength of light.) This approximation is more accurate the smaller the thickness Δl of the absorbing layer. Compute the intensity I_1 transmitted by a *thick* absorbing plate (thickness l_1) on which light of intensity I_0 is incident.

HINT: (*a*) Write the statement for the thin layer as an equation keeping in mind that an *increase* of the thickness l causes a *decrease* of the intensity I. (*b*) Rearrange, replace the sum by the integral, and integrate. The limits are determined by the consideration that, while the thickness traversed increases from 0 to l_1, the intensity decreases from I_0 to I_1. (*c*) Express I_1 in terms of I_0, μ, and l_1.

CHAPTER 13

PERIODIC TABLE OF ELEMENTS

The periodic system of elements, discovered in 1869, gives a systematic survey of the chemical properties of all elements. In our discussion we do not want to present material properly belonging in a textbook of chemistry, since we suppose that the student is familiar with the foundations of that science. Our purpose is to consider the extent to which the theory of the nuclear atom helps us to correlate the chemical properties of the elements with the results of spectroscopy and experiments on controlled electron impact. After a brief survey of certain groups of related elements, we shall try to interpret their chemical behavior jointly with their spectroscopic properties.

13.1. Survey of Some Facts of Chemistry. Certain groups of elements of widely differing atomic weights are chemically closely related. For example, the *alkalies* (Li, Na, K, Rb, Cs) are all metals of low density with the power to decompose water. All are univalent electropositive; *i.e.*, in electrolysis they form singly charged positive ions like Li^+. This property is confirmed in the positive-ray (canal-ray) experiment, where, by electric and magnetic deflection, we find ions like Li^+ in great abundance but no doubly charged ions Li^{++}. We conclude that the alkali atom readily loses 1 but not 2 electrons. The *rare gases* (He, Ne, A, Kr, Xe, Rn) form another group of related elements. All are gases except at very low temperatures. They are chemically inert, hence have molecules identical with single atoms. The *alkaline earths* (Be, Mg, Ca, Sr, Ba, Ra) are bivalent electropositive in electrolysis. Correspondingly, in the positive ray they easily show up singly or doubly charged, but not triply charged. The *halogens* (F, Cl, Br, I) are all univalent electronegative; *i.e.*, in electrolysis they form singly charged negative ions. In the canal ray (which in this case we cannot call "positive ray") they readily form the same ions.

In order to define the atomic number, we write all elements in the order of their atomic weights, beginning with hydrogen (atomic weight, 1.008), continuing with helium (atomic weight, 4.00), lithium (atomic weight, 6.94), etc. The atomic number is defined as the number of the element counted in this order, 1 for hydrogen, 2 for helium, 3 for lithium, and so on through the whole list of elements.

Mendeleeff and Lothar Meyer (1869) discovered the fact that in the row of elements so written their chemical properties are a periodic function of their atomic numbers.   In other words, the same sequence of neighboring elements occurs over and over again.   The simplest example is given by the sequence: a halogen, a rare gas, an alkali, and an alkaline earth, like F, Ne, Na, and Mg.

It is true that, to a minor extent, this regularity is enforced by rearranging the order of the elements at a few places.   For example, argon (atomic weight, 39.94) is placed before potassium (atomic weight, 39.10).   Later, discussing X-ray spectra, we shall find another powerful argument for this rearrangement.   Furthermore, we shall find a certain excuse for it in the discussion of isotopes, where it will be evident that the chemical atomic weight is not a property characteristic of the individual atom but of a mixture of atoms.

This periodic occurrence of the same sequence of elements is well represented in a table when we break off the row of elements after each rare gas and begin a new horizontal line, called a new "period," with the following alkali (see Table 13.1 and Appendix 4).   In this way of writing, all alkalies are the first elements of their periods, the alkaline earths the second elements, the rare gases the last elements, the halogens the last but one.   What we have described is a systematic arrangement of the elements according to their atomic weights and chemical properties and is much older than the theory of the nuclear atom.

Table 13.1.   *Periodic Table of Elements*

| H | | | | | | He |
| 1 | | | | | | 2 |

Li	Be	B	C	N	O	F	Ne
3	4	5	6	7	8	9	10
Na	Mg	Al	Si	P	S	Cl	A
11	12	13	14	15	16	17	18

K	Ca	Sc	Ti	V	Cr	Mn	Fe	Co	Ni	Cu	Zn	Ga	Ge	As	Se	Br	Kr
19	20	21	22	23	24	25	26	27	28	29	30	31	32	33	34	35	36
Rb	Sr	Y	Zr	Cb	Mo	Tc	Ru	Rh	Pd	Ag	Cd	In	Sn	Sb	Te	I	Xe
37	38	39	40	41	42	43	44	45	46	47	48	49	50	51	52	53	54
Cs	Ba	La	Hf	Ta	W	Re	Os	Ir	Pt	Au	Hg	Tl	Pb	Bi	Po	At	Rn
55	56	57*	72	73	74	75	76	77	78	79	80	81	82	83	84	85	86
Fr	Ra	Ac	Th	Pa	U	Np	Pu	Am	Cm	Bk	Cf						
87	88	89	90	91	92	93	94	95	96	97	98	99	100				

*The asterisk indicates the position of the rare earths here omitted (see Appendix 4).

13.2. Nuclear Atom. We wish to correlate this abbreviated description of chemical properties with our theory of the atoms consisting of positively charged nuclei surrounded by electrons. Of basic importance is the rule stating that the atomic number equals the nuclear charge. This rule is well established: for heavy elements, by the investigation of the scattering of alpha particles; for light elements, by Bohr's theory as applied to He, He⁺, Li⁺⁺, etc. The number of external electrons is the same as the nuclear charge for neutral atoms, less than that for positive ions, and more than that for negative ions. We are interested in the arrangement of these electrons in the normal states of atoms because these are the states that play the greatest part in chemical reactions.

13.3. Stability of Rare-gas Electronic Structures. The rare gases are chemically inert, in strong contrast to their neighbors, the alkalies, which are chemically so active that they can even break up water molecules. The same contrast is quantitatively expressed by comparing the energy-level diagrams, for example, of the first rare gas, helium, and its neighbor, the first alkali, lithium. We are interested only in the energies of excitation and ionization, derived from analysis of the spectra and confirmed by controlled electron impact. They are shown in Fig. 13.1. (We indicate all other energy levels summarily by light lines.) Helium has an excitation energy 11 times as high as lithium and an ionization energy 4.6 times as high. These energies may be considered as measuring the high "stability" of the helium atoms since it is plausible to measure the stability of a structure by the energy required to change it. The chemical inactivity of helium is another aspect of this high stability. This is the extreme case of a general rule stating that the rare-gas atoms are much more stable than the alkalies, their successors in the periodic table.

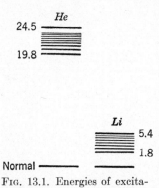

FIG. 13.1. Energies of excitation and ionization of helium and lithium atoms (in electron volts).

What applies to the neutral helium atom applies as well to the lithium positive ion, which carries the same number of external electrons since it consists of the nucleus with the positive charge 3 surrounded by 2 electrons. The spectrum of this ion again indicates a special stability. So we may say in general that the electronic structures of the rare gases, which consist of 2 or 10 or 18 or 36 or 54 or 86 external electrons, are particularly stable. The same applies to any ion which, by loss or gain of electrons, has been changed so that it has the same number of external electrons as a rare gas. In any case the addition to the rare-gas structure of one more external electron (as in Li or Be⁺ or B⁺⁺, etc.) produces an

electronic structure of much less stability.   For the time being we accept
the stability of the electronic structures containing the numbers just
listed as an observed fact without explaining the mysterious significance
of these numbers (see Sec. 13.10).

We may understand the word "stability" somewhat differently.   In
nature there is a general tendency toward the most stable configuration.
For example, a rock located high up on a slope has the tendency to roll
down into the valley, *i.e.*, to its most stable position.   Another example is
given by an electron that is raised to a high and, therefore, unstable orbit;
it has the tendency to fall down toward the nucleus into the stable state.
Correspondingly, the great stability of the rare-gas electronic structure,
just expressed in terms of energies, suggests that there is in nature a general *tendency toward the rare-gas electronic structure*.   Let us tentatively
assume this general tendency as our basis for the following discussion of
the periodic table.

13.4. Neighbors of Rare Gases and Their Ions.   On this basis we easily
interpret some facts surveyed in Secs. 13.1 and 13.3.   The alkalies have
low energies of ionization; in other words, they readily form singly
charged positive ions because these ions have the electronic structures of
rare gases.   For example, Na^+ has the structure of Ne.   Correspondingly, the doubly charged ion of an alkaline earth has a rare-gas structure,
e.g., Ca^{++} the structure of A.   On the other hand, the halogens readily
attach 1 electron to their structure in order to reach the rare-gas status,
like Cl^- which has the same structure as A.   This explains the electronegative behavior of the halogens.

13.5. Polar Molecules and Crystals.   The concept of the tendency
toward a rare-gas electronic structure explains the structure of a large
class of molecules, the "polar molecules."   For example, in NaCl vapor
the diatomic molecule is presumably formed by a sodium and a chlorine
atom bound together because the sodium has lost its excess electron and
the chlorine has swallowed this electron to make up its deficiency.   Thus
a positive ion is formed with a structure like neon and a negative ion with
a structure like argon.   The Coulomb attraction keeps the two ions
together as a molecule.

The same picture applies to numerous molecules.   For example, neutral
$CaCl_2$ is supposed to consist of a doubly charged positive ion Ca^{++} bound
by the Coulomb force to two singly charged negative ions Cl^-.   When we
consistently attribute to the oxygen atom, the precursor of fluorine, the
tendency to capture 2 electrons and so acquire the rare-gas electronic
structure of 10, we understand the structures of CaO, Na_2O, and similar
molecules.   The hydrogen atom, having 1 external electron, is supposed
to have chemical properties similar to the alkalies although the hydrogen
positive ion has no electron at all.   Assuming this similarity, we con-

sistently understand the structures of HCl, H_2O, NaOH, and many other molecules.

The general idea is that atoms belonging to the left wing of the periodic table form polar molecules with atoms belonging to the right wing; in any case, positive and negative ions are formed, all with rare-gas electronic structures, and kept together as molecules by the Coulomb attraction. This picture does not explain the structures of all molecules. Those formed of atoms of the same element, like H_2, O_2, N_2, Cl_2, and many others, because of their symmetry, cannot be described by the same idea. They are called "nonpolar" molecules. Their formation is due to other effects not so simply understood. It will be reported below (Sec. 13.9). It should be added that these other effects contribute to the formation of the polar molecules, too, so that our picture gives only one important aspect of the molecular forces without claiming to be complete.

What applies to molecules applies as well to crystals. For example, the rock-salt crystal, NaCl, which forms a simple cubic structure, is thought of as consisting of Na^+ and Cl^- ions, alternating in their positions at the corners of cubes, the whole structure being held together by the Coulomb attraction (see Fig. 14.6). Again, this explains only one type of crystal, the polar crystal, in which atoms of the right and left wings of the periodic table unite. There are other crystals, *e.g.*, iodine, I_2, which, because of their symmetry, cannot be polar and are held together by the same forces as nonpolar molecules. They will be discussed below (Sec. 13.9).

13.6. Ions in Solution. In our discussion of electrolysis (Sec. 6.1) we gave an outline of the Arrhenius theory of electrolytic solutions (1887). Arrhenius assumed that crystals like NaCl when dissolved in water are dissociated into ions Na^+ and Cl^-. This assumption, giving the sodium particles an independent existence and motion in the water, must appear bold to everybody who is familiar with the violent reaction of sodium and water. Arrhenius was forced to make the additional assumption that the sodium ions Na^+ have chemical properties different from those of sodium metal. This assumption is justified by our theory of the periodic table. By attributing to the ion Na^+ a rare-gas electronic structure, we understand that Na^+ is chemically as inert as a rare gas. This applies to all ions in solution. When the sodium ion arrives at the negative electrode, it is neutralized and goes into a reaction with H_2O.

13.7. Metallic Conduction. Finally, our theory contributes to the understanding of metallic conduction. The left wing of the periodic table contains those elements which have one or more excess electrons and which, at the same time, are metallic conductors. The consistent picture is that these electrons are the ones that are given off and, therefore, are free to move and able to carry the electric current. On the other hand, the precursors of the rare gases, *e.g.*, iodine crystals, are insulators because the halogen atoms have no excess electrons.

13.8. Electronic Structure of Heavy Atoms.   The only hypothesis we need for our elementary interpretation of the periodic table is the general tendency toward a rare-gas electronic structure.   A detailed picture is suggested by the high ionization energy belonging to the rare gases and the much lower values belonging to the alkali atoms, each containing 1 additional electron.   Suppose a lithium nucleus endowed with the positive charge 3 is supplied, to begin with, with only 2 electrons.   The great stability of this structure suggests that the electrons are close to the nucleus.   When the third electron is added and so a neutral lithium atom formed, this last electron goes into a position from which it is comparatively easily torn off.   This fact suggests that it is not located in a position so close to the nucleus as the two other electrons. The same general statement applies to the fourth electron in the neutral Be atom.   This comparison of stabilities indicates that there are only two places provided for electrons very close to the nucleus.   If the nucleus has a larger nuclear charge than 2, it can assemble additional electrons only in more distant orbits.   In other words, the two innermost electrons form a "closed shell" unable to accept more electrons. We do not discuss the cause for

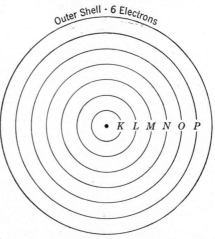

Fɪɢ.   13.2. Electronic   structure   of   the uranium atom.   The designation of the "shells" as K, L, M, N, O, and P will be introduced in the section on X-ray spectra (Sec. 14.2*c*).

this limitation, we only infer this property of the shell from the comparison of the rare gas and the alkali.   The same argument applies to any rare gas and the alkali that follows it in the periodic table.

Suppose we gradually build up the electronic structure of uranium (atomic number, 92) starting from the nucleus, allowing 1 electron after the other to join (Fig. 13.2).   Then the first two electrons form a "shell" which, for unknown reasons, is closed, *i.e.*, excludes any additional electron.   The third electron takes a place farther away and so starts the structure of the second "shell" of electrons, which in turn is closed when it contains 8 electrons (total number of electrons $= 2 + 8$) as is indicated by the rare-gas nature of neon, element number 10.   The eleventh electron, because of its low energy of separation, is assumed to reside farther away, starting the structure of the third shell of electrons, etc.   Finally, as far as this argument goes, a heavy element like uranium, in its neutral state, is supposed to have most of its 92 electrons in closed groups, easily computed from the rare-gas structures as containing 2, 8, 8, 18, 18, and 32 electrons, respectively.   (In Sec. 13.10 it will be reported that, in the more detailed treatment, these numbers are somewhat modified.)   In the discussion of X-ray spectra (Sec. 14.2c) the conventional designation of these shells by the letters K, L, M, N, O, and P will be introduced. The remaining 6 electrons of the uranium atom form the surface shell which is far from completed.

At the present stage of the argument it remains unexplained why just the numbers mentioned are endowed with this mysterious power and, furthermore, why there is no stable element heavier than element 92, uranium.   For many years it was guessed that the nuclei heavier than uranium spontaneously disintegrate like radium.   This was suggested by the fact that all radioactive elements are located near the end of the periodic table.   This guess was finally proved to be correct by the fact that elements beyond uranium have recently been manufactured and actually proved unstable, all being radioactive.   This will be discussed in the chapter on artificial transmutation (Chap. 18).

One may well object that so detailed a picture of the electronic structure of atoms is not warranted by such scanty evidence as the contrast between the rare gases and the alkalies.   However, this picture will help greatly in the understanding of X-ray spectra presented in the next chapter. Thus these spectra will provide a powerful confirmation of the idea of electron shells as constituting the atoms.

13.9. Report on Nonpolar Molecules and Crystals.   What forces are responsible for the formation of nonpolar molecules like H_2, O_2, N_2, or Cl_2?   The answer was suggested by G. N. Lewis and Langmuir (1916), who noticed that saturated molecules are produced when each constituent atom supplies one or several electrons which individually form pairs with electrons supplied by other atoms.   Only those electrons that are not already members of a pair within 1 atom are available for the binding. Hence the number of free valences of an atom is given by the number of electrons that do not form pairs within the atom.

The simplest example is the H_2 molecule, in which each constituent H atom supplies 1 electron, thus forming one chemical bond.   The He atom does not form molecules, since its 2 electrons form an antiparallel pair. The alkali atoms have 1 external electron, hence are univalent like hydrogen.   The alkaline earths have 2 external electrons, hence have no free valence in their normal states.   Nevertheless, they behave differently from He since these 2 electrons are loosely bound, hence render the atoms available for both polar and nonpolar binding.   The nonpolar binding is explained by excited states of the atom in which the 2 external electrons have their spins parallel and hence represent two free valences. The same picture of valence applies to the formation of crystals (see Fig. 13.3).

This successful picture offered by Lewis and Langmuir was correlated to wave mechanics by Heitler and London (1927). They applied to the structure of the H_2 molecule the same theory that had had great success in interpreting atomic spectra. Their results are briefly summarized as follows. When 2 H atoms approach one another, their respective electrons orient themselves so that their spins are either parallel or antiparallel (see Sec. 11.1e). Repulsion occurs when the spins are parallel and attraction when they are antiparallel. This theory even deals quantitatively with the nuclear distance, the energy of dissociation, and the vibration of the hydrogen molecule. The wave-mechanical picture

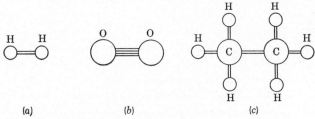

(a)   (b)   (c)

Fig. 13.3. Electron-pair bonds (a) H_2; (b) O_2; (c) C_2H_6.

of the electron pair forming a chemical bond agrees well with the picture boldly introduced by Lewis and Langmuir on the basis of chemical evidence.

13.10. Report on Further Developments. Since in our discussion of atomic spectra (Sec. 11.1e) we did not systematically introduce the elaborate system of quantum numbers required for the description of more complex spectra, we shall only briefly report on the relation between the periodic properties of atoms and their spectra. The more detailed discussion is all based on the picture of the shells of electrons. For example, the spectra of the alkalies, the simplest atomic spectra except that of atomic hydrogen, are satisfactorily explained as due to transitions of *one* easily excited electron. In the lithium atom (atomic number, 3) this electron revolves not simply about the nucleus but about a core consisting of the nucleus of positive charge 3 closely surrounded by the 2 innermost electrons representing the "K shell"; hence this core as a whole has the resulting positive charge 1. Correspondingly, the alkaline earths, which are expected to have 2 electrons outside of a rare-gas structure, show spectra explained in detail as due to *two electron systems*. Thus the investigation of atomic spectra confirms our theory of the shell structure of atoms.

The theory of the periodic table has been developed with the help of spectroscopy far beyond the range just discussed. Progress has been made on the basis of the theoretical interpretation of complex atomic spectra. In this theory, briefly reported in Sec. 11.1e, the assumption is made that each electron, like a planet revolving about the sun, has an angular momentum due to its *orbital motion* and an additional angular momentum due to its *spin about its own axis*. These momenta as well as the mutual orientations of all momenta are described by quantum rules. Similar quantum rules describe the orientation of the resulting angular momentum in a magnetic field. The orientations are described in terms of the quantum numbers originally introduced for the interpretation of atomic spectra. In particular, the quantum number n, introduced by Bohr, largely determines the energy of the electrons in the various shells, $n = 1$ characterizing the lowest shell, which, in the analysis of X-ray spectra (Sec. 14.2c), will be given the name K shell, $n = 2$ characterizing the second shell, the L shell, etc. This system may impress the student as somewhat arbitrary, although it is justified by the fact that it coordinates a vast material of spectroscopic observations.

The confidence in this system of quantum numbers is greatly strengthened by the fact that the same system, although introduced for the interpretation of spectra, is surprisingly successful in predicting the mysterious numbers constituting the rare-gas electronic structures (Sec. 13.8). This requires the additional simple assumption, known as the "Pauli exclusion principle," that within 1 atom no electron can have all its quantum numbers identical with those of any other electron (1925). On this basis Pauli was able to demonstrate that only 2 electrons can be accommodated in the lowest shell and only 8 in the second shell, in agreement with the numbers of elements contained in the first and second periods. Some apparent discrepancies in the higher shells are well explained by spectroscopic and chemical properties of atoms and by no means detract from the validity of the principle.

The student may be disappointed that here one mystery, the preferred atomic numbers of the rare gases, is replaced by two others, the quantum numbers and the Pauli principle. The student may feel that the "understanding" ultimately should imply an explanation based on the familiar laws of classical physics. However, there seems to be no chance of invoking classical physics in the explanation of atomic structure. All we can hope for is to reduce the atomic theory to as few and as simple laws as possible, capable of predicting as large a group of observed phenomena as possible. Keeping this point of view in mind, we recognize the great progress due to the discovery that the same principles introduced for the description of spectra also account for the chemical properties of the elements.

Table 13.2. *Periodic Table of Elements*

Observed Fact	Theory
A. *Nuclei.*	
Scattering of α particles by gold foil	Rutherford's nuclear atom
Scattering of α particles compared for different substances.	Atomic number = nuclear charge (positive)
Spectra of H, He^+, Li^{++}, Be^{+++}, etc.	= number of external electrons of neutral atom
B. *Rare gases.*	
Chemical inactivity; highest excitation and ionization energies	Stability of rare-gas electronic structure. *The hypothesis is assumed that in any case the structure of 2, 10, 18, 36, 54, or 86 outer electrons is particularly stable*
C. *Heavy atoms as built up of electrons.*	
Alkali: univalent; electropositive; in electric discharges only Na^+, never Na^{++} or Na^-; simplest spectra of neutral atoms, except H; follow rare gases in periodic system	Alkali atom has rare-gas electronic structure $+ 1$ outer electron
Alkaline. earth: bivalent; electropositive; in electric discharges Mg^+ and Mg^{++}; follow alkali in periodic system	Alkaline earth has rare-gas structure $+ 2$ outer electrons
Halogen: univalent, electronegative; in electric discharges Cl^-; precede rare gas in periodic system	Halogen atom has rare-gas electronic structure $- 1$ outer electron
Oxygen group: bivalent, electronegative; precede halogens in periodic system	Atom of oxygen group has rare-gas electronic structure $- 2$ outer electrons
D. *Certain molecules and crystals.*	
Vapor molecules: $NaCl$; H_2O; $NaOH$ *Crystals:* $NaCl$; H_2O; MgO	Polar molecules and polar crystals consist of positive and negative ions (each with rare-gas electronic structure) kept together by Coulomb attraction
E. *Electrolysis.*	
Faraday's laws	Theory of electrolytic dissociation; $NaCl$, for example, dissociates into Na^+ and Cl^-. Both ions are chemically inactive, different from the neutral atoms
F. *Metallic state.*	
The elements following rare gases in the periodic system are metals (high electric conductivity)	In the liquid and solid state the elements following the rare gases give off electrons. These represent the free electrons responsible for the electric conductivity of the metals

SUMMARY OF CHAPTER 13

When all elements are written in the order of their atomic weights, certain sequences of elements appear periodically, in particular the sequence given by an element of the oxygen group, a halogen, a rare gas, an alkali, an alkaline earth.

Their properties are interpreted by the theory of the nuclear atom and the additional hypothesis that there is a general tendency toward the rare-gas electronic structure. This assumption explains the valence of the neighbors of the rare gases, their behavior in electrolysis and gas discharges, and the formation of polar molecules and crystals. This interpretation leads to a detailed picture of heavy atoms as consisting of several "shells" of electrons with each rare gas indicating the completion of such a shell. This picture will be confirmed by X-ray spectra (see Table 13.2).

In a nonpolar molecule, like H_2, the binding force is attributed to a pair of electrons whose spins are oriented antiparallel.

The Pauli exclusion principle predicts the lengths of the periods of the Table of Elements by applying a new rule to the same quantum numbers which were originally introduced for the interpretation of atomic spectra.

CHAPTER 14

X RAYS

Our discussion now turns to phenomena which, although related to light, do not abundantly occur at the surface of the earth but are produced in the laboratory by a highly developed technique. In the first section we shall report Roentgen's discovery of X rays and study their properties, largely by comparing these with those of light. Here we shall find a technique of observing X-ray spectra. In the second section we shall discuss these spectra in detail and derive evidence regarding the electronic structure of atoms. This new evidence will corroborate our theory of atomic structure, which so far has been based on optical spectra and chemistry. The third section will bring a discussion of the Compton effect, which was mentioned before as furnishing a striking argument for the concept of light quanta. Finally we shall discuss applications of X rays.

14.1. Properties of X Rays. *a. Discovery.* Roentgen (1895) began the first publication of his new discovery by describing his observation as follows:

When the discharge of a large induction coil passes through an evacuated discharge tube covered by black cardboard, one sees in the darkened room the fluorescence of a paper screen which is painted with platinum barium cyanide, irrespective of which side of the screen is turned toward the discharge tube. The fluorescence is visible over distances up to two meters.

This new and striking discovery was the product of careful observation. There was no theoretical prediction whatever to guide the discoverer. Roentgen made sure that a new kind of radiation of a penetrating power heretofore unknown emanates from glass or metal when they are hit by cathode rays, *i.e.*, by free electrons of high kinetic energy (Sec. 12.2b). This radiation, which he called X rays, was being studied all over the world less than a month after his first publication and is now familiar to all in the form of the X-ray photograph of a hand in which the bones are sharply visible because they are less transparent to X rays than the soft tissue.

In spite of his thorough exploration Roentgen did not succeed in ascertaining the nature of the new radiation. From the numerous speculations as to its nature we quote a letter of J. J. Thomson, addressed to a friend a few weeks after Roentgen's discovery. Thomson offers his guess as follows: "On the whole I incline to the opinion that X-rays are due to waves so short that the wave length is comparable to a molecule. The absence of refraction is, I think, not surprising for these very short waves." Later on we shall discuss experimental proof for this early and remarkably correct guess regarding the nature of X rays (see Appendix 8).

b. X-ray Tubes. There are two types of X-ray tube: gas-filled and high-vacuum tubes. Gas-filled tubes (Fig. 14.1*a*) are similar in construction to Roentgen's original apparatus except that a block of heavy metal like tungsten is provided, which, serving as a target for the cathode ray, emits the X rays. These tubes are rarely used any more. At present, high-vacuum tubes, first designed by W. D. Coolidge, are almost exclusively used. In these the electrons are supplied by a glowing

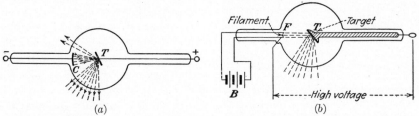

(a)   (b)

FIG. 14.1. X-ray tubes. (a) Electric discharge through a gas of about 1/1,000 mm pressure; (b) highly evacuated tube, electron current supplied by glowing filament (Coolidge tube).

cathode and accelerated toward the target by high voltage. This construction has the great advantage that the potential difference accelerating the electrons can be varied entirely independently of the current hitting the target, which is a function of the temperature of the cathode. Figure 14.1*b* shows an X-ray tube of this type. At present X-ray tubes are operated with potential differences up to a million volts or even more.

c. Effects Produced by X Rays. Roentgen very thoroughly explored the properties of the newly discovered radiation. We briefly list the properties as follows:

X rays produce light on a fluorescent screen.

They affect a photographic plate in the same way as visible light does.

On metal surfaces they produce the photoelectric effect.

They render air and any other gas conducting by ionizing the molecules. (This effect can easily be demonstrated by aiming a bundle of X rays, limited by lead diaphragms, across the space between the plates of a charged condenser in air and observing the discharge.)

The absorption of X rays depends on the atomic weight of the absorber, elements of high atomic weight showing much stronger absorption than those of low atomic weight.

X rays are diffusely scattered by all substances.

X rays are not deflected by electric or magnetic fields.

The most easily evident biological effect is the production of erythema, *i.e.*, reddening of the skin, which leads to permanent destruction of the tissue when a larger dose is applied.   Another biological effect of X rays is the increase in the rate of mutation, which represents a variation of the offspring making them different from the parents.

Roentgen also investigated whether X rays showed any of the properties of light other than rectilinear propagation.   His results were all negative.   He found no reflection from mirrors, no refraction by glass or any other substance, no diffraction by gratings, and no polarization by the passage of the rays through crystals.   Later we shall see that a refined technique has revealed the fact that X rays do show all the familiar effects of light, but most of them only in minute traces.

d. Intensity, Dose, and Hardness.   The outstanding characteristics of X rays are their intensity and hardness (or penetrating power).   In order to measure the penetrating power, first we must measure their intensity. Although the conventional method fails to give results as complete as the physicist wants them, we shall describe it in detail since it is important for medical purposes in the measurement of the X-ray dose.

Arbitrarily we measure the intensity of X rays by their effect of ionizing air.   This effect is measured by the discharge of a plate condenser when an X-ray beam is passing through the air between the plates.   The plates themselves are protected from the X rays in order to exclude photoelectric effect on the metal surfaces.   The simplest wiring diagram of an ionization chamber is given in Fig. 14.2.   Before the exposure to X rays the insulated plate of the condenser is charged; then the rate of the discharge of the electroscope gives a measure of the intensity of the rays.   As the practical unit of *X-ray quantity* or *X-ray dose*, 1 roentgen is defined as follows: The roentgen is a quantity of X radiation such that the associated corpuscular emission of 1 cm³ air under standard conditions produces ions carrying 1 electrostatic unit of electric charge

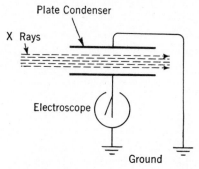

Fɪɢ. 14.2. Measurement of the dose and intensity of X rays by the ionization chamber.

of either sign.   It is evident that the unit roentgen measures the total effect of an exposure to X rays.   The same number of roentgens may be delivered by a short-duration exposure to strong X rays or by a long-duration exposure to weak X rays.   The corresponding unit of X-ray *intensity* is roentgen/second.   This unit characterizes the radiation depending on the power of an X-ray tube and its distance from the exposed body (see Sec. 17.3).

From the point of view of physical measurements, this definition is inadequate. It has been found that X rays, depending upon the construction and operation of the tube, have penetrating powers varying over a wide range. (Later we shall see that the penetrating power, called the "hardness," depends upon the wavelength and, therefore, is analogous to the color of visible light.) Very penetrating rays, called "hard" X rays, deliver much less energy to the air of the ionization chamber than soft X rays, *i.e.*, rays of low penetrating power. Hence, when observing the rate of the discharge, we fail to differentiate between hard rays of high intensity, delivering only a small fraction of their energy, and, on the other hand, soft rays of low intensity delivering most of their energy. The physicist would prefer to base the measurement of the intensity, like that of the intensity of visible light, on the total energy carried per square centimeter per second. But this cannot easily be done since we cannot easily construct a "black body" for X rays, *i.e.*, a body that is sure to absorb them completely. For medical purposes, however, the situation is different. It is assumed that the biological effect of X rays is due to the ionization caused in the tissue. Later, in the discussion of absorption spectra (Sec. 14.2*d*), we shall find that for any hardness of X rays, air shows approximately the same ionization as the animal body. Hence for this special purpose the ionization of air is an adequate indicator of the quantity or "dose" of X rays. The doctor applying X rays must, of course, know the penetrating power of his rays in order to judge whether they will be effective only near the surface of the body or at greater depth as well.

The instrument described (Fig. 14.2), although based on the arbitrary choice of air as the absorbing gas, serves for the measurement of the penetrating power of X rays. For this purpose layers of various thicknesses are placed between the source and the instrument. In some cases the absorption so produced can be represented by the well-known formula describing the absorption of light in colored glass:

$$I = I_0 e^{-\mu d}$$

where I_0 = incident intensity

I = transmitted intensity

d = thickness of absorbing layer

μ = absorption coefficient characteristic of the material and the type of X ray

In many other cases it is found that the transmitted intensity I plotted against the thickness d of the absorbing layer shows a more complicated curve, which can be analyzed as the superposition of two (or possibly more) exponential curves, hence mathematically represented by a formula like $I = I_1 e^{-\mu_1 d} + I_2 e^{-\mu_2 d}$. This observation indicates the superposition of two types of X radiation. Later, when equipped with better techniques for analyzing X rays, we shall find that these two or more types consist of X rays of different wavelengths.

When the absorbing power of various elements for X rays is described, the situation is much simpler than for visible light. Whereas the absorption of yellow light, *e.g.*, by sodium, is entirely different for sodium vapor, solid sodium, sodium compounds, or the same compounds dissolved in water, there are no such differences for the absorption of X rays. The absorption by a certain element is simply proportional to its density in the absorbing body, irrespective of its chemical combination or physical state. This is expressed by the equation $\mu = \mu_m \rho$, where ρ is the density of the element and μ_m, called "mass absorption coefficient," a factor of proportionality which describes the absorption of X rays by the element irrespective of the chemical or physical state (depending, however, on a quality of the X rays which we shall describe in Sec. 14.2 as their wavelength). This definition saves the trouble of giving separate figures for the gas, liquid, solid, and various compounds (see Prob. 14.13).

e. Polarization. Through many years the nature of X rays remained unknown. Because of their high penetrating power, it seemed impossible to explain them as rays of *corpuscles*. On the other hand, at the outset no indications of a *wave* nature could be found. The student will remember that the nature of visible light is elucidated by the following observations (see Sec. 8.2). *Interference* of light demonstrates its *wave nature*. *Polarization* of light indicates the *transverse* nature of the light waves (as opposed to the longitudinal nature of sound waves). In the next sections we shall describe the corresponding development for X rays. Following the history, we shall begin with the discovery of the polarization of X rays and next discuss X-ray interference and diffraction.

Within the ten years following Roentgen's discovery no new effect of fundamental importance was found until, in 1906, Barkla discovered the polarization of X rays. Roentgen had found that crystals, *e.g.*, Nicol prisms, fail to cause polarization. In order to test the polarization, without relying on crystals, Barkla applied to X rays two experiments which are well known in optics. By way of introduction we shall review these experiments. It is known that *nonpolarized* visible light is completely polarized when scattered by small particles (as in dilute soap solution) in a direction perpendicular to the original beam. The electromagnetic theory, which describes light as a *transverse* electromagnetic vibration, explains this polarization as follows (see left half of Fig. 14.3). Since the incident ray is nonpolarized, its (transverse) vibrations occur in all directions perpendicular to the ray. These vibrations, in turn, force the electrons in the scattering atoms to vibrate in any direction perpendicular to the incident ray, but not in the direction of the incident ray itself. The scattering is due to the forced vibrations of these electrons. However, any linear vibration of an electron, as in a straight radio antenna, emits light with maximum intensity in its equatorial plane and zero intensity along its axis. When applying this relation to the forced vibrations of the electrons, we find that the scattered light seen from a direction perpendicular to the incident ray is polarized, since the other transverse component, which would be in the direction of the incident ray, is missing. (In Fig. 14.3, the ray leaving the first scatterer in the horizontal direction to the right is caused only by the vertical vibration occurring in the atom.)

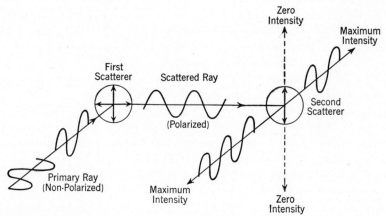

Fig. 14.3. Polarization of X rays demonstrated by double scattering (perspective drawing). All rays travel in the horizontal plane except those marked "zero intensity."

Another, closely related, optical experiment is concerned with the scattering of light which to begin with is *completely polarized* (right half of Fig. 14.3). The incident polarized ray whose electric vibration takes place in the vertical plane is scattered in any *horizontal* direction, but not in the *vertical* direction. This is consistently explained by the idea that the electrons in the scattering atom vibrate only vertically and hence fail to emit light in the vertical direction.

Barkla combined these two experiments in order to demonstrate the polarization of X rays (Fig. 14.3). Double scattering is expected to give the highest intensity in the horizontal direction and zero intensity in the vertical direction. Here finally we arrive at a prediction which can be checked by the measurement of X-ray intensities, *i.e.*, with a technique available to Barkla. The observation confirms this prediction and so proves the polarization of X rays, leading us to infer that X rays have the same character as light.

f. Diffraction; X-ray Spectrometer.   In the endeavor to ascertain the nature of X rays diffraction through very narrow slits was explored (Walter and Pohl, 1909).   Only small traces of an effect presumably due to diffraction were found which, if interpreted by the wave nature of X rays, led to a wavelength as short as 4×10^{-9} cm, *i.e.*, about 1/10,000 of the wavelength of visible light.   Although no reliable conclusion could be drawn from these experiments, they were of importance in that they started von Laue on the way to his discovery of diffraction of X rays by a crystal.   Von Laue's argument was as follows.   The simple theory of diffraction by an ordinary, optical grating, manufactured on the ruling machine, indicates that the distance between adjacent grooves should be somewhat larger than the wavelength of the light to be analyzed.   If the distance is much larger, these maxima are placed so close together that the dispersion is small.   Hence for the analysis of X rays we wish to rule

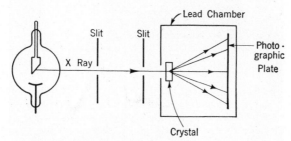

Fig. 14.4. Diffraction of X rays by a crystal; experimental arrangement.

a grating with the grooves as close together as, say, 10^{-8} cm.   Unfortunately this is technically impossible.   However, the mutual distances of the *atoms in a crystal* are just of this order.   Hence one may expect that the scattering of X rays by all the atoms regularly spaced in a crystal should lead to interference maxima in certain preferred directions, comparable to the interference maxima, *i.e.*, the spectral lines produced by a ruled grating.

The experiment of Friedrich, Knipping, and von Laue (1912) is sketched in Fig. 14.4.   A pencil of X rays, narrowed down by two small circular diaphragms, is incident on a zinc blende crystal.   As anticipated, the photographic plate, placed at some distance behind the crystal, shows a striking and complicated diffraction pattern (Fig. 14.5).   This important discovery proves the wave nature of X rays and opens up two avenues of research.   With a given crystal of known structure, X rays from various sources can be analyzed, thereby leading to X-ray spectroscopy, a field nowadays as well developed as optical spectroscopy and equally important for our knowledge of atomic structure.   On the other hand, with X rays of a known wavelength various crystals may be investigated resulting in a detailed knowledge of crystal structure. We are not concerned with crystal structure and shall discuss only X-ray spectroscopy.

Fig. 14.5. X rays diffracted by an iron crystal. (*Courtesy of Dr. G. L. Clark.*)

In order to derive the wavelengths from the diffraction pattern observed, we shall give the argument of W. L. Bragg. Suppose that X rays are incident on a cleavage face of a crystal, *e.g.*, the face of a simple

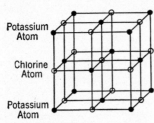

Fig. 14.6. Model of sylvite (KCl) crystal; simple cubic crystal.

cubic crystal like sylvite (KCl) as shown in Fig. 14.6. (Describing X rays, we conventionally measure the angle between the incident ray and the *crystal face*, rather than the *normal to the face*, because we frequently deal with X rays incident at small angles to the face.) We describe the interference by essentially the same argument which applies to interference of light scattered by a ruled grating. According to Huygens' principle we visualize that each atom of the crystal when hit by X rays scatters the rays in any direction (in the same fashion as the grooves of a ruled grating). Since the scattering by all atoms is caused by the same incident ray, the scattered rays are "coherent," which means that the phases of the rays scattered by the various atoms are related to each other. Hence the scattered rays interfere with one another similarly to the rays scattered by the grooves of a grating, however differing from this simpler process because of the arrangement in space of the scattering atoms. In order to explain the resulting spectrum, we arbitrarily consider the scattered ray leaving the face at the angle θ which equals the angle of incidence (*i.e.*, we consider the ray which is apparently reflected; see Fig. 14.7). This will be justified later. Constructive interference takes place; hence an appreciable intensity is produced when the rays scattered from all atoms cooperate. Let us consider two parallel rays belonging to the same bundle, aimed at two adjacent atoms: atom A in the surface layer and atom B in the next lower layer. In order to find the path difference between the corresponding scattered rays, we construct the two normals AN and AM on the

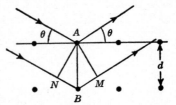

FIG. 14.7. Bragg's equation for constructive interference of X rays; d = grating constant, θ = angle between X ray and crystal plane.

rays. The path difference results by a simple geometrical consideration to $NB + BM = 2d \sin \theta$. As in optics the condition for constructive interference states that the path difference is a multiple of the wavelength λ, hence

$$2d \sin \theta = n\lambda \qquad\qquad (14.1)$$

where n is any integer. This equation, called Bragg's equation, is as important for diffraction of X rays by a crystal as the familiar similar equation for diffraction of light by a grating.

The conventional derivation of Bragg's equation just given should be supplemented by the following argument. Anybody familiar with the ruled grating used for optical spectra may ask: Why do we *presuppose* that the angle of diffraction equals the angle of incidence? Why don't we consider other combinations of angles for which again the path difference would be λ, or 2λ, or 3λ, etc.? We must add another condition for constructive interference. The argument based on Fig. 14.7 is too special in that it considers only the rays scattered by any two atoms, A and B, located on a line *normal to the surface*. In addition, for constructive interference, we must postulate that, at the same angles of incidence and diffraction, *all other atoms* of the crystal add their contributions. By an argument here omitted it can be proved that this requirement is met only if the angle of diffraction equals the angle of incidence, *i.e.*, for the ray which is apparently reflected.

Although geometrically the diffracted ray follows the law of reflection, the process taking place here is widely different. Reflection, *e.g.*, on a metal surface, takes place at the surface proper and requires a well-polished surface. On the other hand, X-ray diffraction is a process that takes place within the body of the crystal although in a layer close to a surface.

In order to compute the distance d between adjacent atoms in a cubic crystal (Fig. 14.6), we equate the density ρ of the crystal, which is easily measured, to the total mass of all atoms contained in 1 cm^3, which is easily computed. The chemical atomic weights of the 2 atoms, for example K and Cl, are called M_1 and M_2; hence the average atomic weight of K and Cl = $(M_1 + M_2)/2 = M/2$, where M = molecular weight of KCl. Then we argue, considering Eq. (2.3):

Number of atoms per cm along edge = $1/d$
Number of atoms per cm^3 = $(1/d)^3$
Mass per cm^3 = $M/2N_0 d^3 = \rho$

Hence,

$$d^3 = \frac{M}{2N_0\rho} \tag{14.2}$$

Here we presuppose that KCl has a *simple cubic* structure. There exist two other types of cubic structure, which, however, are ruled out because, for crystal planes of different orientations in space, they have different values of the grating constant d. We shall not discuss this distinction in detail.

Bragg's equation for the crystal grating, although superficially resembling the equation for the ruled grating, is fundamentally different and leads to a different operation of the spectrometer. This will be evident from a comparison of the two types of grating. Suppose that light of one wavelength λ is incident on a *ruled grating* (d = distance between grooves). Constructive interference takes place if

$$n\lambda = d(\sin \alpha - \sin \beta)$$

where n is an integer, α and β are the angles of incidence and diffraction, respectively. (Here we do not consider the special case of normal incidence, $\alpha = 0$, which leads to the simpler equation given in elementary textbooks.) When we arbitrarily select the angle of incidence α, for any values of λ and n we can compute the angle β, *i.e.*, the position of the spectral line. Hence for a stationary grating and slit we can observe all spectral lines. This is important for the ruled grating as used for the investigation of optical spectra.

The situation is different for the *crystal grating* (crystal constant = d). Again we suppose that light of one wavelength λ is incident. The condition for constructive interference, *i.e.*, Bragg's equation, contains only the one angle θ, the same for incidence and diffraction. Hence for given values of n, λ, and d the angle θ is determined. This means that the spectral line appears on the photographic plate only for the special position of the crystal described by this angle. If the spectrum consists of several spectral lines, we must turn the crystal in order to obtain the spectral lines successively on the photographic plate. The order n is easily determined since the first order belongs to the spectrum recorded at the smallest angle θ.

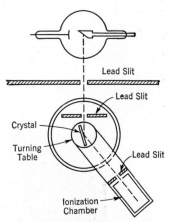

This discussion leads to the construction of Bragg's turning crystal spectrometer (Fig. 14.8). The X rays emanating from the target are narrowed down to a thin beam by two slits. This beam is incident on the turning crystal, and the diffracted beam leaving the crystal under the same angle is registered on the photographic plate. Instead of the plate, an ionization chamber (Fig. 14.2) or Geiger counter (see Sec. 17.2) may serve for recording the ray. The X rays are admitted to one or the other recording device by a slit so narrow that only a thin beam of them can pass through. When the crystal is turned, the recording device

FIG. 14.8. Bragg turning-crystal spectrometer. The ionization chamber is turned through twice the angle through which the crystal is turned.

must be turned by twice the angle since the diffracted ray emerges from the crystal as if it were reflected. The order of magnitude of X-ray wavelengths measured by this method is between several angstroms and a fraction of 1 angstrom, $i.e.$, smaller than the wavelength of visible light by a factor between 1,000 and several thousand.

A different technique, which dispenses with the turning of the crystal, was introduced independently by Debye and Scherrer and by Hull (1916). In this method (Fig. 14.9), a narrow pencil of X rays, selected by narrow holes (not slits), is incident on a small sample of fine crystal powder, containing many small fragments, all of the same material but oriented at random. Most of these fragments are ineffective, since their random orientations are such that the Bragg equation [Eq. (14.1)] is not fulfilled. There are some crystals, however, in such orientations that interference, according to the Bragg equation, occurs. Hence here the turning of the single crystal, which in the Bragg spectrometer is done by the operator, is replaced by the presence of very many small crystals oriented at random. An individual crystal on which the X-ray pencil is incident at an angle θ produces a spectral line emerging at the same angle θ. Hence the X ray is deflected through the angle 2θ. All other little crystals forming the

FIG. 14.9. Powder method.

same angle with the incident pencil will cause numerous pencils to emerge with a deflection through the same angle 2θ. Because of the axial symmetry, all these pencils emerging from the powder occupy a cone and produce a circular trace on the photographic plate (Fig. 14.10). Because of the large number of crystal fragments contained in the powder, the circle appears continuous. The various circles observed are due (1) to different wavelengths present in the spectrum, (2) to different orders of interference, and (3) to reflections on different crystal planes.

The crystal-powder analysis can be carried out with those numerous crystals which are available only in small pieces or in powder form. Hence this method is largely used for crystal analysis. However, the problem we are most interested in, *i.e.*, the analysis of various X-ray spectra, is best solved by the turning-crystal method in which one of the standard crystals, rock salt or, more commonly, calcite, is used.

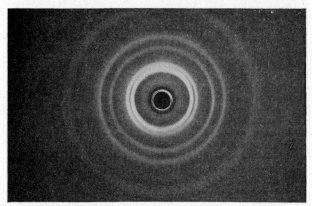

Fig. 14.10. X-ray spectrum taken with X rays of 1 wavelength incident on aluminum powder (photographic positive). The black circle masks the spot of the direct X-ray beam. (*Courtesy of B. E. Warren.*)

g. Other Optical Properties. Before discussing the important results obtained with the turning-crystal X-ray spectrometer, we shall finish the discussion of the optical properties of X rays. In addition to polarization and diffraction, traces of refraction and reflection have been found. In high-precision determinations of X-ray wavelengths it was discovered that the different orders ($n = 1, 2, 3$) did not yield exactly the same results. This was explained by the assumption that within the crystal the wavelength differs slightly from the value it has outside the crystal because the *index of refraction* differs slightly from unity. This explanation led to a measurement of the index of refraction by a technique much more highly developed than that of Roentgen who, in 1896, failed to find any refraction of X rays. Glass, crystals, and metals have indices of refraction for X rays slightly smaller than 1. For example, the index of refraction of crown glass for X rays ($\lambda = 0.708$ A), incident in air on glass, has been determined to be $n = 0.99999836$. The very small deviation from unity explains why the effect escaped detection by the less highly developed technique of Roentgen.

The student may have learned, as a conclusion of the theory of relativity, that "a velocity larger than that of light does not exist." However, an index of refraction smaller than unity, as observed for X rays, seems to indicate such a velocity of X rays in glass. This apparent discrepancy will vanish when the student studies the subtle distinction between "group velocity" and "phase velocity." The theory of relativity actually only claims that a signal, *i.e.*, a group of waves, cannot travel faster than light. In agreement with this statement the *group* velocity of X rays in any medium is smaller than the velocity of light. The fact that the index of refraction indicates a *phase* velocity larger than that of light does not contradict the theory of relativity. For the details we refer to a textbook of optics.

The fact that the index of refraction of X rays is smaller than unity leads to the prediction that *total reflection* may take place when X rays are incident in air on a glass or crystal surface. Here the student is urged to review the argument which, starting from Snell's law of refraction, leads to the following result regarding total reflection: Light traveling in a

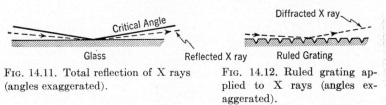

FIG. 14.11. Total reflection of X rays (angles exaggerated).

FIG. 14.12. Ruled grating applied to X rays (angles exaggerated).

medium of *higher* index of refraction (glass) and incident on a surface of *lower* index of refraction (air) can leave the medium (glass) as a refracted ray only if the angle of incidence is equal to or smaller than the limiting value α given by the equation

$$\sin \alpha = \frac{1}{n}$$

where α is measured against the *normal of incidence*, as conventional in optics, and n is the index of refraction characteristic for the combination, *e.g.*, about 1.5 for the glass-air surface (Fig. 14.11). If, however, the angle of incidence is larger than the limiting value α, no refracted ray exists and the incident ray is totally reflected. The same surface would be characterized by an index of refraction 1/1.5 (*i.e.*, smaller than unity) if, contrary to the convention in optics, it is specified that the incident ray travels in glass and the refracted ray, if there is one, in air.

This argument applies to X rays as follows. Here, surprisingly, for the incident ray traveling *in air* and incident on glass we find an index of refraction n smaller than unity. This observation consistently implies that X rays when incident within a certain angle *in air on a glass surface* are totally reflected. It is true that here n is only very slightly smaller than unity, a fact which makes the range of total reflection (see Fig. 14.11) very small indeed, near grazing incidence. On the basis of this prediction

Compton actually found that glass, crystals, and metals near grazing incidence strongly reflect X rays. This is the only method of making a mirror for X rays.

h. Determination of the Electronic Charge. This discovery led to further progress. On a metal surface a grating is ruled of the same type as the well-known Rowland grating, which is used for ordinary light. The grating is ruled with lines so fine that between the grooves appreciable strips of the polished metal surface are left, able to reflect X rays if they arrive at grazing incidence (Fig. 14.12). This device serves as a spectrograph for X rays. Although for X rays the dispersion of a ruled grating is vastly inferior to that obtained for visible light, it is possible to apply the grating to the measurement of X-ray wavelengths with an error of a few parts in 100,000.

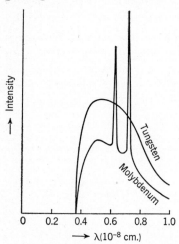

FIG. 14.13. Typical X-ray spectrum at 35,000 volts. Molybdenum shows the lines of the K series superimposed on the continuous spectrum. Tungsten (wolfram) has no lines within this range.

This new application of the ruled grating was applied to an independent determination of Avogadro's number N_0 and the electronic charge e. In Sec. 14.1f we determined the wavelength of X rays by computing the crystal constant d with the help of Avogadro's number N_0, which, in turn, follows from the electronic charge e (Sec. 7.2). Now we reverse the procedure. First a ruled grating supplies the wavelength λ of X rays, independently of our knowledge of N_0 and e. This serves for the computation of d from the Bragg equation [Eq. (14.1)] and of N_0 from Eq. (14.2). Finally, we compute the electronic charge e from $F = N_0 e$ without referring to the oil-drop experiment. The recent development, after the correction of an error, led to a full agreement of the results obtained by two entirely different methods. At present, the method here discussed, which involves X-ray spectra, yields the most accurate values of Avogadro's number N_0 and the electronic charge e.

14.2. X-ray Spectra. Von Laue's discovery of X-ray diffraction and Bragg's construction of the turning-crystal spectrometer opened up the wide field of X-ray spectroscopy. A typical X-ray emission spectrum is given in Fig. 14.13. It consists of a spectrum which *continuously* covers a wide wavelength range superimposed by *sharp lines*. In the first section we shall investigate the continuous spectrum, which is independent of the material of the target. Next we shall discuss the sharp-line spectra, which are as characteristic of the target material as optical spectra are.

   a. Continuous-emission Spectrum. The continuous-emission spectra emitted from a tungsten (wolfram) target at various potential differences applied to the X-ray tube, hence various energies of the impinging electrons, are plotted in Fig. 14.14a. Each continuous spectrum shows a strikingly sharp limit on the short-wavelength side. This sharp limit does not depend on the material of the target but only on the energy of the electrons. With increasing energy the limit is shifted to shorter wavelengths, *i.e.*, higher frequencies. (In Fig. 14.14a the superimposed sharp-line spectrum of tungsten fails to show up, since it happens that

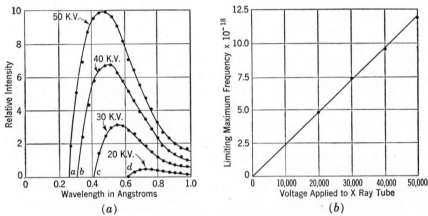

                                      (a)   (b)

Fig. 14.14a. Continuous X-ray spectra of tungsten at various voltages.   (*Courtesy of C. T. Ulrey.*)
Fig. 14.14b. Relation between frequency limit and voltage, derived from Fig. 14.14a. (*Courtesy of C. T. Ulrey.*)

there are no tungsten lines in the range represented.)   From the data given in Fig. 14.14a one derives the relation between the limiting frequency ν_l of the spectrum and the potential difference V accelerating the electrons. The surprisingly simple result is that ν_l is proportional to V (Fig. 14.14b). The factor of proportionality turns out to have the value e/h (e = charge on the electron; h = Planck's constant). Hence the experiments lead to the simple law

$$h\nu_l = eV \tag{14.3}$$

called the law of Duane and Hunt (1915). Duane assumed this law to be valid and used it for one of the most precise determinations of Planck's constant. He measured the limiting frequencies ν_l for given accelerating voltages V and used Millikan's value of the electronic charge e.

Let us summarize the various methods for the determination of Planck's constant. (1) The constant was discovered and first determined in Planck's work on black-body radiation (Sec. 8.3). The further measurements are based (2) on the photoelectric effect (Sec. 8.3), (3) on Bohr's expression for the Rydberg constant (Sec. 10.4), (4) on an excitation energy measured both spectroscopically and electrically (Sec. 12.1), and (5) on the continuous X-ray spectrum as just discussed. All these methods, although based on different experiments, lead to the same numerical value of h.

How are the experimental results just reported interpreted by the quantum theory? The law of Duane and Hunt bears a striking resemblance to Einstein's equation of the photoelectric effect $h\nu = P + eV_s$ [Eq. (8.1)]. Einstein interpreted this equation by the idea that a quantum of light $h\nu$ expends the energy P in the liberation of an electron from a metal surface and the balance eV_s ($V_s =$ stopping potential) in imparting kinetic energy to the same electron. For the photoelectric effect by X rays the same equation is true, but it may well be simplified by neglecting the work function P, because the energy $h\nu$ is so high—many thousand electron volts—that the work function P of a few electron volts is negligible. Thus the equation for the photoelectric effect due to X rays, $h\nu = eV_s$, still more strikingly resembles the law of Duane and Hunt describing a different process.

This similarity of the equations suggests the explanation of the continuous X-ray spectrum. While in the photoelectric effect the energy of one quantum $h\nu$ is changed into kinetic energy of one electron, in the emission of the continuous spectrum the reverse process takes place, i.e., the kinetic energy eV of the impinging electron is changed into the energy of a quantum $h\nu$. This idea implies a process in which the frequency emitted is not prescribed by quantized energy levels of an atom. In particular, since the sharp limit of the spectrum does not depend on the material of the target, we must assume that at the limit the total kinetic energy of the electron ($= eV$) changes into a quantum ($= h\nu$) without producing excitation of an atom. As the intensity is vanishingly small at the limit and has its maximum at longer wavelengths (Fig. 14.14a), we further assume that, in general, the electron does not give away its kinetic energy at one step but at random in several consecutive steps, any one step being responsible for one frequency in the continuous range. We are unable to describe the mechanism of the emission process in greater detail. We do not even believe that "classical" electrodynamics will help us in describing this process. In this respect the situation is the same as in the theory of the photoelectric effect (Sec. 8.3) in which all we know is a certain energy relation. But "classical" electrodynamics fails to describe the mechanism by which a quantum ejects an electron from a metal surface.

Summarizing, we note that the continuous X-ray spectrum fits well into the quantum theory; it is emitted in a process that may be described as the reverse of the photoelectric effect.

b. Sharp-line Emission Spectra; Moseley Diagram. So far in our discussion of X rays we have described experimental results and referred to the theory of light quanta. We have not yet made use of the picture of the atom that consists of a nucleus surrounded by shells of electrons. The contribution of the *X-ray line spectra* is important for the analysis of the electronic structure and our knowledge of the periodic table. This is the subject of the present section. We shall pay particular attention to the X-ray spectra of the heavy elements in which the simplest conditions prevail.

It is a striking fact that X-ray line spectra are much simpler than optical spectra. While we had to omit the description of the more complicated optical spectra, it will be easy to describe X-ray spectra. We

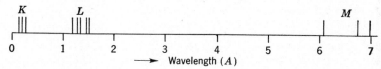

Fig. 14.15. X-ray spectrum of tungsten (wolfram) omitting the weak lines and those of longest wavelengths.

shall omit only the detail of their fine structure. A heavy element, serving as the target in the X-ray tube, emits an X-ray spectrum which consists of several series of lines. Each series converges toward high frequencies as far as one can tell, considering the fact that each series consists only of a few lines, not infinitely many lines like the series in optical spectra. The various X-ray series of tungsten (wolfram) are sketched in Fig. 14.15. The series located at the highest frequencies is called the "K series"; next comes the L series; and so on. The series spectrum is characteristic of the element of which the target consists, unlike the continuous emission spectrum discussed above.

Moseley, in 1913, investigated the relation between the X-ray spectra of the various heavy elements. In optical spectra, there is no simple relation whatever between the spectra of atoms adjacent in the periodic table. (Here we mean neutral atoms, not atoms compared with ions as in Sec. 11.1*b*.) However, in X-ray spectra Moseley discovered a simple relation, which is evident in the graphical representation of the spectra (Fig. 14.16). The X-ray spectra of all elements closely resemble each other; with increasing atomic number they are systematically shifted to higher frequencies. In X-ray spectra, there is no trace of the periodicity that is strikingly demonstrated by the optical spectra and chemical properties of the elements. When tracing any one X-ray line through the table of elements, Moseley found simple relations between ν and Z, for example, for the first line of the K series, called K_α, the relation

$$\nu = \tfrac{3}{4}cR(Z - 1)^2$$

where c = velocity of light

R = Rydberg constant (the same as in the Balmer formula of the hydrogen spectrum)

Z = atomic number

When $\sqrt{\nu}$ is plotted against Z, this relation is represented by a straight line. Such straight lines for various X-ray spectral lines are shown in

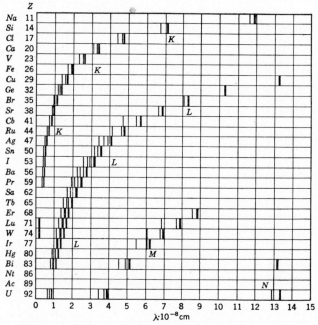

Fig. 14.16. Comparison of X-ray series of the various elements. (*After Siegbahn.*)

Fig. 14.17. This diagram, called the "Moseley diagram," is of outstanding importance, not only to our knowledge of X-ray spectra, but beyond that to our knowledge of the periodic table. First of all, independently of any theory, the diagram tells us that in one respect our knowledge of the chemical elements is complete. No new element can be fitted between two of the known elements because this would disrupt the smooth straight lines of the diagram, which obviously represent a law of nature. However, this argument leaves unknown whether or not new elements may be found beyond the heaviest element known at the time of Moseley, *i.e.*, No. 92, uranium.

Historically it is better to say that Moseley discovered a gap in the table of elements by kinks in his straight lines, which, however, disappeared when he assumed the existence of an element, $Z = 43$, previously unknown, discovered many years later.   Furthermore, Moseley had to reverse the order of nickel (atomic weight, 58.69) and cobalt (atomic weight 58.94) in order to obtain smooth lines.   He confirmed two similar rearrangements previously proposed by the chemists (see Sec. 13.1).   These exchanges of order seem less objectionable nowadays than they may have appeared in 1913 because now we know that any chemical

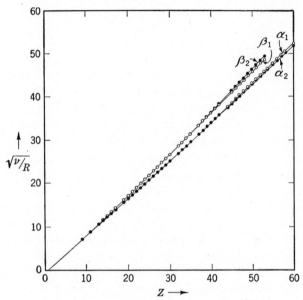

Fig. 14.17. Moseley diagram of the K series.

atomic weight is not characteristic of an individual atom but of a mixture of "isotopes" (see Sec. 16.2), the concentrations of which are determined by nuclear processes.

The X-ray spectrum of an element is the same for the solid, the liquid, and the gas; it is even independent of the formation of chemical compounds.   In this respect, too, X-ray spectra are much simpler than optical spectra.

Moseley's diagram accurately predicts the X-ray spectra of the few elements not found in nature.   Therefore, since Moseley's time, any claim of the discovery of a new element has had to be substantiated by the X-ray spectrum.   Only if the element is produced by artificial transmutation (Chap. 18) in quantities too small for the spectroscopic test are other arguments acceptable.

c. Theory of Shells of Electrons.   So far we have described observations of X-ray spectra.   How do they fit into the theoretical picture which we introduced on the basis of the periodic table (Sec. 13.8)?   The principal idea of this theory is that the atom consists of a nucleus surrounded by shells of electrons, each completed shell accommodating only a limited number of electrons.   Our answer will begin with a qualitative picture; then we shall try to estimate the frequencies on the basis of Bohr's theory. Historically, the early exploration of X-ray spectra had the benefit of the interpretation by Bohr's theory which became known only one year after von Laue's discovery of X-ray diffraction.

From Bohr's theory we take the idea that the emission of an X-ray spectral line is due to the falling down of an electron from an upper to a lower quantized energy level.   Since X rays have much higher frequencies than optical spectra (say a thousand times higher), we are dealing with much higher energy levels.   Therefore, we attribute X-ray spectra to the *inner* electrons of an atom, since they are bound to the highly charged nucleus with much larger energies than are the *surface* electrons to which we attribute the optical spectra.

The K series contains the highest frequencies, *i.e.*, the largest quanta emitted.   Hence this series is associated with the electrons closest to the nucleus.   These are the two electrons of the innermost shell, called the "K shell" (see Fig. 13.2).   But here we encounter a difficulty.   Since we assume that the inner shells are complete, we cannot, as in the theory of the hydrogen atom, assume that in the excitation process a K electron is lifted to the next higher orbit.   We are forced instead to assume that the excitation of any line of the K series consists in the *complete removal* of a K electron from the atom.   This process creates a vacant place in the K shell into which an electron from one of the outer shells drops, thus emitting a spectral line.   In this picture the first line of the K series, *i.e.*, the line of lowest frequency, is emitted when an electron from the adjacent shell, the L shell, drops in, the second line of the K series if an M electron drops in, and so on.

The corresponding idea applies to the higher series.   An atom that has just emitted the line K_α has now a vacancy in the L shell.   (The same vacancy may be created when the impinging free electron knocks out one of the L electrons.)   If now one of the M electrons drops into the L shell, the first line L_α of the L series is emitted, etc.   The diagram (Fig. 14.16) indicates that only for the heaviest elements has the N series been observed.   For this and the still higher series, the technique of observation is difficult since they are strongly absorbed by air.

We represent this idea in the schematic energy-level diagram of Fig. 14.18.   The atom is raised to the highest level when a *K* electron is removed, to a somewhat lower level when an L electron is removed, and so on. The line K_α is emitted when the K vacancy changes to the L vacancy.

The energy-level diagram (Fig. 14.18) predicts a relation closely resembling the "combination rule" (Sec. 10.5d) of the optical spectra. Let us suppose that a K electron is knocked out. If an M electron falls into the empty place, the line K_β is emitted. If instead an L electron goes into the K shell and next an M electron into the L shell, the same total change of the configuration takes place in two successive steps; hence the total change of the energy is the same. Consequently, the frequencies should bear the simple relation

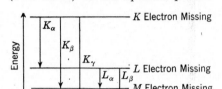

Fig. 14.18. Schematic energy-level diagram.

$$\nu_{K\beta} = \nu_{K\alpha} + \nu_{L\alpha}$$

The experiments confirm this prediction. Another combination rule will be discussed in the section on absorption spectra (Sec. 14.2d).

The theoretical importance of the Moseley diagram will be clear when we compare X-ray and optical spectra. Optical spectra of neighbors in the periodic table, e.g., those of neutral helium and neutral lithium, are widely different since the addition of one external electron produces different types of the *outer electron orbits* (Sec. 11.1). On the other hand, the *inner shells* have once and for all their specified number of electrons. This explains why the X-ray spectra are all essentially the same. The only noticeable difference consists of different values of nuclear charge and the consequent increase of all energies and frequencies with increasing atomic number. The fact that this change progresses steadily along the table of elements explains the fact that the Moseley diagram shows a steady progression of ν instead of the periodicity which is evident in optical spectra and chemistry. Thus the Moseley diagram gives evidence of the closed nature of the inner shells and the gradual increase of the nuclear charge over the table of elements.

When we attempt a quantitative prediction of an X-ray spectrum on the basis of Bohr's theory, we can expect only a crude approximation since the theory applies only to the case of *one* external electron. This case is widely different from our picture of the K emission in which all inner shells are filled with the exception of the one K electron just knocked out. Nevertheless, let us tentatively apply Bohr's theory (Sec. 10.4) to one of the innermost electrons. (The neglect of all effects of the outer shells is theoretically justified by the consideration that an electrically charged sphere does not produce an electric field in its interior.) Thus we try to predict the line K$_\alpha$, *i.e.*, the first line which is due to the fall of an electron from the second to the first orbit ($n' = 2$ to $n'' = 1$).   For this line Bohr's theory predicts the frequency

$$\nu = cRZ^2 \left(\frac{1}{1^2} - \frac{1}{2^2} \right)$$
$$= \tfrac{3}{4} cRZ^2$$

This crude theoretical approximation approaches Eq. (14.4), discovered empirically by Moseley, surprisingly well, since for heavy atoms there is little difference between $Z - 1$ and Z.   (The factor $Z - 1$ instead of Z is explained by the fact that the electron considered is not confronted with a nucleus alone but with a nucleus whose charge is slightly "screened" by one or two of the innermost electrons.)   The success of Bohr's theory in predicting Moseley's empirical formula may well be counted as an additional confirmation of the statement that the atomic number Z equals the nuclear charge.   Altogether, the picture of the shells of electrons, introduced for the interpretation of optical spectroscopy and chemistry, gives an excellent account of X-ray spectra.

In our discussion of optical emission spectra we learned that liquids and solids show continuous or diffuse spectra, whereas gases show sharp-line spectra (Sec. 12.4c).   Furthermore, the optical spectra of compounds are completely different from those of the constituent atoms (Sec. 11.2). On the other hand, the sharp-line X-ray spectra are not at all affected by the state of the emitter or its binding in a compound.   This is theoretically explained by attributing all X-ray lines of an atom to its *inner shells*, which are not affected by closely adjacent atoms, unlike the external shell, which is responsible for the optical spectrum.

d. Fundamental Processes.   Following our treatment of optical spectra, we shall next compare the various fundamental processes that occur in excitation by electron impact, absorption of X rays, or fluorescence.   In all these experiments we shall notice great differences between X-ray spectra and optical spectra which are fully explained by the theory of electron shells.

In order to excite X rays by *controlled electron impact*, we simply vary the voltage that accelerates the electrons from the filament to the target. The results differ widely from those obtained for optical spectra (Sec. 12.1).   While we can excite the first line of the optical "principal series" separately, there is no separate excitation of the first line of any X-ray series, say of the line K$_\alpha$.   This line appears only when the impinging electrons have enough energy to *knock out* K electrons, *i.e.*, the energy computed from the *series limit* of the K series.   Then the whole K series appears at once, combined with all the other series.   The L series can be excited without the K series, simultaneously with all series of longer wave-lengths, by electrons impinging with an energy computed from the limit of the L series. The corresponding statement applies to any series of longer wavelength.

This is exactly what the theory predicts. We cannot expect to excite the line K_α separately by raising a K electron to the L orbit because this orbit has no place vacant. Because of the closed nature of the shells, we must completely knock out K electrons in order to give rise to the emission of the complete K series and all other series. Although, in our argument, one individual excitation process causes the emission of one or a few quanta, the X-ray spectrograph, in which a photographic plate is exposed through several minutes, is not sensitive enough to record a single emission process but shows all possible quanta emitted, *i.e.*, all possible spectral lines, on the photographic plate.

In a gaseous atom, theoretically, one may distinguish between knocking out a K electron and raising it to an excited level outside the external electrons. However, this distinction, which amounts to a few electron volts, is not noticeable experimentally, since in removing a K electron we are dealing with energies of many thousand electron volts.

Correspondingly, by knocking out L electrons, which requires much less energy, we give rise to the radiation of the whole L series and the series of lower frequencies. In any case, the excitation consists of eject-ing an electron from a closed shell, in other words, ionizing the atom.

The simultaneous observation of the continuous spectrum and the sharp-line spectrum as in Fig. 14.14a forces us to assume alternative processes by which the impinging electron may expend its energy. Either it is suddenly stopped, possibly in several steps, without exciting an atom, and so emits a frequency or several frequencies of the continu-ous spectrum. Or, instead, it knocks out an electron from a target atom and so causes the emission of sharp X-ray lines.

The *X-ray absorption spectra* fit equally well into the theoretical picture. To begin with, we must make sure that X-ray spectroscopy permits a definition of the absorption coefficient better than that which we dis-cussed and criticized above (Sec. 14.1d). In that primitive method a measurement is made of the hardness of a composite X ray which in general contains spectral lines of several frequencies. There the transmitted intensity I is not represented as a simple exponential func-tion of the thickness d. We refine the method by measuring the absorp-tion coefficient of X rays *of one well-defined wavelength*, separated by the spectrometer. For this purpose we proceed as follows. First we measure the intensity of an emission line by the ionization current I_0 produced in the Bragg spectrometer of Fig. 14.8. Next we insert the absorber, say a metal plate of thickness d, between the X-ray tube and the spectrograph.

This reduces the ionization current to the smaller value I. The ratio of the currents I/I_0 gives the ratio of the X-ray intensities. From the equation

$$I/I_0 = e^{-\mu d}$$

we derive the absorption coefficient μ for this particular wavelength. When varying the incident intensity I_0 or the thickness d, we always obtain the same value of μ. We repeat this measurement for different wavelengths and finally plot the absorption coefficient μ against the wavelength λ. The curve so obtained describes an important property of the absorber.

As discussed above (Sec. 14.1d), the absorption coefficient μ does not depend on the state of the absorber but only on its density. This justifies the definition of the "mass absorption coefficient"

$$\mu_m = \frac{\mu}{\rho} \qquad (\rho = \text{density})$$

which depends on the wavelength in the same way as μ does.

The resulting X-ray absorption spectra differ from optical absorption spectra (Sec. 12.4) in a way that is readily understood on the basis of the theory. We remember that the optical absorption spectrum, *e.g.*, of sodium vapor (Fig. 12.7), shows all lines connected with the normal state of the atom, *i.e.*, the principal series, and, beyond its convergence limit, a continuous range which gradually decays toward higher frequencies.

We accept this gradual decay as an observed fact which, on the basis of our simple theory, cannot be predicted. It indicates that those quanta whose energies exceed the energy of liberation of an electron only by small amounts are most readily absorbed.

The X-ray absorption spectrum differs from the optical absorption spectrum by the complete absence of the sharp lines, while the continuous ranges beyond the series limits are evident. This is illustrated by Fig. 14.19, in which we schematically compare the emission spectrum and the absorption spectrum of the same heavy element. Each continuous absorption range starting at the frequency of a series limit gradually decays toward higher frequencies. The explanation of these absorption spectra agrees entirely with the argument just given for excitation by controlled electron impact. Since the shells do not contain vacant places, incident X rays (as well as impinging electrons) fail to *raise* a bound electron, for example, from the K to the L shell. The only possible effect of incident X rays consists in *removing* an electron; this process gives rise to absorption beyond the convergence limit, and it may happen to the K shell as well as to any other shell.

This argument explains only the sharp absorption edges. Again we must accept the gradual decay of the absorption coefficient from the edges toward higher frequencies as a fact which, on the basis of the present simple theory, remains unexplained. The continuous *absorption* spectra, whose *long*-wavelength limits are characteristic of the absorbing atoms, bear no relation to the continuous *emission* spectra (Sec. 14.2*a*), whose *short*-wavelength limits are characteristic of the kinetic energy of the impinging electrons, irrespective of the material of the target.

The theory of electron shells predicts a special combination rule. As an example we shall use the line K_α. In the *initial* state of its emission an electron is missing from the K shell; in the *final* state it is missing from the L shell; hence the quantum $h\nu$ of the line K_α measures the energy difference between these two atomic states. On the other hand, the K absorption limit is a measure of the energy required to remove an electron from the K shell, and the L absorption limit has the same significance for the L shell. Consequently the difference between the two absorption limits

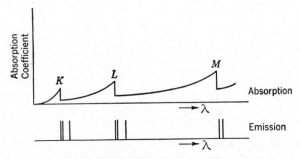

Fig. 14.19. Schematic comparison of X-ray absorption and emission spectra of a heavy element (omitting the structures of the lines and edges). Each absorption edge coincides with the short-wavelength limit of an emission series. The sharp lines show up only in emission.

should equal the frequency of the line K_α. Observation confirms this theoretical prediction (see Fig. 14.18).

The location of the various absorption limits all over the table of elements can be visualized from Fig. 14.16, which shows all the emission series, each represented by only two or three lines. In the absorption spectra all sharp lines shown on this diagram are absent. Instead of each series there is a *continuous absorption range* stretching from the convergence limit of the series to the left (to shorter wavelengths) with gradually diminishing intensity (Prob. 14.14). Visualizing these continuous ranges we derive the answers to specific questions. For example, when operating an X-ray tube with a tungsten target on 70,000 volts, we excite the tungsten K_α line (0.21 A) with considerable intensity. How is this line absorbed by the various elements, considering equal numbers of absorbing atoms? Light elements are transparent, because their K series, as far as one can identify them, are located at much longer wavelengths.

Thus the diagram explains the transparency of the tissue of the animal body consisting largely of carbon, oxygen, nitrogen, and hydrogen. Furthermore, it explains the fact (utilized in the measurement of the X-ray dose by the ionization chamber) that air shows about the same ionization as animal tissue (Sec. 14.1d). Bones absorb considerably more because they contain the heavier element calcium.

For long X-ray wavelengths, say 20 A, all elements except the very lightest ones are opaque. For very short wavelengths, like those of gamma rays emitted from radioactive elements (of the order 10^{-2} A), all elements are transparent, the lighter elements more so than the heavier ones.

Now we are able to predict that in X-ray fluorescence the same contrast should show up between optical and X-ray spectra as in absorption.

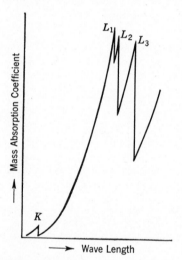

FIG. 14.20. Structure of the L-absorption limit of a heavy element.

Although in sodium vapor the first line of the principal series excites fluorescence of the same wavelength, we cannot do the corresponding experiment with the line K_α of a heavy element. However, when we irradiate a heavy element with a line that is strongly absorbed (*e.g.*, barium with the line K_α of tungsten), we ionize the K shell. Then the whole K series and all other series of the element that is irradiated appear in fluorescence, *i.e.*, are emitted in all directions. The corresponding statement applies to the other series, in close analogy to excitation by electron impact discussed above. Here Stokes' law is valid just as in optical fluorescence (Sec. 12.6). X-ray fluorescence represents X radiation produced by absorption of X radiation. Hence absorption of X rays does not necessarily indicate that radiant energy is *lost* as such: it may merely be partly *deflected* to other directions and *deteriorated* into smaller quanta. Only that part of the absorbed quantum that goes into kinetic energy of the liberated electron is really lost as radiant energy.

e. Report on Further Developments. Our description of X-ray spectra, in emission and absorption, has been simplified. Many X-ray lines show fine structure. Furthermore the absorption edges, except for the K absorption, show structures, *e.g.*, the L absorption a subdivision into three separate limits (Fig. 14.20). They indicate that not all 8 electrons constituting the L shell are equivalent; they may be subdivided into three separate groups which are bound to the nucleus with slightly different energies.

Let us summarize the evidence for the arrangement of the electrons in closed shells. (1) The chemical inactivity and the high excitation energies of the rare gases indicate that they have closed (or complete) electron shells. The alkalies, which follow the rare gases in the periodic table, indicate by their chemical activity and their spectra that they have one external electron in addition to the rare-gas structure. (2) The Moseley diagram shows that the inner shells of electrons differ only by the nuclear charges which are increasing with the atomic number. (3) By controlled electron impact or absorption of X rays we cannot separately excite the first line of any series because we cannot lift, *e.g.*, a K electron into the L shell.

In our discussion of optical spectra and the periodic table it was briefly reported (Secs. 11.1*e* and 13.10) that the theory of the fine structure of spectral lines requires a more detailed picture of the atom, involving more quantum numbers. It is highly satisfactory to note that the same system of quantum numbers as was introduced for the interpretation of optical spectra and substantiated by their bearing on the periodic table gives a thorough account of all the detail of X-ray spectra.

We limited ourselves to the consideration of the X-ray spectra of the heavy elements. This is justified by their simple structure as well as by the historical development. There is a wide range of wavelengths between optical spectra and X-ray spectra in which the spectroscopic technique is difficult, partly because the air is opaque, still more so because the crystal grating fails, and the ruled grating reflects light only with low intensity. Hence, for many years there was a wide gap between the ranges explored in optical and X-ray spectra; through the work of Lyman, Millikan, and others, this gap has gradually been closed. In the intermediate wavelength range, the transition is evident from the simple structure of X-ray spectra to the complex structure of optical spectra. For example, it is in accord with the theory that for lighter atoms, or for the higher shells of the heavy atoms, the shells are not completely independent of what happens at the surface of the atom. There the spectrum of an element is, to a certain extent, affected by the state or the formation of chemical compounds.

The simple structure of X-ray spectra discussed above provides overwhelming confirmation of the theory of atoms as constituted of nuclei endowed with positive charges and surrounded by shells of limited numbers of electrons.

14.3. Compton Effect. When introducing the quantum theory of light (Part IV), we based our argument largely on Einstein's equation of the photoelectric effect and its interpretation. We supported his argument by a qualitative discussion of the Compton effect (Sec. 8.6). Having discussed the X-ray spectrometer, we are prepared to discuss

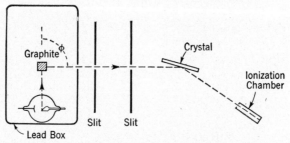

F<small>IG.</small> 14.21. Compton effect, experimental arrangement. Angle ϕ between the incident ray and the ray scattered by graphite can be varied.

Compton's discovery in detail.   A. H. Compton investigated the spectrum of scattered X rays.   Figure 14.21 shows his arrangement.   X rays of a sharply defined frequency, *e.g.*, of a characteristic line of molybdenum, are incident on a block of carbon.   The angle between the incident and the scattered rays can be varied.   The scattered X ray is analyzed in a spectrograph.   Compton found that the spectrum of the scattered ray shows the same sharp lines as the "primary ray" and, in addition to each line, another line shifted to longer wavelengths.   The wavelength difference between this new line and the original line increases with the angle ϕ at which the scattering is observed.   The experimental results are given by Fig. 14.22.

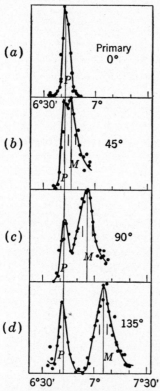

F<small>IG.</small> 14.22. Compton effect. The modified line *M* is shifted with respect to the primary line *P*, depending upon the angle ϕ of scattering.

Compton interpreted this effect by a bold application of the quantum theory of light.   He assumed that the incident light consists of quanta of energy $h\nu$ which travel with velocity c and hit the electrons of which the carbon atoms are largely constituted.   In this collision process each quantum imparts some of its energy and momentum to an electron, according to the same laws as govern the collisions between billiard balls, *i.e.*, the laws of conservation of energy and momentum.   With this idea in mind, we describe first the scattering material and then the incident X ray.   In a light atom the detachment of electrons requires energies so small as compared with the X-ray quantum $h\nu$ that the electrons may be considered to be free. Since their velocities are small as compared with the velocities that, as we shall see, will be imparted to them, we may neglect their original velocities. Thus, rather strangely, the scattering material is described as consisting of free electrons with negligible velocities.

For the description of the quantum, we must specify its energy, well-known as $h\nu$, and also must make a plausible hypothesis ascribing a momentum to the quantum as follows. In our discussion of cathode rays (Sec. 6.4) we introduced what we called the "principle of the equivalence of mass and energy." (We stated that historically Einstein derived this equivalence from his more fundamental principle of relativity; Appendix 7.) The principle states that any energy represents a mass = energy/c^2, where c = velocity of light. Thus we ascribe to the quantum of energy $h\nu$ the "equivalent mass" $h\nu/c^2$. Furthermore, to this mass we attribute the linear momentum = mass × velocity, hence

$$\text{Momentum of quantum} = \frac{h\nu}{c}$$

Attributing an equivalent mass $h\nu/c^2$ to a quantum $h\nu$ does not imply that a *material body* of this finite mass travels through space, because, according to Einstein, no *material body* can travel with the velocity of light. The equivalent mass is only based on a mathematical operation which leads to a momentum of the quantum $h\nu/c$. The argument is justified by the success of the theory of the Compton effect.

Now, by applying the laws of conservation of energy and momentum to the collision of a quantum and an electron, we compute the energies and momenta of both the scattered quantum and the "recoil electron." Since we wish to avoid formulas that we have not derived, we shall not use the relativistic expressions for the energy and momentum of the electron. By applying the expressions of Newtonian mechanics, we restrict ourselves to an approximation that is valid only for velocities of the electron small as compared with the velocity of light.

Notation:

ν = frequency of incident X ray
ν' = frequency of scattered X ray
m = mass of electron
v = velocity given to the electron
ϕ = angle between incident and scattered X ray (see Fig. 14.23)
θ = angle between incident X ray and recoil electron

We are sure that the recoil electron will move in the plane defined by the incident and the scattered rays, because there is no component of momen-

tum available which would throw the electron out of this plane. We
define the angles which are counterclockwise to the direction of the
incident beam, such as ϕ in Fig. 14.23, as positive, which makes the
angle θ negative.

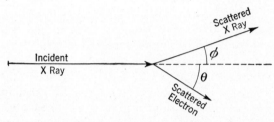

FIG. 14.23. Conservation of momentum at the scattering of an X-ray quantum.

Our equations will state the same ideas as in Prob. 9.2 as follows: The
conservation of energy is stated in one equation since the energy is a
scalar quantity:

$$h\nu = h\nu' + \frac{mv^2}{2} \tag{I}$$

The conservation of momentum is stated in two equations, since the
momentum is a vector and the law of conservation applies to each of the
components:

$$\frac{h\nu}{c} = \frac{h\nu'}{c} \cos \phi + mv \cos \theta \tag{II}$$

$$0 = \frac{h\nu'}{c} \sin \phi + mv \sin \theta \tag{III}$$

(In the last equation we give $mv \sin \theta$ the positive sign, expecting that the
resulting θ will have a negative value.)

Which quantities should we consider as known and which as unknown?
The fundamental constants h, m, and c are known once and for all.
Furthermore, the experimental physicist knows the frequency ν of the
incident X ray and the direction ϕ at which he observes the scattered
X ray. Thus the three unknowns ν', v, and θ are to be computed from
the three equations. In order to compare the result of the theory with
Compton's experiment, we are not interested in the velocity v and the
angle θ of the scattered electron. Therefore, we solve the equations for
the wavelength shift $\lambda' - \lambda$. This, unfortunately, is an awkward problem, the solution of which is carried through in Prob. 14.15. The result is

$$\lambda' - \lambda = \frac{h}{mc} (1 - \cos \phi)$$

(The rigorous, relativistic treatment leads to the same final formula.) This simple result states that the wavelength shift $\lambda' - \lambda$ depends only on the angle ϕ, not on the wavelength of the incident X ray. For the observation of the scattered ray in the direction normal to the primary ray, the wavelength shift always has the value $h/mc = 0.0242 \times 10^{-8}$ cm. The final formula of the theory successfully predicts the observed shift of the spectral line. The fact that the scattered light contains the unshifted line in addition to the shifted line is explained as the contribution of the nuclei, which, by their greater mass, cause only a negligible wavelength shift. Moreover, in a heavy element the numerous firmly bound electrons cannot be considered as free and hence scatter the X rays as parts of a much larger mass. Consistently the nonshifted line shows high intensity when X rays are scattered by heavy atoms which have many firmly bound electrons.

This argument explains at the same time why visible light fails to show Compton scattering; there are no electrons bound with an energy small as compared with the energy of the quanta of visible light. On the other hand, visible quanta have a chance for another division of their energy when scattered from molecules; they may transfer a part of their energy and so start molecular vibration. This describes the Raman effect discussed in Sec. 12.7.

Compton's theory predicts that in each scattering process an electron is ejected. With the Wilson cloud chamber (discussed in Sec. 17.2a) such "recoil electrons," ejected by X rays from gaseous atoms, have actually been observed. We shall not discuss the complicated detail because the evidence is not so straightforward as the observation of the wavelength shift (see Prob. 14.18).

The excellent agreement of Compton's theory and his observations provides a striking confirmation of the theory postulating that light consists of quanta endowed with a certain energy and momentum.

The same fundamental idea leads to a theoretical derivation of the *radiation pressure*. Such a pressure was predicted by Maxwell (1874) on an entirely different basis. From his electromagnetic theory he derived the result that radiation, at normal incidence, exerts a pressure on a reflecting surface, amounting to twice the energy density of the radiation. How is the radiation pressure treated in the quantum theory of light? Here we assume that, at the reflecting surface, each quantum bounces back, reminding us of the treatment of the pressure exerted by a gas on a surface. The computation is given in Prob. 14.19, where the result of the quantum theory is found to agree with the result of Maxwell's theory.

14.4. Applications. The medical applications of X rays are known so universally that they will be only briefly mentioned. X rays are used for diagnosis and for treatment. For most purposes of *diagnosis* a potential difference between 50,000 and 90,000 volts generates rays of a sufficient hardness.   Bones and metals are easily visible, and the digestive tract can be made visible by mixing a compound of a heavy element, *e.g.*, bismuth, with the food.

Treatment by X rays depends on the fortunate fact that diseased tissue, like a tumor, is susceptible to destruction to a greater degree than the surrounding healthy tissue.   In order to reach a deep-seated tumor with minimum destruction of the skin, very hard X rays, generated by potential differences between 200,000 and 1,000,000 volts, or even more, are applied.   For this purpose some hospitals are equipped with special X-ray apparatus operated with Van de Graaff electrostatic generators.   In the

Fig. 14.24. Radiograph of a steel casting showing internal defects.   (*Courtesy of Dr. G. L. Clark.*)

radiation emitted from a million-volt X-ray tube the continuous spectrum is much more effective than the line spectrum whose quanta, even for heavy elements, do not exceed about 90,000 ev.

Testing of materials represents another important application of X rays.   For example, X-ray pictures of heavy steel plates may show defects which reduce their strength (Fig. 14.24).

The structures of complex organic molecules may be analyzed by X-ray diffraction since such molecules show regularities in their structures similar to the regularities in crystals.   Thus atomic distances within organic molecules are being determined.

SUMMARY OF CHAPTER 14

1. *Properties of X Rays.*   Roentgen discovered that glass and metals when hit by fast electrons emit rays which penetrate through black paper

or any light material and produce light on a fluorescent screen. These rays he called X rays.

Other outstanding effects of X rays are as follows: They affect the photographic plate. They are diffusely scattered by all substances. They ionize air. They are absorbed, in general, by heavy elements more strongly than by light elements.

The dose of X rays is measured by the rate of discharge of a condenser containing air which is ionized by the rays.

Polarization of X rays may be produced by scattering and tested by a second scattering process (Barkla).

Von Laue discovered that X rays diffracted by the atoms of a crystal interfere with each other. This effect gives evidence of the wave nature of X rays. Since constructive interference depends on the wavelength, a spectrum is produced. The wavelengths are of the order 1 A, *i.e.*, about 1/5,000 of the wavelength of visible light, and are measured by Bragg's turning-crystal spectrometer.

Since for X rays the index of refraction of glass, crystals, and metals is slightly smaller than unity, total reflection takes place within a small angle near grazing incidence. This observation makes X rays accessible to spectral analysis by a ruled grating. The combination of this experiment with diffraction by a crystal grating leads to a new determination of the electronic charge e. The result agrees with the result of the oil-drop experiment.

2. *X-ray Spectra.* A heavy target bombarded by fast electrons emits two types of spectrum superimposed: a sharp-line spectrum characteristic of the material of the target and a continuous spectrum. The continuous spectrum has a sharp high-frequency limit ν_l depending only on the voltage V accelerating the electrons, not on the target material. The frequency ν_l can be computed from the equation $h\nu_l = eV$. The limit is explained by the complete conversion of the electronic kinetic energy eV into energy of a quantum $h\nu_l$. This process is the reverse of the photoelectric effect produced by X rays.

The characteristic line spectrum of a heavy element consists of a few series called the "K series" at the highest frequency, the "L series," etc., each series consisting of only a few lines. Comparing the emission spectra of the heavy elements, Moseley discovered a linear relation between $\sqrt{\nu}$ and the atomic number Z. For example, all first lines of the K series of the various elements are described by the equation

$$\nu = \tfrac{3}{4}cR(Z - 1)^2$$

The Moseley diagram representing these relations proves that our knowledge of elements is complete except, possibly, at the end of the periodic table.

X-ray spectra do not depend upon the state of an element nor the formation of compounds. All observations on line spectra are satisfactorily explained by the theoretical picture of the atom consisting of a nucleus and shells of electrons. See the survey given in Table 14.1. Altogether, the X-ray line spectra provide a strong confirmation of the theoretical picture of an atom consisting of a nucleus surrounded by shells of electrons (see Table 14.2).

Table 14.1.   *Comparison of Optical Spectrum and X-ray Spectrum*

	Optical spectrum	X-ray spectrum
Spectrum is due to..	An *outer* electron	An *inner* electron (normally all available places occupied)
Excitation by controlled electron impact	An *outer* electron raised to higher orbit. Single line (*D* line of Na) excited by excitation potential computed from λ of this line	An *inner* electron knocked out. No individual excitation of lines. Whole series excited by excitation potential computed from λ of series limit
Absorption of radiation	All lines connected with normal state and continuous spectrum beyond series limit	Only continuous spectrum beyond series limits of K, L, etc., series
Radiation..........	The electron just excited falls to lower level	One of the electrons of one of the next shells falls into the vacated place of the inner shell. *Example:* Line Kα due to L electron falling into K shell

Table 14.2.   *Properties of Outer and Inner Shells and of the Nucleus*

Chemical and spectroscopic properties	Depend on state and formation of compound; *periodic*	Due to outer shell
X rays..............	Largely independent of state and formation of compound; *nonperiodic*	Due to inner shells
Isotopes, radioactivity, transmutation	Independent of state and formation of compound; *nonperiodic*	Due to nucleus

3. *Compton Effect.* Compton effect is observed when X rays of a sharply defined wavelength λ are scattered by a light substance. The spectrum of the scattered rays contains the same wavelength λ and a new, longer wavelength λ', the difference λ' − λ depending only on the angle at which the scattering is observed. The shifted spectral line is explained by an application of the "corpuscular" theory of light, which describes the scattering process as a collision between the quantum and an electron belonging to the scattering material.

4. *Applications.* The medical applications for diagnosis and therapy are widely known. X rays are further used for the testing of materials

and for the analysis of the structures of crystals and complex organic molecules.

PROBLEMS

14.1. *X-ray dosimeter.* A parallel-plate condenser in air (capacitance $C = 50$ esu; volume $= 50$ cm^3) is charged to 110 volts. Exposure to X rays removes 10 per cent of the initial charge. Calculate the dose (in roentgens) applied to the condenser (1 volt $= \frac{1}{300}$ esu).

14.2. *Grating constant.* Calculate the grating constant d of a sodium chloride crystal (density $\rho = 2.15$ g/cm^3). Use Appendix 4.

14.3. *Bragg spectrometer.* Given the crystal constant of rock salt, $d = 2.820$ A. In the Bragg spectrometer the first-order reflection of a spectral line is observed at an angle $\theta_1 = 15°53'$. Calculate its wave length λ and the angle θ_2 of the second order.

14.4. *Limit of spectrometer.* Calculate the longest wavelength that can be analyzed by a NaCl crystal ($d = 2.820 \times 10^{-8}$ cm) (a) in the first order, (b) in the second order.

14.5. *Total reflection.* The index of refraction of glass for X rays traveling from air into the glass is $n = 1 - 1.59 \times 10^{-6}$. Calculate the small angle α of grazing incidence in air that limits total reflection.

14.6. *Electronic charge.* Calculate the charge e on the electron on the basis of the following measurements: the line K_α ($\lambda = 0.712 \times 10^{-8}$ cm) of molybdenum (measured by a ruled grating) is diffracted in the first-order spectrum given by a NaCl crystal at the angle $\theta = 7°15'$. The density of the crystal is $\rho = 2.15$ g/cm^3. (a) Calculate Avogadro's number N_0. (b) Using the value of the Faraday constant F given in Appendix 3, calculate the charge e on the electron.

14.7. *Continuous X-ray spectrum.* With the turning-crystal spectrometer we measure the continuous X-ray spectrum excited by a potential difference of 75,000 volts. Compute the short-wavelength limit of the spectrum and the adjustment of the spectrometer with which we observe this limit in the first order (rock-salt crystal, $d = 2.820 \times 10^{-8}$ cm).

14.8. *Determination of Planck's constant.* Duane and Hunt observed that an X-ray tube operated with 30,000 volts emits a continuous X-ray spectrum with a short-wavelength limit $\lambda = 0.414 \times 10^{-8}$ cm. Calculate Planck's constant h, using the electronic charge e as given in Sec. 7.1.

14.9. *Moseley diagram.* Make a qualitative sketch of the Moseley diagram for the line K_α as Moseley first found it, *i.e.*, omitting the element 43.

14.10. *Bohr's theory applied to K series.* From the approximate relation derived in Sec. 14.2b, predict the wavelength K_α of tungsten ($Z = 74$).

14.11. *Energies of X rays.* The first line of the K series of tungsten (K_α) has the wavelength 0.213 A and the last line of the same series the wavelength 0.178 A. (a) Calculate the stopping potential (in volts) of the photoelectrons liberated from any metal by the line K_α of tungsten. (b) Calculate the minimum voltage (to be applied between the filament and the tungsten target) required to excite the same line.

14.12. *Screens.* You are asked to build a screen protecting you from the highly penetrating line K_α of tungsten. The absorption coefficients μ of aluminum and lead are, respectively, 0.688 and 41.8 cm^{-1}. What percentage of the intensity will pass through plates 1, 2, 4, mm thick of aluminum and lead, respectively? What thickness of aluminum is equivalent in absorbing power to 2 mm lead?

14.13. *Absorption of X rays.* Given the mass-absorption coefficient $\mu_m = \mu/\rho$ of mercury for the wavelength 0.098 A: $\mu_m = 3.31$ cm^2/g. Compute the ratio of transmitted to incident intensity I/I_0 for the following cases: (a) a layer of liquid mercury, 1 mm thick, density 13.55 g/cm^3; (b) the same, 3 mm thick; (c) a 1/10 molar solution in water of mercuric nitrate, Hg(NO$_3$)$_2$, in layer 5 cm thick (the molar solution contains

1 mole in 1 liter of the solution). Assume that the solution occupies as much space as the water alone; the absorption by the atoms other than Hg is negligible; (d) monatomic mercury vapor, 1 atm at 357°C, in a layer 30.0 cm thick.

14.14. *X-ray absorption spectra.* (a) Using red pencil, enter the X-ray absorption spectra of the various elements into the diagram of Fig. 14.16. Indicate the fading of each absorption range toward short wavelengths. (b) Consider the L absorption range of silver (element 47). Does it absorb the emission lines L_α of silver, L_α of tin (element 50), or L_α of iodine (element 53)?

14.15. *Compton effect.* Solve Eqs. (I), (II), and (III) given in the text for the wavelength shift $\lambda' - \lambda$ which is observed by Compton. Apply the following procedure:

a. Introduce λ and λ' instead of ν and ν'. The equations so produced are called (IV), (V), and (VI).

b. In order to eliminate the unknown θ, write Eqs. (V) and (VI) such that the members containing θ are on one side. Square and add these equations.

c. As the resulting equation contains h^2/λ^2 and h^2/λ'^2, simplify it by squaring and subtracting Eq. (IV) (after transferring the members containing λ and λ' to one side).

d. Since we restrict our consideration to velocities v of the electrons small as compared with the velocity c of light, neglect $v^2/(4c^2)$ as compared with 1.

e. In order to eliminate the unknown v, divide Eq. (IV) into the last equation. Express $\lambda' - \lambda$ in terms of the universal constants and the angle ϕ.

14.16. *Compton effect I.* For the primary line molybdenum $K_\alpha (\lambda = 0.707$ A) calculate the wavelength shifts $\lambda' - \lambda$ predicted by Compton's theory for the angles $\phi = 0, 45, 90, 135,$ and 180 deg. Calculate the shifted wavelengths λ' and the corresponding angles θ which will be observed for the first order of a Bragg spectrometer equipped with a calcite crystal ($d = 3.029$ A). Compare with Fig. 14.22.

14.17. *Compton effect II.* Calculate the wavelength λ' of the ray scattered at an angle $\phi = 90°$ (a) for a "soft" X ray, $\lambda = 2.00$ A; (b) for a "hard" X ray, $\lambda = 0.200$ A; (c) for a "hard" gamma ray, $\lambda = 0.00400$ A.

14.18. *Recoil electron.* Compton effect is observed for the scattering of X rays of wavelength λ at the fixed angle $\phi = 90°$. Express the angle θ at which the recoil electron is ejected (in terms of λ and λ') and its velocity v (in terms of λ and θ). For λ introduce the line K_α of copper ($\lambda = 1.541$ A).

14.19. *Radiation pressure.* Applying Compton's idea of light quanta as endowed with momentum, express the pressure exerted by radiation at normal incidence on a reflecting surface in terms of the intensity (= energy incident per cm² and per sec) of the radiation. Using the data of Prob. 8.4, compute the force exerted by yellow light emitted from a source of 1,000 candlepowers on a mirror (area A = 5.00 cm²) placed in a position normal to the rays at the distance of 2.00 m from the source. Express the force in dynes and gram weights. (*Notation:* n = number of quanta per cm² and sec.)

HINT: Follow the procedure applied in the kinetic theory of gases.

CHAPTER 15

SOLID STATE

In our brief study of the vast field of solid-state physics our aim will be to interpret electric conductivity of metals, emission of electrons from hot metals, specific heats of solids, the crystal counter, the photographic plate, and the transistor. This program, which follows the historical development, will make it clear for what purpose one or the other theoretical idea has been introduced. However, here more than in other chapters we can only briefly, perhaps not quite satisfactorily, outline basic ideas and results of the mathematical treatment without giving derivations.

15.1. Metallic Conductivity. Emission of Electrons from Hot Metals. We begin with the discussion of electric currents in metals and emanating from heated metals, since these phenomena are explained by the simplest theoretical idea.

The conduction of electricity through *metals* is fundamentally different from *electrolytic* conduction, where ions, electrically charged atoms or molecules, are transported through the solution, as evidenced by the visible effects on the electrodes. However, when a copper wire has carried an electric current even for many years, no chemical change can be detected in, or at the ends of, the copper. More than a century ago it was first postulated that electricity is an agent that can flow freely through a metal. The sign of this agent, flowing in one direction or the other, was unknown, but it was assumed to flow from the arbitrarily defined "positive" terminal to the opposite or "negative" terminal. At present we believe that this agent is identical with electrons which flow in the opposite direction. Although electrons can freely move through the *body* of the metal, its *surface* presents an obstacle. This is demonstrated by the ability of a metal, when supported by an insulator, to keep an electric charge.

This theoretical picture of electrons in metals has been refined in order to include electron emission from a glowing metal, commonly called "thermionic emission" (Sec. 6.2b). Suppose that in high vacuum a glowing filament is surrounded by a metal cylinder. This simple apparatus is called a "diode." We easily determine the total number of electrons per second emitted by the filament when we connect the filament and cylinder to the negative and positive terminal of a battery, respectively. The current produced by a sufficiently strong electric field is due to all the electrons given off (Fig. 15.1). The reason why a strong field is needed for this process will be explained later. When the filament is at low temperature, the current is not noticeable; at red heat, depending on the properties of the material, it starts, and with further increasing temperature the current rapidly increases.

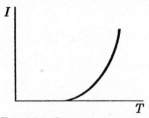

Fig. 15.1. Saturation current from glowing filament plotted against absolute temperature.

This observation has led to a much more detailed picture of electrons in metals (Richardson, 1901). It is assumed that electrons take part in the thermal motion of matter. The electrons, however, are not bound to fixed positions but are free to move like the atoms of a gas. The surface of the metal represents a barrier preventing the electrons from leaving the metal. The kinetic energies of the electrons are distributed over an unlimited range, as described by Maxwell's velocity distribution (Sec. 3.3), so that their mean energy is represented by the expression we derived for gaseous molecules (Sec. 3.2). Thus, some electrons, although only few, have a kinetic energy far exceeding the average. If such a fast electron shoots against the wall with a velocity component perpendicular to the wall exceeding a certain limit, the electron escapes and is registered as part of the current reaching the anode.

This process is illustrated by the following mechanical model (Fig. 15.2). Suppose that on the flat bottom of a washbasin that has a sloping rim there are many small steel spheres violently shaken by some mechanism. They are rolling all over the bottom. When a sphere runs against the rim, it climbs part of the slope. If the component of its velocity perpendicular to the rim exceeds a certain

Fig. 15.2. Mechanical model of electrons escaping from a metal.

well-defined value, the sphere climbs over the top and escapes. In order to escape, the sphere must have a kinetic energy which equals or exceeds the work required to lift the sphere from the bottom to the edge of the basin. The mechanical picture indicates that we must characterize each metal by the energy required to liberate an electron from its surface. This is the same concept which we introduced in our discussion of the photoelectric effect and called the "work function" ϕ of the metal.

This is a general outline of the idea that Richardson carried through mathematically. He derived an expression for the electron current in terms of the temperature in good agreement with the measurements.

Here we must meet an obvious objection to our determination of e/m of electrons emitted from a glowing filament (Sec. 6.2b). We assume that the electrons take part in the thermal motion in the interior of the glowing filament.   Therefore, they are expected to leave the metal with a certain initial velocity, which should be higher at a higher temperature. Does this affect the kinetic energy of the electrons outside the metal, which we simply expressed in terms of the accelerating potential as Ve, disregarding this thermal energy?   As a matter of fact, in most experiments the thermal velocities are negligible.   This is evident from a numerical example.   It is a convenient standard that at room temperature the kinetic energy of a particle, irrespective of its mass, equals $\frac{1}{25}$ ev (Sec. 3.2).   Then in a glowing filament of, say, 2100°K the thermal energy would be only $\frac{1}{4}$ ev.   This is negligible unless the accelerating potential is low.   However, for high-precision determinations of e/m we must consider that not all electrons emitted from a filament have the same velocity.

Finally, we must explain why, in the experiment described above, a considerable potential difference is needed to pull all electrons from the glowing filament to the anode, although apparently an electron leaving the filament would be free to cross the highly evacuated space to the surrounding cylinder. A more detailed experimental investigation will lead to the explanation.   In Fig. 15.3 the electron current I leaving the filament is plotted against the potential difference V between filament and plate for constant filament temperature.   The electron current increases with the potential difference and reaches a limiting value at a potential of, say, 100 volts (depending on the filament temperature and the geometry of the apparatus).   This current is called the "saturation" current.   It is supposed to represent all electrons emanating per second from the glowing filament. This is the current we plotted in Fig. 15.1 against the temperature.

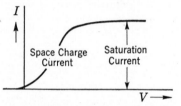

FIG. 15.3. Current-potential curve of a diode at constant temperature of the filament.

Why is the current smaller for the lower voltages although in high vacuum there are apparently no obstacles to prevent the passage of electrons?   The electrons themselves form such an obstacle.   At low potential difference the electrons travel slowly enough so that a certain accumulation in space occurs, known as a "space charge." The electrons are accelerated by the electric field on their way from the filament to the anode.   As the accumulation is largest where the velocity is smallest, the space charge has the greatest value immediately in front of the filament where the electrons have not yet picked up an appreciable velocity.   The effect of the space charge is that an electron just leaving the filament has a good chance of colliding on its way to the anode with other electrons.   They may deflect the newcomer back into the filament.   On the other hand, a high accelerating potential speeds up all electrons to such an extent that no appreciable space charge is formed, and all electrons leaving the filament reach the plate.   Space-charge effects are of outstanding importance in electron tubes.

The energy ϕ required to lift an electron from the metal surface enters into the discussion of both the photoelectric effect (Sec. 8.3) and thermoelectric emission. Hence here we have a chance for testing our theory of metals by measuring this quantity for the same metal independently by the photoelectric and the thermoelectric method. The results so obtained agree, although it must be admitted that this comparison can be carried out for only a few metals like tungsten and platinum, which stand white heat and can be prepared with very clean surfaces. This is necessary since impurities of the surface are liable to affect the energy of liberation ϕ.

The structure of electricity as consisting of electrons is of importance for the *noise* of very weak currents, *e.g.*, a very weak current emanating from a glowing filament. While a strong current consists of so many electrons per second that it appears entirely uniform, this is not the case for a very weak current, which inevitably shows random fluctuations, called "noise," which are due to the fact that electricity is liberated as individual electrons. From the fluctuation observed one can even determine the charge on the electron. In radio and radar great efforts are made to detect the weakest possible signals. Our ability to detect them is limited by the inevitable noise, since no signal that is smaller than the noise can be noticed. This limitation gives an outstanding practical importance to the noise problem.

Other processes by which electrons may be liberated from a metal surface have been incidentally mentioned. The emission of "secondary" electrons by *electron bombardment* is utilized in the photomultiplier (Sec. 8.4). The emission due to bombardment by *positive ions* forms an important source of free electrons in the low-pressure discharge (Sec. 12.2a). The emission due to *very high electric fields* leads to the field electron microscope (Sec. 6.2d).

15.2. Specific Heats of Metals.

The specific heats of most elements in the solid state are nearly 6 cal/(mole degree). Dulong and Petit discovered this law, which bears their names, as early as 1819.

This law is well explained on the basis of classical physics. The value for the solid is twice as large as that for the monatomic gas, which, according to Table 4.1, is 3 cal/(mole degree). This relation is understood on the basis of the equipartition theorem (see the discussion of the diatomic molecule in Sec. 4.2), which applies to any state, not only the gaseous state. According to this theorem, each degree of freedom is endowed with the same *average kinetic energy* $= \frac{1}{2}kT$. While the atom of a monatomic gas carries only energy of *rectilinear motion*, *i.e.*, *kinetic* energy, each atom of a solid may be considered to be bound to an equilibrium position determined by its neighbors. Hence we visualize that in the solid each atom, which again has three degrees of freedom corresponding to the three coordinates in space, is a *vibrator* (instead of a freely moving body). The study of the simple pendulum shows that each vibrator is endowed with *potential* as well as *kinetic* energy. More specifically the average potential energy equals the average kinetic energy. (This may be shown by plotting the potential and kinetic energies of a pendulum as functions of the time. Apart from a phase shift, the two curves have the same shapes and maximum values, since these values equal the total energy.)   Hence, according to the equipartition theorem, each degree of freedom of the vibrator has an average total energy kT and the vibrating atom of a solid an average energy of $3kT$. The same simple reasoning which we applied to gases (Sec. 4.2) leads to a specific heat of the solid body $= 3R = 5.96$ cal/(mole degree), in satisfactory agreement with the law of Dulong and Petit.

Our satisfaction, however, is marred when we remember the theory of electric conduction and electron emission from hot metals (Sec. 15.1). There we learned that the "conduction electrons" may be compared to a gas which is free to move within the metal.   The quantitative theory predicts that the number of free electrons in the metal is about as great as the number of atoms, in other words, that, on the average, each atom contributes 1 electron.   Thus the metal is visualized as consisting of an assembly of stationary positive ions permeated by an electron gas which makes the metal as a whole neutral.   On this basis we should expect the specific heat of the metal to consist of two parts: the share of the ionized atoms, which we just computed (representing each ion as a vibrator), plus the share of the electron gas, which, according to our earlier theory, amounts to $\frac{3}{2}R$ [Eq. (4.2)] and brings the total to $\frac{9}{2}R$, in glaring disagreement with the measurements.   Instead, the numerical values indicate that, unexpectedly, the electron gas makes no contribution to the specific heat of a metal.

How can we reconcile the assumption of free electrons in the metal with the fact that they fail to contribute their share to the specific heat?   The answer is given by quantum theory (Sommerfeld, 1927).   Our assumption that the rectilinear motion of atoms in a gas is simply described by classical mechanics is too primitive.   Quantum theory predicts that a gas that consists of *extremely light* particles like electrons follows very different laws.   The theoretical prediction is that the electrons' energies are not distributed over a continuous range but *limited to quantized values,* which are quantized not with respect to individual atoms but with respect to the metal as a whole.   At absolute zero not all the electrons are found at the energy zero, since the Pauli exclusion principle (Sec. 13.10) limits the number of electrons admitted to any one energy level and thus forces many electrons into higher levels.   Thus at absolute zero all levels up to an energy E_0 are filled with the maximum number of electrons allowed by the exclusion principle; above E_0, levels are empty.   When the metal is heated, however, thermal collisions throw a small fraction of all electrons into the higher levels, and as the temperature increases, the probability increases that a particular level above E_0 will be occupied. At red heat a sufficient number of electrons have been excited into levels with energy great enough so that electrons can escape through the surface, and a detectable current is emitted. For typical metals only a small minority of all the "free" electrons occupy levels above E_0, even if the metal can be heated to 2500°C.

This quantum theoretical probability of finding an electron in a level with a certain energy is given in Fig. 15.4. If the electrons followed the laws of classical physics, this probability would be given by Maxwell's distribution curve, which is strongly affected by changes of temperature as indicated by Fig. 3.1. However, in quantum theory, at absolute zero this distribution is represented by the box-shaped curve (solid line). When the metal is heated, this curve changes but slightly, as is indicated by the rounding off of the corners at the high-energy side (dotted line). For energies considerably greater than E_0 (half an electron volt at room temperature, say) the quantum theoretical distribution does not differ

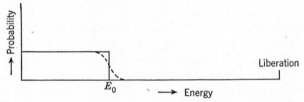

FIG. 15.4. Distribution of energy of the electrons in a metal. At 0°K solid line; at high temperature dotted line.

much from a Maxwell-type distribution. This explains qualitatively why *electron emission*, which usually requires that escaping electrons have energies several electron volts above E_0 in order to penetrate the surface, was successfully described as early as 1901 on the basis of Maxwell's distribution law.

The *specific heat*, on the other hand, is not even described qualitatively by classical theory; we can understand it only through the quantum theory, which predicts that the great majority of all electrons are not affected by the temperature. The minority of electrons (given by the high-energy wing of the distribution curve) is much too small to affect the specific heat. Hence we are right in disregarding the share of the electrons when computing the specific heat of a metal.

A certain deviation from the standard value $3R$ of the specific heat of a solid (conductor or nonconductor) is fully explained by an argument which applies to diatomic gases too (Sec. 4.2). In solids, as in gases, specific heats are constant only within a limited temperature range. The standard value of 3 cal/(mole degree) applies to most elements in the solid state within a wide range near room temperature. At very low temperatures, however, the specific heats decrease. (The diamond shows this decrease over a wider temperature range.) We explain this deviation consistently by the idea that the vibrational energy of the atoms can take up only quantized values. If the average energy of thermal collisions *far exceeds these quanta*, the substance behaves as if each vibrator could accept energy in a continuous range. Then our theory is valid. At low temperature, however, the average energy becomes *smaller than the quanta* so that many collisions are too feeble to excite vibration. Then many atoms fail to contribute their shares to the specific heat and its value decreases.

15.3. Insulators and Semiconductors; Crystal Counter; Photographic Plate. Only a brief outline can be given of research on insulators and semiconductors, which has led to the important development of the "transistor." In this complicated field our simplified discussion cannot give the satisfaction of a thorough understanding.

The name "semiconductor" refers to a solid, whose low conductivity is attributed to an *electronic* process rather than an *electrolytic* process. In a metal at any temperature many electrons occupy levels in which they behave as free electrons, moving through the metal and readily providing a current under the influence of an electric field. In an insulator like diamond or an alkali halide (*e.g.*, KBr) at room temperature the electrons occupy levels in which they are tightly bound to the atoms and cannot drift through the crystal when a field is applied. However, in an insulator there exist other levels of much higher energy in which the electrons are free to move. Ordinarily at room temperature these levels are empty, but an electron can be excited into one of them from a bound level by absorbing a light quantum or suffering a collision with a high-energy particle. This electron provides conductivity for a short time until it falls back into a bound level. It may fall back into a level like that from which it was originally freed, or it may be "trapped" in a new sort of bound level of higher energy. Semiconductors are very much like insulators in the arrangement of their electronic energy levels except that the energy gap between the bound levels and the "free" conducting levels is so small (though not zero) that at room temperature a small number of electrons are excited to the conducting levels as a result of thermal collisions.

The "crystal counter," which is of importance in nuclear research, represents a practical application of the principles discussed. The diamond and some other crystals like silver chloride, which normally are excellent insulators, show an instantaneous conductivity when hit by X rays or high-energy particles. The instantaneous electric current (produced by an external emf) is recorded and indicates the passage of a high-energy particle. Thus the device serves as an indicator or counter of nuclear events, equivalent to the more familiar Geiger counter (Sec. 17.2*a*).

In the Geiger counter the conductivity of the gas produced by a high-energy particle persists through a longer period (10^{-4} sec), during which the instrument is insensitive to new particles. For the crystal counter, however, the period of conductivity is as short as 10^{-8} sec and thus makes the instrument a valuable tool for high-speed counting.

In the *photographic plate* the primary effect of the illumination is the same, *i.e.*, the light lifts electrons to conducting levels in the high-energy range within the AgBr or AgCl grain, which is embedded in the gelatin. Here, however, we explain the permanent effect of the illumination (called the formation of the "latent image") by assuming that these electrons can be trapped permanently in a special type of bound level associated with tiny specks possibly consisting of normal silver. Once trapped, the electrons attract positively charged silver ions from the crystal. (These can move toward the speck, since at room temperature the silver halide exhibits appreciable ionic conductivity due to silver ions.) The ions neutralize the electrons previously trapped by the silver speck and so add to the amount of normal silver. We are not concerned with the processes which occur during the development of the plate. They cause the accumulation of a visible grain of silver which is responsible for the blackening of the plate.

Photoconductivity is closely related to the photographic process, for while the electrons are in the conducting levels, they drift under the influence of an electric field and thereby constitute a current. As expected, then, crystals of AgBr which are much larger than grains of the photographic plate are rendered conducting by the same range of wavelengths which affect the photographic plate.

15.4. Electrons and Holes in Semiconductors. Transistor. The work of Bardeen and Brattain at the Bell Telephone Laboratories, culminating in the invention of the "transistor," heralds important developments in the field now dominated by electron tubes. We shall first discuss the rectifier effect at the junction of two semiconductors and later the transistor.

Let us compare the diamond, an excellent insulator, to another crystal of the same chemical family, the semiconductor germanium. As the carbon atoms, constituting the diamond, are tetravalent, each atom is linked to four neighbors, symmetrically placed in space. The good insulating quality of the diamond proves that all electrons are in bound positions described. However, as mentioned before, the diamond can be rendered conducting by ultraviolet light or X rays or corpuscular rays. This indicates that, although normally all electrons are bound, there exist excited energy levels even in the diamond in which electrons are free to move. When an electron is lifted to an excited level, there are two entities contributing to electric conduction, first this electron, second the hole left in the structure of valence electrons, creating a positive ion.   We do not assume that this ion migrates bodily, but only that under the effect of an external emf an adjacent electron may jump into this hole, so creating a shifted hole into which another electron may jump, and so on.   The result is that under the effect of an electric field the hole migrates in the direction opposite to that of the electron and so acts like a positive ion in a gas discharge.   This motion of the hole represents a current in addition to that caused by the opposite motion of the electrons.   When the illumination stops, the conduction electrons quickly recombine with the holes, and the diamond crystal returns to its normal state.

While this picture explains the temporary conductivity of a crystal which otherwise is an *insulator*, in a *semiconductor* electrons are so loosely bound that thermal motion is sufficient to create conduction electrons and the corresponding holes.   Here decreasing temperature reduces the concentration of carriers and thus decreases the conductivity.   At very low temperature the semiconductor germanium is as good an insulator as the diamond is at ordinary temperature.   Hence we assume that both materials have essentially the same structure but that the electrons are not so firmly bound in germanium as they are in the diamond.

While the currents here considered are those flowing in an ideal pure semiconductor, the conductivity may be greatly increased by impurities of a concentration as small as 1/10,000,000.   As the first example we add to the *tetravalent* germanium a trace of arsenic, which has a valence of *five*. We explain the increase of conductivity so produced by assuming that the arsenic atom occupies a position in the crystal which in pure germanium would be occupied by a germanium atom and that consequently only 4 of the arsenic's 5 valence electrons are used in forming the usual four valence bonds with the neighboring germanium atoms.   Since the bond structure has no use for the fifth electron, this goes to the range of conduction electrons.   (It does not give a negative charge to the crystal, since its charge is compensated by the nuclear charge of the arsenic atom.) Germanium with arsenic impurity is called an "*n*-type semiconductor," where *n* stands for negative.

Whereas a *pentavalent* impurity gives to the germanium conduction *electrons*, a *trivalent* impurity brings about conduction by *holes*.   In detail, the process is as follows.   When we add the trivalent boron to germanium, its 3 valence electrons form bonds with 3 of the 4 neighboring germanium atoms; the fourth possible bond is incomplete, the missing electron constituting a hole.   (This deficiency is not noticed as a positive charge of the crystal since the boron nuclei contribute correspondingly less positive charge.)   For the understanding of the transistor the assumption is important that these holes can migrate through the germanium crystal and hence render it conducting. Germanium with boron impurity is called a "*p*-type" semiconductor, where *p* stands for positive. Except at very low temperatures, the electrons or holes which are placed in the crystal by the respective impurities are free to move. Heating increases the conductivity as it liberates additional electrons from the germanium itself and, simultaneously, creates more holes.

Next we want to study the rectifying action of the "*p-n* junction": two adjacent layers of semiconductor, one *n*-type, the other *p*-type (Fig. 15.5). The current-potential curve of this device is given in Fig. 15.6. In the quadrant marked "forward" the metal electrode in contact with the *n*-type semiconductor is made negative with respect to the other electrode. The situation is reversed in the quadrant marked "reverse." A simplified explanation of the marked dissymmetry of the curve is as

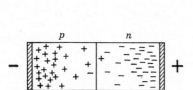

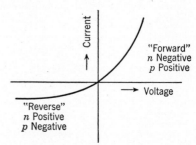

FIG. 15.5. Deficiency of carriers near *p-n* junction ("reverse" quadrant of Fig. 15.6).

FIG. 15.6. Current-potential curve of *p-n* junction.

follows. When the emf applied to the metal plates drives the electrons from right to left and the levels from left to right, electrons and holes meet near the common surface and may partly even pass through the surface. In this region they neutralize each other and thus allow the free flow of the current ("forward" quadrant). When, however, the sign of the emf is reversed, the electrons and holes are both pulled away from the common surface of *n* type and *p* type. Thus, near this surface a deficiency of carriers of electricity is created, hence a layer of high resistance. This explains the low current in the "reverse" quadrant and thus the rectifying effect. For the following argument we summarize the effect: when electrons and holes are driven toward the common surface, high conductivity results; in the opposite case, low conductivity.

This effect is used in the *transistor*. A thin slice of a *p*-type semiconductor is sandwiched between two *n*-type semiconductors. Metal electrodes are connected, as shown in Fig. 15.7. (To begin with, we disregard the transformers indicated in the figure.) A battery gives a *negative* bias to the *left n* type with respect to the central *p*-type semiconductor.   This brings the left junction into the "forward quadrant," where an increase of the voltage produces a strong increase of the current. Another battery gives a *positive* bias to the *right n* type with respect to the central *p*-type semiconductor and so makes the right junction less sensitive to changes of voltage (reverse quadrant).   Here, however, we must consider a new effect.   The *p*-type slice is so thin that electrons which copiously arrive from the left side drift through the slice and materially increase the conductivity of the right junction.   This effect leads to the following application.   When a signal is superimposed through the transformer on the left circuit, the supply of electrons drifting through the slice will vary.   Thus the right circuit will respond to the signal and transmit it to the right transformer.   The effect is similar to that of a

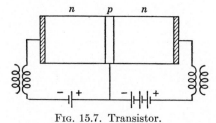

Fig. 15.7. Transistor.

triode in which an input signal applied to the grid affects the output plate current.

This simple argument is not sufficient to predict the important fact that the output signal carries larger power than the input signal, hence that the device acts as an amplifier.   This depends on the voltages applied.   Low voltage on the input side and high voltage on the output side favors power amplification.

It is anticipated that the transistor will profoundly change the whole field of electronics.   The outstanding advantage of the transistor over the conventional vacuum tube is due to the fact that free electrons and holes are available all the time and do not need to be produced by a glowing filament.   The useful life of the transistor is expected to be much longer than that of the vacuum tube, since the transistor has no filament that may burn out and no vacuum that may deteriorate.   The ensuing gain of reliability will be appreciated when we consider the enormous numbers of vacuum tubes required in radio sets, computing machines, etc.   As an example we cite the fact that more than 12,000 vacuum tubes operate during a transatlantic telephone call.

PART VI

NUCLEAR STRUCTURE

In preparation for the discussion of spectra we had to insert a chapter on nuclei (Chap. 9) reporting Rutherford's discovery of the *nuclear atom* and the ensuing measurement of *nuclear charges*.* The conclusion that the nuclear charge equals the atomic number has been amply confirmed by other arguments. Furthermore, it may seem that we know the *nuclear masses* (with particularly great accuracy the relative masses which are derived from the atomic weights). We shall find, however, that we must revise our understanding of the significance of the atomic weights.

To what extent do nuclear properties affect the electronic system? In the study of optical and X-ray spectra we had little interest in any nuclear property other than the *nuclear charge*. The *nuclear mass* is simply assumed to be very large in comparison to the electronic mass; it is exceptional that in Bohr's theory of the relative motion of the nucleus a very small effect is explained by taking into account the finite value of the nuclear mass. (Nuclear masses have noticeable effects on molecular spectra, which we have not studied in detail.) The possible *instability* of a nucleus, one of its very important properties manifest in its disintegration or transmutation, is not noticeable at all in the study of the electronic structure. For these reasons, nuclear physics is a field largely independent of the physics of the electronic structure.

In Part VI we shall first study the separation of elements into isotopes. Next we shall study natural radioactivity, which is due to the spontaneous disintegration of some elements occurring in nature. Finally, we shall discuss the wealth of new observations made since physicists succeeded in breaking up nuclei by high-energy projectiles, thus transmuting elements and even creating new elements heretofore unknown. This new technique opens up a vast new field of physics. Moreover, the new observations profoundly modify what seemed to be firmly established fundamental laws of physics. We shall find new evidence regarding the fundamental particles (neutrons, positrons, mesons), the equivalence of mass and energy, annihilation of material particles, fission of the heaviest nuclei, and fusion of the lightest nuclei, processes which make vast stores of nuclear energy available to the human race.

* A student beginning the study of nuclear physics should first read Chap. 9.

CHAPTER 16

ISOTOPES

16.1. Apparatus. The discovery of isotopes was the result of a refined technique in positive-ray analysis (Sec. 6.3). J. J. Thomson's parabola method discussed above gave the first, rather vague evidence of the new phenomenon (1913), while modern apparatus using the same method gives clear-cut evidence (Fig. 6.13). Owing to the need for accurate determination of specific charges, such instruments have been vastly refined. They are called "mass spectrographs" because they collect ions of the same mass along sharp lines on photographic plates and thus produce pictures resembling optical spectra. We shall describe two types, that of Aston and that of Dempster.

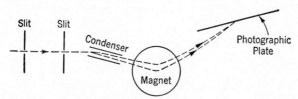

Fig. 16.1. Aston's mass spectrograph. Electric and magnetic deflection.

Aston's mass spectrograph (Fig. 16.1) avoids a drawback of the parabola method. In this early method (Figs. 6.12 and 6.13), positive ions of each type are present within a considerable range of velocity because the individual ions are created in the discharge at various distances in front of the cathode and, therefore, accelerated by various potential differences. The corresponding spread of the positive ray over the length of any one parabola is a nuisance since it dilutes the intensity on the photographic plate. Aston succeeded in concentrating the ions of one value of e/m but a wide velocity range into one short line and so increased the intensity of this line. This device enabled him to introduce improvements, such as longer paths of the ions, which materially increased the accuracy of the results.

Aston's mass spectrograph is sketched in Fig. 16.1. The positive ions, which originate in a low-pressure discharge (not shown on the diagram), form a ray which is narrowed down by two consecutive slits. The ray is first deflected in one direction by an electric field (indicated by a pair of condenser plates) and next in the opposite direction by a magnetic field (indicated by the circular cross section of a magnetic pole piece with the lines of force perpendicular to the paper). While the *electric* field deflects the slow ions *further downward* than the fast ones, the *magnetic* field, acting in the opposite sense, deflects the same ions *further upward* and so finally combines on the photographic plate all ions of one value of e/m, although they may have different velocities. This is called "velocity focusing." The separation on the photographic plate of the different types of ion is explained as follows. Ions *heavier* than those whose paths are drawn in Fig. 16.1 are *less* deflected by the electric and magnetic fields. This stretches their paths and makes them appear further to the

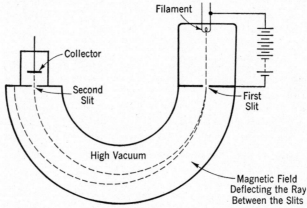

Fig. 16.2. Dempster's mass spectrograph. Positive ions from the filament are accelerated toward the first slit and bent on a circular path by a magnetic field acting between the slits.

right on the photographic plate. Thus the ions of any one value of e/m form a separate sharp line on the plate.

Simpler is the principle of the mass spectrograph designed by Dempster (Fig. 16.2), who independently made the discovery to be discussed. It was reported in Sec. 6.2*b* that glowing filaments, impregnated with certain salts, give off positive ions, a large fraction being alkali ions. By the use of this source of ions, Dempster's instrument is applicable to different materials and so supplements that of Aston. In high vacuum these ions are subjected to electric and magnetic fields in the same way as described for electrons (see Sec. 6.2*b*). First the ions are accelerated toward a plate by the potential difference V. Those ions which pass through a narrow slit cut in the plate (the first slit) enter another evacuated chamber in which they are subjected to a uniform magnetic field directed perpendicularly to their path. The force exerted by this field on the moving charges bends their path into a circle. After passing around one-half of its circumference the ray is incident on another plate in which a second slit is cut. But only for a special adjustment of all variables will the ray pass through the second slit and be incident on some recording device, e.g., an isolated metal plate connected with an electroscope. The electric charge per second carried by the ray is measured by the rate of charge of the electroscope. In the figure two rays are shown with slightly different values of e/m; one of them passes through the second slit and hits the recording device.

The theory of the instrument was given in Sec. 6.2b. The specific charge of the particles recorded is easily computed from

$$\frac{e}{m} = \frac{2V}{B^2 r^2} \tag{16.1}$$

In most cases we are dealing with singly charged positive ions. The radius r of the circular path is given by the rigid construction of the apparatus, and the magnetic induction B is kept constant. By variation of the accelerating voltage V the various rays can have the radii of their respective circular paths so adjusted that these rays pass successively through the second slit. For every such value of the voltage V we compute the mass m of the particles in the corresponding ray from the last equation. Next we may compute their atomic weight M from the equation $M = N_0 \times m$ [N_0 = Avogadro's number; Eq. (2.3)]. Conversely, Aston, knowing the atomic weight M of the ray, could predict the position of the line on the photographic plate. Hence the outcome of the experiment is apparently fully predictable.

16.2. Whole-number Rule. In our discussion of the results we shall follow the work of Aston. He started with an accuracy of one-tenth of 1 per cent in his measurements. Continuing the work of Thomson, he applied his mass spectrograph to neon gas (atomic weight, 20.20). The unexpected result of this experiment was that at the spot of the photographic plate computed for the atomic weight 20.20 no trace of a ray showed up—an indication that such atoms, although supposedly well-known, do not exist at all. Instead there were revealed on the plate two types of atom, unknown previously, with whole-number atomic weights, namely, 20.00 and 22.00. (See the mass spectrum of Fig. 6.13, taken by the parabola method; it even shows a faint trace of the very rare Ne 21.00.) Their intensities are observed as 9 for the ray 20.00 and 1 for the ray 22.00. Thus the average atomic weight results as $(9 \times 20.00 + 1 \times 22.00)/10 = 20.20$, just the well-known value of the "chemical atomic weight" of neon. This observation leads to the conclusion that neon gas is a mixture of two kinds of atom with different masses that cannot be distinguished by their chemical and spectroscopic properties. Hence to both types of atom we must attribute the same nuclear charge, *i.e.*, the same position in the periodic table of elements.   Aston gave to these different types of atom of the same element the name "isotopes," meaning atoms that have the same position in the periodic table.

When applying the same analysis to other elements, Aston found the same result over and over again.   For example, chlorine (atomic weight 35.46) consists of the isotopes 35.00 and 37.00 in such proportions that their average is 35.46.   Figure 16.3 shows the more complex mass spectra of tin and xenon.   The general law, called the whole-number rule, states that *each chemical atomic weight that deviates from a whole number is due to a mixture of isotopes, each of them with a whole-number atomic weight.*

116 120 124

Tin   Xenon

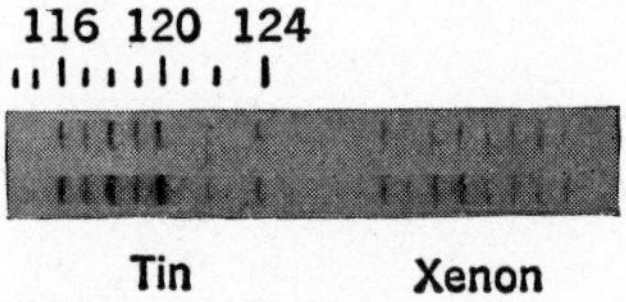

Fig. 16.3. Mass spectra of tin and xenon.   (*After Aston.*)

Only hydrogen noticeably deviates from this rule; its atomic weight 1.008 is not due to a mixture but the individual hydrogen atoms (see Sec. 16.5).   At present nearly 300 stable isotopes are known.   (The much more numerous *radioactive* isotopes will be discussed in Sec. 18.7.)

Aston's discovery is of such fundamental importance that it necessitates a new definition of an element.   We now define elements and isotopes as follows: *Elements* are the ultimate constituents beyond which matter cannot be analyzed by chemical processes (or can be analyzed only to a very small extent).   *Isotopes* are the ultimate particles into which elements can be analyzed by the determination of e/m for charged particles, as in the mass spectrograph.   Analysis by the mass spectrograph shows that atoms of the same element may differ in their nuclear masses, although they have the same nuclear charge.   However, atoms of the same isotope have the nuclear charge and mass in common.

It had been known for a long time that many elements have whole-number atomic weights when that of oxygen is defined as 16.0000. Examples are helium (4.00), fluorine (19.00), and sodium (23.00).   These elements are not analyzed into several isotopes (except possibly into one isotope of major abundance and one or several very rare isotopes).   In some cases the same integer serves as atomic weight for the isotopes of several elements.   For example, the atomic weight 40 is found among the isotopes of argon, calcium, and potassium.   Such atoms of the same atomic weight but different atomic numbers are called "isobars."   A survey of stable and unstable isotopes is given below on Fig. 18.4.

The discovery of isotopes makes it evident that the chemical atomic weight of an element is not a property of individual atoms but represents an average of the atomic weights of the several isotopes.   Here we remember that the chemist is able to demonstrate the periodic properties of the elements only after certain rearrangements, reversing, *e.g.*, the order that would be given to argon and potassium by their atomic weights (Sec. 13.1). These rearrangements are strongly supported by the X-ray spectra of the elements (Sec. 14.2*b*). Now, finally, we find an excuse for the rearrangements in the consideration that the chemical atomic weights are not fundamental constants of nature. The relative abundances of isotopes which affect the chemical atomic weights can even be changed within certain limits by manipulations at the laboratory.

16.3. Structure of Matter. As early as 1815, Prout had noticed that the atomic weights show a marked preference for whole-number values. He had suggested the important hypothesis that the atoms of all elements are built of the same fundamental particle, presumably the lightest atom, hydrogen, with the atomic weight 1. Thus carbon would contain 12 of these particles, nitrogen 14, oxygen 16, etc. This hypothesis became untenable as more accurate values of the atomic weights became known, and many deviations from the simple rule were found. Aston's discovery revives the whole-number rule and so gives striking evidence in favor of the hypothesis that all matter is constituted of one or a few fundamental particles. The great progress due to this idea is evident when we compare it with the older idea of the nature of matter. In chemistry, the infinite variety of all substances is analyzed into elements. Here we used to assume 92 different types of atom. The discovery of isotopes seems to complicate our picture greatly because so many elements, in turn, are analyzed into different types of atom, the isotopes. Now we seem to have several hundred different types of atom. The great simplification, finally, comes in through the whole-number rule, which indicates one or a few fundamental particles as building blocks of all matter.

What is the fundamental particle? The obvious guess attributing this role to hydrogen leads into two difficulties. (1) Since the atomic weight of hydrogen is appreciably larger than unity (1.008), 4 hydrogen atoms are heavier than 1 helium atom (atomic weight 4.00). (2) Since the helium nucleus has only one-half the charge supplied by 4 hydrogen nuclei (Sec. 9.1), these are unable to form 1 helium nucleus.

We begin with the discussion of the second difficulty. It is solved by the discovery of the *neutron*, a particle of nearly the same mass as the proton but uncharged (Sec. 18.2*b*). This discovery suggests the assumption that all composite nuclei are constituted of protons and neutrons, *e.g.*, the helium nucleus consists of 2 protons and 2 neutrons.

The atomic weight of the neutron turns out to be even slightly larger than that of the proton (Sec. 18.2*c*). Hence our first difficulty persists in that 2 protons and 2 neutrons represent a larger atomic weight than a helium nucleus. This difficulty is removed by invoking Einstein's principle of the equivalence of mass and energy (Sec. 6.4). Let us consider the separation of a helium nucleus into the four constituent particles.

To overcome the binding we must spend energy. Einstein's principle predicts that this energy which is finally stored in the separated particles (2 protons and 2 neutrons) gives to these particles additional mass and hence a total atomic weight larger than that of the helium nucleus. The accurate values of all atomic weights involved (Sec. 18.2c) permit the computation of the energy of separation. The result (28.2×10^6 ev; see Prob. 18.7) is nearly 7 million times the energy of dissociation of the hydrogen molecule, which has a value typical for chemical energies. This is the first example of the large energies inherent in nuclear changes.

It is not claimed that this argument represents an experimental confirmation of Einstein's principle. That would be the case only if we were able to perform an independent measurement of the energy predicted by the principle. Later, when discussing nuclear reactions, we shall find processes in which all energies are accessible to measurement. They will provide a test of the principle (Sec. 18.7). It is a fascinating idea that the same vast amount of energy is *gained in the combination* of 4 hydrogen atoms to form 1 helium atom. It has been computed that the energy gained, if we should so combine all hydrogen atoms contained in a glass of water, would be sufficient to drive a transatlantic liner across the ocean (see Prob. 19.11). But it must be remembered that this result is based solely on atomic weights and their interpretation on the basis of Einstein's principle. There is no laboratory experiment known in which the combination of all hydrogen contained in a glass of water is actually performed, or which even shows some promise that it can be performed. We shall come back to this process in the chapter on energy production in nuclear reactions (Sec. 19.7).

From the study of nuclear reactions (Chap. 18), we shall find that, within nuclear physics, the energy of separation of helium has a very high value. This indicates a very high stability of the helium nucleus. (We are familiar with the idea that the stability of a structure is expressed by the energy required to break it up; Sec. 13.3.) This stability, here derived from the atomic weights, is confirmed by other observations. In the chapter on the scattering of alpha particles (Sec. 9.1), we argued that they are identical with helium nuclei. They are projectiles that are able to break up other nuclei; but no such experiment is known in which an alpha particle itself goes to pieces. It is a curious coincidence that helium has the most stable *electronic* structure (Sec. 13.3) as well as the most stable *nuclear* structure, of all elements.

The general assumption is that any nucleus consists of as many protons as are given by its atomic number, with the addition of as many neutrons as are required by its atomic weight. Hence the isotopes of any one element differ by the numbers of neutrons present. Protons and neutrons as constituents of nuclei are called "nucleons." The whole-number atomic weight which indicates the total number of nucleons present in any isotope is called its "mass number." The conventional notation gives both the mass number as a *superscript after* the chemical symbol and the atomic number as a *subscript before* this symbol. For example, the two isotopes of neon are written $_{10}Ne^{20}$ and $_{10}Ne^{22}$.

The determinations of the nuclear sizes of many atoms (Sec. 9.3) lead to the result that their nuclear *volumes* are approximately proportional to their nuclear *masses*. Hence the *densities* of all nuclei are nearly the same. The value is as large as 10^{14} g/cm³.

Although in the chapter on Isotopes we apply Einstein's principle only to the *mass defects, i.e.*, to small quantities of the order of a few thousandths of a proton mass, a convenient standard is obtained by computing the energy equivalent of the mass belonging to unit atomic weight (see Prob. 16.10). The result is 931 Mev. However, the use of this unit does not imply that the exchange between mass and energy has ever been observed in such large quantities. *Million electron volt*, abbreviated Mev, is the conventional energy unit in nuclear physics. It is applied as well to the energies of charged particles accelerated by high voltage as to any other energy, *e.g.*, of quanta or nuclear reactions. The energies of cosmic rays are measured in *billion electron volt* (Bev).

Positive-ray analysis may impress the student, to begin with, as a remote field of physics without any general interest, merely indicating that the rays consist of charged atoms and molecules. Here the great importance of this field becomes manifest. Positive rays give us a more profound understanding of the nature of matter by revealing the fact that the great variety of the different elements known in chemistry are actually built of one or a few building blocks. Moreover, the example of hydrogen and helium shows that positive-ray analysis, interpreted by Einstein's principle of the equivalence of mass and energy, gives evidence of the relative energies of nuclei. When accepting Einstein's principle, we discard the principle of conservation of mass which for centuries had been accepted as one of the cornerstones of physics and chemistry. We applied Einstein's principle only to the slight *excess beyond unity* evident in the atomic weight of hydrogen. One may go a step farther and assume that *all matter* is an accumulation of energy. Then the principle of conservation of energy fully replaces the two old principles, which seemed to be independent: that of mass and that of energy. No exception has been found, however, to the principle of conservation of electric charge.

16.4. Deviations from the Whole-number Rule. The whole-number rule is the outcome of the high technical development of the mass spectrograph. The further development of this instrument enabled Aston to measure the relative weights of isotopes with still higher accuracy. In this way he discovered that all isotopes deviate from the rule by noticeable amounts. Because these deviations are highly significant indications of nuclear energies, many of them, in particular those of the light elements, have been determined with a special mass spectrograph of high precision designed by Bainbridge. We shall mainly apply his numerical results.

Figure 16.4 demonstrates the accuracy of Bainbridge's results. The O atom and the CH_4 molecule, although differing in their atomic weights only in the higher decimal places, appear widely separated. The same is true for the ordinary hydrogen molecule and the heavy hydrogen atom, which we shall discuss in the next section. If we define the atomic weight of oxygen O = 16.00000, the atomic weight of helium becomes He = 4.00389. Whoever has tried to improve the accuracy of a measurement will appreciate this successful extension to three more significant

FIG. 16.4. Mass spectrum. The molecule CH_4 and the atom O have both the same mass number 16; the light hydrogen molecule and the deuterium atom have both the same mass number 2. The mass defects are evident. (*Courtesy of K. T. Bainbridge.*)

figures. The accuracy is so high that one must take into account the fact that the positive-ray method furnishes the atomic weight of a *charged* atom like He^+, which is less than the atomic weight of the *neutral* atom by the contribution of 1 electron, *i.e.*, 0.000549.

Now we find that the mass of 4 helium atoms (4 He = 16.01556) exceeds the mass of 1 oxygen atom (O = 16.00000). Each one of the two systems has 8 external electrons. Therefore, the larger mass of the four heliums must be attributed to their nuclei, not to external electrons. Consistently, we explain it by the same idea by which we correlated 1 helium and 4 hydrogens, *i.e.*, the equivalence of mass and energy. The corresponding computation leads to the result that an energy of 14.49 Mev is required to separate an oxygen nucleus into 4 helium nuclei.

Aston applied his analysis to all elements accessible to his method. All show deviations from the whole-number rule. So we have the strange situation of a vast array of atomic weights, stretching from 1 to 238, all figures very nearly being whole numbers, but all deviating from whole numbers in the third and higher decimal places. The nearest whole number indicating the number of fundamental building blocks, was called by Aston the "mass number" (= 4 for helium).   The deviation from the whole number (atomic weight − mass number) is called the "mass defect" (= 0.00389 for helium).   Aston plotted the quotient, mass defect/mass number, which he called the "packing fraction," against the mass number.   His results are given in the curve of Fig. 16.5, which shows no trace of periodicity, as would be expected since we attributed the *periodicity* of the table of elements to the *external* electronic structure.   It is a striking fact that a smooth curve, although branching on the side of the light elements, represents all packing fractions.   In this respect the nuclei show a much simpler regularity than the electronic structures.

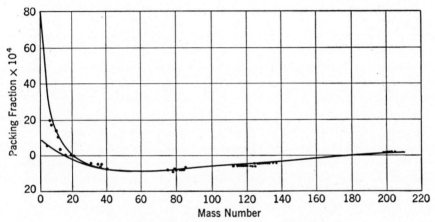

FIG. 16.5. Packing-fraction curve.   (*After Aston.*)

The zero value attributed to the packing fraction of oxygen has no physical significance since it is due to the arbitrary definition of the atomic weight of oxygen as a whole number.   Only the difference between the values belonging to two elements has significance.   This difference indicates the energies *spent* or *liberated* by the various nuclear reactions.   (This application of the curve will be demonstrated by Probs. 16.9, 18.3, 18.4, and 18.7.)   Our computation makes it evident that energy is *liberated* when $_2He^4$ form $_8O^{16}$, or $_8O^{16}$ form $_{16}S^{32}$.   In general the formation of a nucleus with a smaller packing fraction liberates energy.   The same idea applies to the right wing of Aston's curve. There the situation is complicated by the fact that a heavy element, *e.g.*, the uranium isotope $_{92}U^{235}$, cannot simply split into two lighter elements like $_{36}Kr^{84}$ and $_{56}Ba^{138}$.   Although their nuclear charges add up to 92, the sum of their mass numbers, 222, is deficient as compared with the mass number 235 of U.   (We found a related difficulty in the relation between $_1H^1$ and $_2He^4$; see Sec. 16.3.)   We shall remove this difficulty by assuming neutrons as essential building blocks of the atoms. The accurate determination of their atomic weight will be discussed below (Sec. 18.2c). This assumption will allow us to express the same information, which here is presented as Aston's packing fraction, in terms of the "average binding energy per nuclear particle" (Prob. 18.7).

Great practical interest is connected with the question: How can we *gain* energy? In other words, which are the nuclear processes in which energy is *liberated?* The general answer is closely connected with the slope of the curve of packing fractions. Let us first consider the simple case in which several light nuclei supply both the charge and mass of a heavy nucleus. This is the case for 3_2He^4 forming $_6C^{12}$ or 4_2He^4 forming $_8O^{16}$, etc. In this simple case the packing-fraction curve makes evident that the constituent nuclei represent a larger total mass than the product nucleus, hence that energy is *liberated* when several light nuclei *form one heavy nucleus.* This will turn out to be true even in the cases in which neutrons have to be added to form the heavy nucleus. The most important case is *"fusion"* of 2 protons and 2 neutrons to form a helium nucleus with the liberation of a large amount of energy.

Qualitatively we may apply the same argument to the right wing of the curve, *i.e.*, to the heavy elements, although here the situation is complicated by the numbers of neutrons built into the various nuclei. On this basis we reach the following conclusion. Since the packing fractions of the heavy elements are larger than those of the intermediate ones, the heavy elements contain stored energy; hence energy may be *liberated* when a heavy nucleus *disintegrates* to form several light fragments. Thus the curve indicates that heavy nuclei are explosives. They may *disintegrate spontaneously* like radium and many other heavy nuclei. Or we may induce their disintegration in a process called *fission.*

The deviations from the whole-number rule represent a case in which the painstaking exploration of the higher decimal place results in a great new discovery which is not anticipated from the less accurate figures.

16.5. Abundances of Isotopes. The atomic weights of the *chemical elements* (with very few exceptions) are as sharply reproducible as the accuracy of the measurements permits. Therefore, before the discovery of isotopes, these atomic weights were considered to be fundamental constants. Now we know that an important factor determining a chemical atomic weight is the relative abundance of the isotopes which, by a refined technique, we may well alter. The fundamental significance is now attributed to the atomic weights of the individual *isotopes*, as discussed in Sec. 16.4. It is a striking fact that, with few exceptions, for each element the relative abundance of the isotopes is the same once and for all. As a matter of fact, the measurement of the relative abundance combined with the atomic weights of the isotopes provides a very accurate determination of the chemical atomic weight.   The relative abundance is measured by the currents registered in the ionization chamber.   Figure 16.6 shows the relative abundance of the mercury isotopes.

Are the relative abundances so measured characteristic only for the earth?   The little material that may serve to answer this question is derived from the investigation of meteorites, which presumably are members of the solar system, too.   They show the same relative abundances as the elements known in the laboratory.

A striking exception to the rule is given by lead.   Figure 16.7a shows the isotopic constitution of "ordinary" lead, i.e., the lead found in many

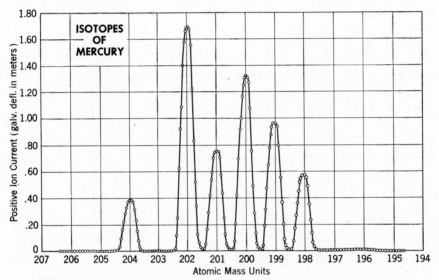

FIG. 16.6. Abundance of mercury isotopes.   (*Courtesy of A. O. Nier.*)

ores.   Entirely different is the constitution of lead found associated with radioactive elements.   As we shall see in the next chapter, these elements decompose in many steps, which end with lead as the stable product. Figure 16.7b shows the constitution of lead found at Katanga in the Belgian Congo, one of the rich sources of uranium and radium.   Katanga lead shows a striking preeminence of the isotope 206 which has only a rather low abundance in ordinary lead.   We shall come back to this fact when discussing the radioactive series (Sec. 17.4).   Closely connected with the case of lead is that of helium, since radioactive decay produces both Pb^{206} and, by alpha emission, He^4.   Thus it is understood that the helium contained in radioactive minerals is exclusively He^4. The helium contained in the air is largely He^4 with a small admixture of He^3; presumably the He^4 originates from the weathering of rocks and the He³ from cosmic-ray processes (see Chap. 20).   In nonradioactive minerals the ratio of the helium isotopes varies widely.

In the elements C, O, N, and S the relative abundances of the respective isotopes vary very slightly.   But this effect is not due to the terrestrial origin of certain isotopes (as Pb²⁰⁶ and He⁴) but to chemical processes occurring through geological time.   For example, matter that has been dissolved in water and later deposited shows a very slight preference for

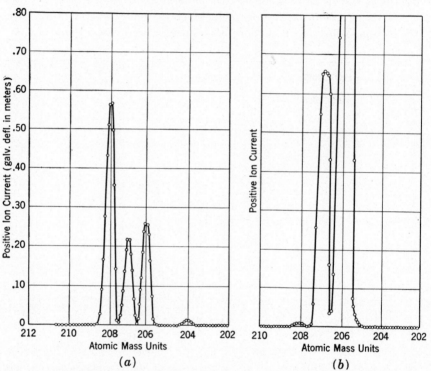

Fɪɢ. 16.7. Abundance of the isotopes of lead.   (*Courtesy of A. O. Nier.*)   (*a*) Ordinary lead; (*b*) Katanga lead.

the rare isotope O¹⁸ (see Sec. 16.9).   Apart from these minor exceptions, it appears that in the early geological period in which the minerals were formed, a certain isotopic constitution prevailed all over the whole material now accessible to our investigation.   This constitution remained unchanged through the ages except for the few elements that are spontaneously disintegrating and so giving rise to the gradual formation of elements like Katanga lead.

In many elements, in addition to the well-known isotopes, rare isotopes have been discovered.   The most important example is the rare heavy isotope of hydrogen $_1H^2$, frequently called "deuterium"; its nucleus is called the "deuteron." Its existence was inferred by a slight discrepancy between the values of the atomic weight of hydrogen determined by chemical methods and by the mass spectrograph. However, the mass spectrograph used was not so sensitive that it showed the heavy isotope. Urey, Murphy, and Brickwedde (1932) went through a laborious procedure intended to increase the concentration of the heavy isotope, if it were present. They relied on the fact predicted by theory that a light atom should evaporate more readily than a heavy atom. Hence they evaporated a large quantity of liquid hydrogen and searched the residue for heavy hydrogen. They investigated the line spectrum which, for the heavy isotope, should show all Balmer lines slightly displaced to shorter wavelengths, as predicted by Bohr's theory of the relative motion of the nucleus (Sec. 10.6b). Actually, the displaced lines appeared and proved the existence of a new isotope in the element hydrogen, which had seemed so thoroughly explored. Heavy hydrogen has a relative abundance of 1/4,500. Its effect on the chemical atomic weight is small but just noticeable. However, the striking deviation of the chemical atomic weight of hydrogen from unity (Sec. 16.3) is not due to the presence of deuterium but is a property of the most abundant isotope $_1H^1$. A still heavier isotope, $_1H^3$, called tritium, is radioactive and does not occur in nature (Sec. 18.7).

Many other rare isotopes have been found. $_{10}Ne^{21}$ (abundance $\frac{1}{4}$ per cent) is evident in Fig. 6.13. $_6C^{13}$ and $_7N^{15}$ are other examples. Oxygen has two rare isotopes, $_8O^{17}$ (0.04 per cent) and $_8O^{18}$ (0.20 per cent). This fact causes a curious ambiguity in the definition of our standard. The chemist attributes the atomic weight 16.0000 to the chemical element containing all three isotopes. (This definition is not absolutely sharp, since the relative abundance of the heavy rare isotopes of O is slightly variable as discussed in Sec. 16.9.) On the other hand, the mass spectroscopist attributes the value 16.00000 to the most abundant isotope, the only isotope recorded on most mass spectra. Hence he computes for the mixture, i.e., the natural element, the atomic weight 16.0044. For this reason the atomic weights derived from mass spectra must be corrected by the factor 0.999725 in order to convert them to the scale used in chemistry (Prob. 16.8).

In this section we have restricted ourselves to the consideration of the isotopes found in nature. In the chapter on the transmutation of elements we shall study many new isotopes produced in the laboratory. We reported only the numerical values of the relative abundances. What processes are responsible for determining these abundances remains a mystery. In the section on energy production in stars (Sec. 19.6) we shall find a partial answer to this question.

16.6. Separation of Isotopes. For many purposes of research and practical application (see Sec. 16.9) a separation of isotopes in larger quantities is desired. It is true that the *mass spectrograph* provides a complete separation; but it yields only small quantities. This, at least, was considered to be a fact before the Second World War. In the meantime, the rare uranium isotope $_{92}U^{235}$ (abundance 0.7 per cent) has been separated by the mass spectrograph in quantities not made public but sufficient to destroy a city.

Fractional distillation of hydrogen has been mentioned as increasing the abundance of the heavy isotope in the residue. A complete separation of the neon isotopes has been accomplished by *gaseous diffusion*. When a steady stream of mercury vapor is maintained in a glass tube and neon gas is diffusing against the stream, the lighter isotope passes at the higher rate because of the larger speed of its atoms (Sec. 3.2). In order to apply diffusion to the isotope separation of solid elements, gaseous compounds are formed, such as UF_6 for the separation of the uranium isotopes (Sec. 19.4). Related to this method is the separation by the *flow of gas through a porous clay pipe*. In order to explain this process, we go back to the well-known determination of the density of a gas by "effusion." A very small hole is drilled through the wall of a glass bulb containing two gases. If the hole is small as compared to the mean free path, we predict the rate of escape of one or the other gas by considering molecular collisions with the wall. Any molecule that happens to hit the hole escapes. Light molecules, since endowed with higher speed than heavy ones [see Eq. (3.5)], hit the wall more frequently and so have a priority for escape. Light hydrogen will escape more readily than heavy hydrogen. The residue will show an increasing concentration of heavy hydrogen.

The separation of light and heavy hydrogen is comparatively easy since the mass ratio of the two isotopes is as large as $2:1$. Even in nature the relative abundance of the two is not strictly constant, and their physical properties are noticeably different. For example, heavy water, *i.e.*, water built of 2 heavy hydrogen atoms combined with 1 ordinary oxygen atom, has a melting point 3.8°C higher than ordinary water. Much more difficult is the isolation of the rare isotopes C^{13}, N^{15}, and O^{18}. Their great importance will be discussed in Sec. 16.9.

16.7. Report on Nuclear Magnetic Moments. The magnetic moment of a nucleus is a property that gives important evidence concerning its structure. As briefly mentioned in Sec. 11.1e, the hyperfine structure of spectral lines allows the determination of the spins and magnetic moments of some nuclei. One may predict that *nuclear* magnetic moments are of much smaller order of magnitude than *electronic* magnetic moments, since quantum theory postulates *mechanical angular momenta* of the same order of magnitude (multiples or half-multiples of $h/2\pi$) for electrons and nuclei. The same value of angular momentum would impart a much slower rotation, hence presumably a smaller magnetic moment than that of electrons to the larger mass of any nucleus.

Only a brief report will be given on modern measurements of nuclear magnetic moments. They are based on the theoretical prediction that, in a stable molecule like hydrogen or water or paraffin, the *electronic* structure has no resulting magnetic moment since all moments of the individual electrons (orbital and spin moments) cancel each other. Hence only the *nuclei* are responsible for the resulting magnetic moments. As the simplest example, let us consider hydrogen. Suppose that hydrogen nuclei are subjected to an external, constant magnetic field H. Quantum theory predicts that each hydrogen nucleus, representing a tiny magnet (magnetic moment $= M$), has two quantized orientations, parallel or antiparallel to this field (see Sec. 11.1e). These two positions differ by a certain energy that is computed as the energy required to turn a magnetic needle of moment M in the magnetic field H from the parallel into the antiparallel position. The computation (see Prob. 16.13) gives this energy as $2MH$. The nucleus may change its position either from parallel to antiparallel or vice versa. We are interested in the associated absorption of radiative energy. Its frequency ν is predicted by Bohr's quantum condition $h\nu = 2MH$.

For the magnetic fields available at the laboratory this frequency lies in the radio-frequency range. Here the experimental problem of observing this frequency, like that of an absorption spectrum, cannot be solved with the familiar technique (Sec. 12.4a) since no spectrographs are available for these frequencies. Most of the accurate information that we now have on nuclear magnetic moments is due to Rabi and his collaborators (beginning 1936), who used their elegant method of molecular beams. Omitting the description of their experiment, we give an outline of the device recently used by Purcell, Torrey, and Pound (1945) and its application to the hydrogen nucleus. A small coil of wire, which is part of a resonance circuit (frequency 29.8×10^6 cycles/sec), surrounds the sample to be tested, *e.g.*, paraffin, which provides a great density of hydrogen atoms. (The carbon atoms contained in the paraffin are ineffective.) Thus the hydrogen nuclei are subjected to alternating magnetic fields of the high frequency just mentioned. The coil is put into an adjustable magnetic field H which, as explained, imparts quantized orientations and thus a characteristic frequency ν to the nuclei. If this frequency coincides with the high frequency of the circuit, the nuclei absorb energy. Observation shows that, at a sharply defined value of the magnetic field, in this case $H = 7,000$ oersteds, the paraffin contained in the coil increases its apparent resistance. For these values of frequency and magnetic field the above equation yields a value for the magnetic moment of the proton as

$$M = 1.406 \times 10^{-23} \text{ erg/oersted}$$

As expected, this value is of a smaller order of magnitude than the magnetic moment of the electron, which is $\frac{1}{2} \times$ Bohr's magneton (Sec. 10.5e), 4.64×10^{-21} erg/oersted. For nuclear magnetic moments, the conventional unit is the "nuclear magneton," defined as Bohr's magneton multiplied by the mass ratio of electron and proton. In this unit the magnetic moment of the proton is 2.79.

The new method described here is applied to the precise measurement of the magnetic moments of many nuclei. The resulting values are characteristic of the individual isotopes of an element; *e.g.*, protons and deuterons have different magnetic moments. The inadequacy of our present theoretical concept is evident from the fact that the neutron, in spite of its lack of electric charge, has a magnetic moment.

This fruitful field of research has contributed a great deal of evidence regarding an important nuclear property. The great accuracy of the results, which are given to six significant figures, reveals minor perturbing effects due to the very weak magnetic fields of neighboring nuclei. The theoretical interpretation of such effects is of great importance for our knowledge of liquids and solids.

16.8. General Rules. The complete list of stable isotopes gives evidence of the following rules: (1) Many elements of even atomic number have many stable isotopes, the most numerous being those of tin, which has 10 stable isotopes. (2) The elements of odd atomic number have few, not more than two, stable isotopes. (3) The majority of atoms have even numbers of protons and even numbers of neutrons. (4) Elements with odd numbers of protons combined with odd numbers of neutrons are very rare. There are four cases among the light elements. The reader can identify them on the list given in Appendix 5.

The preference for even numbers is striking. The most common combination (even numbers of protons and of neutrons) is experimentally distinguished by the resulting spin zero. This result suggests that the nucleons combine in pairs, each pair not necessarily consisting of 1 proton and 1 neutron. (In the combination of 1 single proton with 1 single neutron, known as the deuteron, the two constituents line up their spins, each $\frac{1}{2} \times h/2\pi$, to form $h/2\pi$.)

Discussing the electronic structure of atoms, we found certain "magic numbers," *i.e.*, the atomic numbers of the rare gases, which indicate a preferred stability of structures attributed to the closing of certain "shells" of electrons. They are responsible for the periodicity that is evident in the chemical and spectroscopic behavior of the atoms. Are similar magic numbers evident in the nuclear structure? A much less

pronounced evidence was discovered by M. G. Mayer (1950).   Among
the light atoms the packing fractions are so accurately known that we
can recognize He, O, and Ca as more stable than their neighbors.   This
evidence supplies the nuclear "magic numbers" 2, 8, and 20.   Calcium
is further distinguished by having the unusually large number of six
stable isotopes.   This quality may serve as a plausible, new criterion to
be applied to the heavier elements.   Thus, for example, we single out tin
(atomic number 50), which has the record number of 10 stable isotopes.
Here we become aware of another property of the atomic number.   While
the *proton number* (= atomic number) 50 shows up in combination with
as many as 10 different numbers of neutrons, the same *neutron number*
(= 50) shows up in combination with many different proton numbers
(five).   This symmetry between protons and neutrons is corroborated
when we go back to calcium; while the proton number 20 occurs in combination with six different numbers of neutrons, the neutron number 20
occurs in combination with five different proton numbers.   Therefore, we
may use the neutron number as a criterion for a magic number.   The
neutron number 28 is unusually common (five cases), while the proton
number 28 (nickel) is as common, showing five isotopes (admittedly not
an unusually large number).   The neutron number 82 is unusually
common, as it occurs in seven stable nuclei.   Finally 126 is evident as
a magic number from the unusually large energy that is liberated by the
binding of the 126th neutron.   This argument gives us the list of magic
numbers: 2, 8, 20, 28, 50, 82, 126.   These numbers of protons *or* neutrons
give unusual stability to the nucleus.

While, to begin with, this list seems to be based on arbitrary definitions,
it is corroborated by some different lines of evidence.   They are provided
by the nuclear spins and the nuclear volumes.   The nuclear volumes are
inferred from very small shifts of the spectral lines, the smallest shift
indicating the smallest volume.   There is some evidence that the nuclei
endowed with magic numbers have smaller volumes than those with the
next higher numbers (Kopfermann).

16.9. Applications.   Rare isotopes find important applications as
"*tracers*" in physical, chemical, and biological research.   For example,
suppose we want to trace the distribution in the animal body of a certain
carbohydrate, occurring in the food.   This compound is prepared with
carbon that contains an artificial extra abundance of the heavy isotope
C^{13}, and the food containing this compound is fed to mice.   After a
certain time, the mice are killed, and the carbon, extracted from the
various organs, is analyzed in the mass spectrograph.   One or the other
organ may show an extra-high abundance of the heavy isotope and so
indicate that this organ is a preferred consumer of the carbohydrate
under investigation.

Here, as in similar experiments, we rely on the fact that the various isotopes of one element show the same chemical properties, since these are determined by the *electronic structure* common to the isotopes, and not by the *nuclear masses*. Hydrogen represents the only case in which this assumption may be questioned, since, in a reaction, the mass ratio 2/1 of the isotopes may give a slight priority to one or the other isotope.

A very slight priority for one of the O isotopes is utilized in Urey's measurement of the temperatures at which certain rocks were formed. Let us assume that water has contained the isotopes O^{16} and O^{18} throughout the geological periods in unchanged relative abundance. In the precipitation of carbonates, however, O^{18} is slightly preferred by virtue of its higher atomic weight. This preference depends on the temperature. Urey measures the relative abundances of the two isotopes in the oxygen of carbonates deposited in rocks by organisms. From these data he is able to derive the temperature at which the rock was formed. He applies a calibration that is based on theory and confirmed by laboratory experiments, the higher abundance of O^{18} being associated with the lower temperature. It is surprising that rocks furnish the equivalent of thermometer readings made at the time of their formation with an accuracy of a few degrees centigrade.

In organic chemical analysis the *isotope dilution method* is based on the following argument. The organic compound A can be separated from the mixture $A + B$, but only with an unknown yield. In order to determine this yield, we prepare the compound A with a *known* extra abundance of a rare isotope and add a *known* quantity of this preparation to the mixture. When we now separate A from the mixture, this product A reveals the yield by the relative abundance of the rare isotope. Later we shall discuss *radioactive* isotopes as tracers (Sec. 19.8). The method here discussed, dealing with *stable*, rare isotopes, has particular value for oxygen and nitrogen, both elements that have no radioactive isotopes of convenient half-lives.

The experiments discussed above give only special examples of a highly developed field which makes the mass spectrograph indispensable in chemical and biological research.

SUMMARY OF CHAPTER 16

By positive-ray analysis, Aston (1921) discovered that neon (atomic weight 20.20) does not contain individual atoms with the atomic weight 20.20 but consists of a mixture of two types of atom with the whole-number atomic weights 20.00 and 22.00 and relative abundances 9 and 1. This gives the average atomic weight 20.20 in agreement with the well-established chemical value. In general, any element with an atomic weight deviating from a whole number is analyzed into several types of atom, each of whole-number atomic weight. They are called "isotopes." A slight exception is given by hydrogen whose atomic weight 1.008 belongs to the individual atoms. Isotopes of the same element have the same nuclear charge, the same chemical and spectroscopic properties (with minor exceptions), but different nuclear masses.

This discovery revives Prout's hypothesis stating that all atoms are built of one or a few fundamental particles, the outstanding particle presumably being the hydrogen atom. However, the helium nucleus cannot be composed of 4 hydrogen nuclei, since these would supply twice the charge required. This difficulty is solved by the discovery of the *neutron*, an uncharged particle of nearly the same mass as the proton. The helium nucleus is supposed to consist of 2 protons and 2 neutrons. Another difficulty is the fact that these four particles have a total mass slightly larger than a helium nucleus. This discrepancy is explained by Einstein's principle of the equivalence of mass and energy. The larger mass of the four separate particles is a measure of the energy required to take the helium nucleus apart (28.2 Mev). Any nucleus is supposed to be built of as many protons as are given by its atomic number with the addition of as many neutrons as are required by its atomic weight.

A further improvement of technique results in atomic weights given to six significant figures. In most atomic weights the third figure after the decimal point shows a deviation from the whole-number rule. Aston plotted the packing fraction (= mass defect — mass number) against the mass number. Thus he found a simple curve without a trace of the periodicity evident in chemistry and spectroscopy. From the data given by Aston's curve energies of nuclear separation (*e.g.*, $O \rightarrow 4He$) can be computed. The curve gives evidence of the instability of elements, the lightest elements tending to combine, the heaviest elements tending to disintegrate, and energy is liberated by both processes.

The elements have well-defined chemical atomic weights. This fact indicates that the relative abundances of the isotopes are once and for all the same. A notable exception is given by lead found in uranium minerals, presumably present as the end-product of radioactive decay.

Many elements have rare isotopes. Examples are $_1H^2$, $_6C^{13}$, $_7N^{15}$, $_8O^{17}$, $_8O^{18}$. Here only stable isotopes are considered, not the radioactive isotopes to be discussed in Chap. 18.

The isotopes of an element can be partly or wholly separated. Rare isotopes are valuable as tracers in physical, chemical, and biological research.

Nuclear magnetic moments are measured by subjecting a substance that has no resulting *electronic* magnetic moment to an external magnetic field. This causes quantized orientations of the nuclei, which differ by sharply defined energies. Transitions between such quantized states are produced by quanta of the corresponding energy, *i.e.*, by radiation in the radio-frequency range.

PROBLEMS

16.1. *Mass spectrograph.* In Dempster's mass spectrograph an ion beam is bent into a circle of 5.00 cm radius by a magnetic induction of 3,840 gauss. What voltages must be applied to accelerate the following types of singly charged ion to such a velocity that they are recorded: (*a*) $_3Li^6$; (*b*) $_3Li^7$; (*c*) $_{19}K^{39}$; (*d*) $_{19}K^{41}$? See Appendix 5.

16.2. *Mass spectrograph.* In Dempster's mass spectrograph (Fig. 16.2) ions belonging to an impurity are accelerated by a potential difference of 772 volts and, after passing the slit, bent by a magnetic induction of 3,840 gauss into a half-circle of 5.00 cm radius. What is the nature of these ions? Assume singly charged ions.

16.3. *Resolving power.* In one of Dempster's mass spectrographs, positive ions, after being accelerated by an electric field, are bent by a magnetic induction of 3,840 gauss into a half circle of 5 cm radius. Discuss the resolving power of this instrument on the following basis: Suppose that the first slit is 0.5 mm wide and that each positive ray, when incident on the second slit, has the same width. Furthermore, suppose that, at the place of the second slit, Dempster is able to resolve rays that do not overlap and even are separated. This means that some "darkness" exists between such rays. For this to occur, they must be more than 0.5 mm apart (measured from the middle of one ray to the middle of the other). Can he resolve lithium isotopes (mass numbers 6 and 7)? Can he resolve mercury isotopes (mass numbers 200 and 201)?

HINT: For given values of voltage and magnetic induction, two adjacent rays belong to two adjacent isotopes. Both rays emerge from the first slit. They are separated after passing through one-half circle because their masses differ. When they come near the second slit, they are assumed to have a width of 0.5 mm each. Assume that one ray (*e.g.*, Li^6) just hits the second slit ($2r = 10$ cm, V to be computed). Where does the ray that belongs to the other isotope hit the plate into which the slit is cut? If, for the same voltage, darkness exists between the two rays, these two isotopes can be resolved.

16.4. *Atomic weight from mass spectrum.* Calculate the atomic weight of natural mercury by taking the abundances of the isotopes from Fig. 16.6. Disregard the deviations from whole numbers. Use the slide rule. Compare with Appendix 4.

16.5. *Abundances from chemical atomic weight.* Calculate the relative abundances of the neon isotopes (20.00 and 22.00) on the basis of the "chemical" atomic weight of neon, 20.18.

16.6. *Packing fractions I.* Using Appendix 5, calculate the packing fractions of $_1H^1$, $_2He^4$, $_8O^{16}$, and $_{15}P^{31}$. Satisfy yourself that they fit on Aston's diagram (Fig. 16.5).

16.7. *Packing fractions II.* Using Fig. 16.5, calculate the atomic weight of $_{18}A^{40}$. Estimate the accuracy of your result.

16.8. *Scale of atomic weights.* Compute the atomic weight of natural oxygen (abundances of isotopes, see Appendix 5) in the "physical scale" in which the atomic weight of the most abundant isotope is defined as exactly 16.

16.9. *Nuclear energy.* How much energy (in Mev) is required to separate (*a*) $_6C^{12}$ into three $_2He^4$; (*b*) $_8O^{16}$ into four $_2He^4$; (*c*) $_8O^{16}$ into $_2He^4$ and $_6C^{12}$? The answer to (*c*) serves as a check for the answers to (*a*) and (*b*).

16.10. *A standard energy equivalent.* Compute the energy equivalent of the mass of an atom having unit atomic weight.

16.11. *Energy equivalent of 1 kg.* Suppose that the *total mass* of 1 kg is transformed into energy. How large is this energy (in kwhr)? The answer about equals the energy produced by all electric-power plants of the United States (as of 1939) running for 2 months (H. D. Smyth).

16.12. *Separation of uranium isotopes.* Using the conventional laboratory technique, you may produce a positive ray of 10^{-4} amp of singly charged *natural* uranium ions. How long a time will it take to separate 1,000 g of U^{235} from the bulk?

16.13. *Work required to turn a magnet (calculus problem).* A magnetic needle is turned in a uniform magnetic field, starting from its stable position (parallel to the field), into the opposite position. By integration, compute the work required in terms of the field strength H, the pole strength m, and length l of the needle.

HINT: Obtain the expression for $\Delta W =$ work required to turn the needle by the small angle $\Delta\alpha$. Take α as the variable of integration and integrate. (ml is called the "magnetic moment" M of the needle.)

CHAPTER 17
NATURAL TRANSMUTATION AND RADIOACTIVITY

Natural radioactivity was discovered more than half a century ago by A. H. Becquerel. This discovery, together with those of X rays and of free electrons, marks a turning point in the history of atomic physics. Two difficulties retarded the exploration of this new field: (1) Only exceedingly weak samples of active material were available at the beginning. (2) Since radioactivity was completely foreign and even contradictory to all that was known of physics and chemistry, there was no theory whatever to guide the exploration; it developed only gradually, guided by the experiments. Although historically these great difficulties made the progress devious, we can well go through arguments more straightforward than those of history since we have grams of radium as well as the theory of the nuclear atom at our disposal.

While the investigation of isotopes discussed in the preceding chapter is concerned only with *stable* nuclei, here we are concerned with an *instability* that occurs, in particular, among heavy nuclei. After describing the discovery, we shall analyze the penetrating rays emitted by heavy nuclei. Next we shall discuss what happens to the emitters by exploring their half-lives and the radioactive series. Finally we shall investigate the bearing of the observations on the theory of nuclear structure which we are developing from chapter to chapter (Summary in Sec. 19.3).

17.1. Discovery and Fundamental Properties. Roentgen's discovery of X rays (1895) led, within a few months, to the discovery of radioactivity by Becquerel (1896). He found that uranium minerals permanently give off a radiation as penetrating as X rays, *i.e.*, able to affect a photographic plate contained in a *closed* plateholder. Contrary to any plausible expectation, this radiation does not derive its energy from an agent, like light, X rays, or cathode rays, that acts on the uranium mineral. Instead the radiation emanates uniformly all the time.

Becquerel's starting point was a theoretical guess. Although it turned out to be mistaken, it led to the first discovery in the wide field now called nuclear physics. A few months after Roentgen's discovery Becquerel was searching for a relation between X rays and visible fluorescence (Sec. 12.6). He used uranium compounds which are known to emit both types of radiation. He placed a piece of pitchblende (U_2O_8) on the outside of a *closed* plateholder charged with a photographic plate. After exposing this device for a few days to bright sunlight, he found that the plate was blackened. At first he attributed the effect to a new radiation which emanates from uranium when exposed to sunlight and which penetrates, like X rays, through the substance of the plateholder. During a rainy period he kept such a device in his closed desk. After several days, the sun came out again. Since he did not want to use the old material he developed the plate without having exposed the uranium to sunlight. To his surprise he found a strong effect of a radiation that had penetrated the plateholder. Becquerel's discovery that such a radiation emanates from the uranium mineral is still vastly more surprising than the discovery of X rays, since in Becquerel's experiment it is not even evident where the energy of the new radiation comes from. Apparently, the uranium mineral contains an inexhaustible supply of energy.

The uranium minerals were then subjected to a painstaking chemical analysis by Pierre and Marie Curie. Many kinds of chemical separation were applied. After each separation, the products were tested, the inactive part discarded, and the active part further analyzed. The result was that there are several active elements, prominent among them being one associated with barium and thus recognized as an alkaline earth. By fractional crystallization the inactive barium was gradually removed. The progress of the purification was tested by two criteria: the appearance of an atomic spectrum hitherto unknown and, more conclusive, the increase of the activity of the sample. We continue with the words of Mme. Curie:

After a long effort I succeeded in obtaining radium as a pure salt in a quantity sufficient for the determination of the atomic weight. So I assigned to it its place in the periodic table of elements.

The atomic number, 88, of radium found by Mme. Curie was later confirmed by its X-ray spectrum. Soon thereafter it was found that many other heavy elements show more or less strongly a similar activity. Radium is conspicuous by the strength of this new effect. The outstanding effects produced by radioactive elements are as follows:

1. They continuously emit radiations of various grades of penetrating power; each species (later we shall say each radioactive isotope) emits its characteristic radiation. We have already studied alpha rays (Chap. 9). In the next section we shall find two more types of ray, still more penetrating than alpha rays. All these rays blacken photographic plates and ionize air.

2. All radioactive elements are continually creating small quantities of new elements. An example is radium, which continually generates small quantities of helium and radon (abbreviated Rn), both rare gases. Helium, of course, is well known chemically. Radon, however, is found only as a product of radium. It is chemically identified as a heavy rare gas. As such, it belongs to number 86 of the periodic table, preceding radium, which is an alkaline earth, by two numbers. (No sufficient

quantities of radon are available for producing a measurable X-ray spectrum and so identifying the new element.)

3. A tube containing radium always has a temperature slightly higher than the surroundings.

The conclusion, unheard of at the time of the discovery, is reached that we must assume a hidden source of energy to be responsible for the effects observed. In order to judge this mysterious energy, we compare the decomposition of radium with a chemical decomposition as follows: (1) While the disintegration of radium into helium and radon goes on spontaneously all the time, nobody has ever succeeded in combining radon and helium and so producing radium in the same way in which any chemical molecule can be synthesized. (2) The disintegration is an intrinsic property of the radium atom and is entirely independent of anything we can do to it, like heating it or bombarding it with electrons or combining it chemically with any other substance. (3) The energy content of radioactive rays, amounting to several Mev, contrasts with all known chemical energies that are only about one-millionth of this value. (4) In the disintegration process new elements are created.

All these facts prove that the spontaneous disintegration of radium bears no relation to a chemical process. Radium is not the only element that shows this activity. Many other heavy elements do the same to various extents. In particular, each radon atom, itself a product of a decomposition, in turn decomposes with the emission of another alpha particle and so creates more helium.

The experimental facts described, which are entirely different from anything observed in other fields of physics and chemistry, force us to assume a hitherto unknown process within atoms. We assume that *radium, as well as other radioactive elements, has an intrinsic tendency, which we cannot affect, to disintegrate into other elements* (Rutherford and Soddy, 1902). In some elements the probability of this disintegration is so high that only minor concentrations of the element can accumulate, as in the case of radon. In other elements, like radium itself, it is so low that, within days or a few years, the mass of the element does not appreciably decrease.

The creation of new elements can occur only by a splitting of the nucleus. Hence we must conclude that in the radium nucleus, as in an explosive, energy is stored which, at the explosion, spontaneously breaks it up into a helium and a radon nucleus. Since the atomic numbers of radium, radon, and helium are 88, 86, and 2, respectively, we notice the conservation of the *nuclear charge*. The *atomic weight* of radon cannot be determined accurately, but we can predict it as the difference of those of radium and helium, *i.e.*, $226 - 4 = 222$. The energy exchange in the disintegrations of radioactive elements is of the order of several Mev.

The corresponding change of mass may be computed on the basis of Einstein's principle, as pointed out in Sec. 16.4. The change of mass shows up only in the higher decimal places of the atomic weight and is by no means large enough to affect the mass number.

In the next sections, we shall explore the three outstanding aspects of radioactivity: (1) the nature of the various rays emitted, (2) the rate at which they are emitted, expressed by the half-life of the parent substance, and (3) the chemical transmutations caused by the emission of the rays.

17.2. Radioactive Rays. Methods of Observation. The nature of the radioactive rays is brought out in the experiment schematically represented by Fig. 17.1. A pencil of radiation that is subjected to a magnetic field perpendicular to its direction is separated into three rays. One of them is only slightly deflected in a direction that shows it to be positively charged; this is the "alpha" ray discussed above. Another ray, called "beta" ray, is deflected in the opposite direction and hence possesses a negative charge. Finally, the third type of ray, called "gamma" ray, is not deflected at all by electric or magnetic fields; it has all the properties of a very hard X ray, in particular a very high penetrating power. Thus there exist two corpuscular rays and this additional ray which must be supposed to have a quantum structure like the X rays. Various devices, the most important ones based on the ionization of gases caused by these rays, have been built for their detailed investigation. We shall illustrate all these devices by the effects they show when alpha rays are used. Afterwards we shall describe the effects of beta and gamma rays.

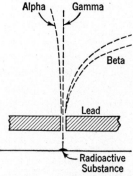

Fig. 17.1. Schematic drawing showing the separation of the three types of radioactive ray by a magnetic field deflecting a bundle of rays.

a. Alpha Rays. We anticipated the discussion of alpha rays (Chap. 9) in order to have the background for Rutherford's theory of the nuclear atom, which is based on observations of the scattering of alpha particles. Here we summarize their properties.

It is *observed* that alpha particles accumulating in a glass tube consist of helium gas. We *conclude* that the alpha particle is essentially identical with a helium atom; hence its mass is $m = 6.64 \times 10^{-24}$ g. We assume that the charged particle when traversing matter is gradually losing its kinetic energy and may pick up the electrons needed for its neutralization so that finally it represents an atom of helium that does not show any symptom of its origin.

It is *observed* that the alpha particle is positively charged and has a specific charge $e/m = 4.82 \times 10^3$ emu/g. Combining this figure with the preceding result, we *conclude* that its absolute charge is $e = 3.20 \times 10^{-20}$ emu. As this is twice the electronic charge, we further conclude that alpha particles are identical with doubly positively charged helium ions.

It is *observed* that alpha particles penetrate gold foil, 2,000 atoms thick. We *conclude* that gold and other matter have their mass concentrated in very small nuclei and that the alpha particle itself is a very small projectile, presumably a helium nucleus, written He^{++}.

For many years the principal method of observing and counting alpha particles was the laborious observation of *scintillations* on a fluorescent screen. Rutherford made some of his greatest discoveries by counting scintillations. Now we ask: Does each incident alpha particle produce an observable scintillation? This question is answered by combining two measurements as follows: Using the same alpha ray, the scintillations per second are counted and, independently, the number of particles arriving is measured by the total charge they convey to an insulated condenser plate. Both measurements lead to the same figure. Thus their combination proves that each alpha particle produces an observable scintillation.

Scintillations can be observed as follows. The bright spots on the luminous dial of a watch consist of fluorescent material in which traces of an element related to radium are embedded. In a dark room a dark-adapted eye can see through a good magnifying lens that the light emitted from the luminous spots is not uniform but consists of many local bright flashes. Each flash is a scintillation indicating the emission of one alpha particle.

Another outstanding property of alpha rays is their limited range. A radium sample that produces ample scintillations when close to the screen becomes ineffective beyond a well-defined distance. The range of alpha rays so determined is a characteristic property of the emitting atom; *e.g.*, in 1 atm of air the range of alpha rays from radium is 3.39 cm.

In most devices we use the ionization of air in order to examine the radiation. The simplest apparatus is the *ionization chamber*, a closed vessel containing a charged condenser connected to an electroscope. For the observation of alpha rays the radioactive sample is placed inside the chamber or in front of a very thin window. It is easy to measure the *over-all effect* by the decay of the charge on the electroscope. The ionization due to one *individual particle* can be measured in a similar device if the short burst of electric current, due to the effect of the particle, is amplified. This permits the counting of particles as well as the differentiation between more or less heavy bursts of ionization and is of **great** value for distinguishing the various particles.

A very useful device, simple enough to be used by uranium prospectors, highly developed for research, is the *Geiger (or Geiger-Müller) counter* (Fig. 17.2; 1928). It consists of a low-pressure electric discharge tube of cylindrical symmetry. A thin axial wire serves as the anode and a concentric metal cylinder as the cathode. The tube is filled with argon or, better, a mixture of argon and alcohol vapor at a few cm pressure. The self-maintained discharge would require for its start a minimum voltage of, say, 2,000 volts. Actually, we apply a voltage a little below this threshold so that ordinarily no current is flowing. Only when a sudden ionization of the gas is produced, *e.g.*, by a high energy particle, will the discharge start. But as soon as the current flows, the high series resistance reduces the voltage available at the terminals of the counter so drastically that the discharge goes off again. Hence the brief duration discharge, which is heard as a kick of the loudspeaker or operates a mechanical counting device, reveals the passage of an ionizing particle.

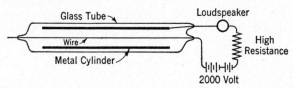

F<small>IG</small>. 17.2. Geiger-Müller counter; schematic diagram. Low-pressure discharge between a wire and a coaxial metal cylinder.

As soon as the discharge is extinguished, say after 10^{-4} sec, the counter is ready to receive the next particle. Since the short, self-maintained discharge that occurs in the counter does not depend on the strength of the triggering pulse of ionization, the counter does not differentiate between alpha, beta, and gamma rays.

In order to distinguish between strongly and weakly ionizing rays, say, alpha and beta rays, we reduce the voltage applied to the counter to a value so low that the self-maintained discharge, characteristic of the Geiger counter, does not occur at all. Still the voltage accelerates the positive ions and free electrons created by the fast particle. Thus electron impacts cause a certain multiplication of the original charges and so produce a weak short-duration current that is proportional to the initial ionization. This device is called the *"proportional counter,"* as distinct from the Geiger counter.

The counter is a highly developed device specially adapted to various purposes. For example, it may be provided with a thin mica window to admit alpha particles which are unable to pass through glass and metal walls. Circuits of great complexity have been developed to increase the maximum rate at which the counter may serve. For this purpose, first, the duration of each burst of electric current must be reduced. Next,

since the mechanical recorder has some unavoidable inertia, an intermediate circuit is built that has the function of feeding only every second
burst into the recorder. By combination of two or more such devices
one can have the recorder show only one response, say, for each 64 particles incident on the counter tube. This makes possible the recording
of thousands of counts per second. Another development, the combination of several counters for "coincidence counting," will be discussed in
the section on annihilation (Sec. 18.5) and applied to cosmic-ray investigations (Chap. 20).

A diamond or a cadmium sulfide crystal, although ordinarily an excellent insulator, is rendered conducting when a high-speed particle or a
gamma-ray quantum traverses it (Chap. 15.3). Hence it can be used
instead of a Geiger counter. Because of their very short recovery time,
such *"crystal counters"* are useful for high-speed counting.

The author assumes that, at the present stage of the discussion, the reader needs no
further experimental proof of the atomic structure of matter and the consistency of
our argument. However, one piece of additional evidence must be discussed, since
alpha rays permit the determination of Avogadro's number by the most direct method
imaginable, *i.e.*, the direct counting of the atoms contained in 1 gram atom of helium.
In the first experiment we determine the number of *alpha particles* emitted per year
from 1 g of radium. (Using a counting device, we determine the number emitted per
second from a small mass of radium within a limited solid angle and calculate the total
number per gram and year.) We assume that each alpha particle after slowing down
changes into a neutral helium atom. In the next experiment we measure the total
amount of *helium gas* emitted per year from 1 g of radium. Finally, combining the
two measurements, we calculate the number of helium atoms per cubic centimeter
and the number per gram atom, which is Avogadro's number N_0. For the numerical
values see Prob. 17.2. The result agrees with those of other determinations within
the limit of experimental error.

Here we survey the methods for the determination of Avogadro's number N_0.
(1) Measurement of the Faraday constant F and the electronic charge e (Sec. 7.2).
(2) Measurement of X-ray wavelengths by both the ruled grating and crystal grating
(Sec. 14.1h).   (3) Counting of the helium nuclei which when neutralized form 1 gram
atom helium.

The *Wilson cloud chamber* (C. T. R. Wilson, 1911) is another device
utilizing the ionization of air. It supplies surprisingly detailed information of a different kind. It is a familiar view that, on a perfectly clear
day, a light cloud hangs around the top of a high mountain. The condensation of water is explained as follows. Air is lifted by the wind as it
approaches the slope of the mountain. Thus the air expands and also
cools since it does mechanical work in the process of expansion. If,
before the expansion, the content of water vapor is slightly below saturation, it may happen that, after the expansion and cooling, the saturation
limit is passed and condensation takes place. This is made evident by
the cloud. The process going on in Wilson's cloud chamber is similar.

Figure 17.3 shows a simple chamber. A glass cylinder is closed on one side by a glass plate, on the other by a piston or rubber diaphragm. The cylinder contains air and a few drops of liquid water, which readily provides water vapor at the saturation pressure. To begin with, the piston is pushed in, compressing and slightly heating the air. A short time is allowed to provide exchange of temperature. Next, by the release of the piston, a *sudden* expansion of the air in the chamber is produced. The corresponding cooling brings the water vapor, mixed with the air, below the saturation point so

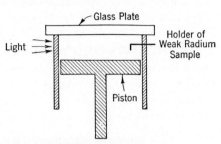

Fig. 17.3. Wilson cloud chamber. The space above the piston contains air saturated with the vapor of water or alcohol. Electrodes for the electric field sweeping out the ions are not shown.

that condensation of water follows and is seen as cloud formation. (Practically alcohol vapor is used.)

It is known that condensation occurs preferentially on dust particles and on ionized molecules. At the first expansions, the inevitable dust present in air causes a cloud to form all over the chamber. This is easily swept out by an electric field since the dust particles and the little water droplets carry electric charges. (The electrodes needed for sweeping are not shown in the figure.) Now the chamber is ready for the main experiment. When a weak radioactive sample carried by a metal wire is introduced, the cloud formed after an expansion forms on the ionized air molecules. Each track indicates the path of one alpha particle (Fig. 17.4). Although these clouds drift away very soon, for a moment the paths of the particles can be clearly seen or photographed. Striking is the straight character of each ray, its well-defined end, and the uniform length, or "range," of all rays. The range of the alpha ray in 1 atm air is characteristic of the emitting atom. In the figure the rays from two radioactive elements, each with its characteristic range, are superimposed. This direct observation of the range confirms the result of the study of scintillations.

The cloud chamber, now an outstanding tool for the investigation of rays from radium, was introduced before the discovery of X rays and radioactivity. C. T. R. Wilson reports on his work as follows: "In September 1894 I spent a few weeks in the observatory on the summit of Ben Nevis, the highest of the Scottish Hills. The wonderful optical phenomena shown when the sun shone on the clouds surrounding the hill top . . . greatly excited my interest and made me wish to imitate them at the laboratory. At the beginning of 1895 I made some experiments for this purpose— making clouds by expansion of moist air. Moist air which had been freed from dust particles [failed to produce a cloud] even when a considerable degree of supersaturation was produced by expansion.   In the autumn of 1895 came the news of Roentgen's great discovery.   At the beginning of 1896 J. J. Thomson was investigating the conductivity of air exposed to the new rays, and I had an opportunity of using an X-ray tube . . . I can well recall my delight when I found at the first trial that a fog which took many minutes to fall was produced."   (For reference see Appendix 8.)

We want to correlate the observation of tracks by the cloud chamber with Rutherford's theory of the scattering of alpha particles.   Rutherford and his coworkers investigated the scattering by the simple technique of counting scintillations (Sec. 9.1).   He explained the high penetrating power of the rays by the hypothesis of the nuclear atom.   This leads to

Fig. 17.4. Cloud-chamber photograph of alpha rays from thorium C and C'.   Each group has its characteristic range.   (*Courtesy of C. T. R. Wilson.*)

the assumption of two different types of collision process suffered by alpha particles when passing, for example, through gold foil.   We distinguished them on the basis of the laws of mechanics.   The alpha particle bounces off when colliding with a *nucleus*, since this is much heavier than the alpha particle.   However, the particle continues in a straight path when colliding with an *electron* and throws this light body out of the way.   These two types of collision are beautifully demonstrated by cloud-chamber pictures.   Figure 17.4 shows a group of alpha rays, all shooting in straight lines.   Each water droplet of the apparently continuous track indicates one collision of the alpha particle *with an electron*.   That is one ionization process.   This is so common an event that the high density of the droplets gives the impression of a continuous cloud in the shape of the track.

The numerous collisions cause the alpha particle to slow down, until at the end of the track, by picking up two external electrons, it is transformed into a neutral helium atom.

Most alpha tracks are straight lines, a fact that indicates that most alpha particles do not collide with heavier bodies, *i.e.*, nuclei. Some tracks, however, show sharp kinks. Such a kink indicates a close approach of the alpha particle to a nucleus which causes a deflection. These kinks occur principally near the ends of tracks since there the alpha particles have slowed down and, therefore, are more readily deflected (noticeable on Fig. 17.5*b*). Much rarer events are more conspicuous on Fig. 17.5. There alpha particles collide bodily with nuclei, giving off appreciable shares of kinetic energy. In the cloud chamber, in contrast to the case of the gold foil, the atoms of the gas are not neces-

(a)   (b)

FIG. 17.5. Collisions of alpha particles with nuclei. (*a*) With helium; (*b*) with oxygen. (*Courtesy of P. M. S. Blackett and Proceedings of the Royal Society.*)

sarily heavier than the alpha particle. Figure 17.5*a* shows the scattering in helium, *i.e.*, by nuclei of masses equal to those of the particles. The two tracks so produced, that of the original alpha particle deflected by the collision and that of the "recoil nucleus," are both well-defined. In gases heavier than helium, like oxygen (Fig. 17.5*b*), the track of the recoil nucleus is very short, as would be expected, since because of its smaller mass the alpha particle keeps most of its energy.

We must study all the information we can derive from the tracks observed in a cloud chamber because in artificial transmutation (Chap. 18) a great variety of particles are being generated and *identified* by their cloud-chamber tracks and, moreover, reveal their *kinetic energies* by these tracks. Figure 17.5 shows that fast nuclei of various kinds are produced by the impacts of alpha particles. The velocity of the alpha particle originating, say, from radium, is known once and for all, having been determined by electric and magnetic deflections. We compute the velocity given to the target particle on the basis of the velocity of the impinging particle, the masses of both particles, and the angles observed in the cloud chamber. This is a familiar problem of elementary mechanics.　If we want to avoid the complication due to the occurrence of various angles, we select only tracks due to head-on collisions, easily recognized by the direction of the target particle which is thrown along the same line in which the alpha particle travels.　This simple case is covered by the theory given in Prob. 9.1.　The result is, for example, that a proton picks up a velocity $8v/5$ while the alpha particle, after the impact, continues its path in the original direction with the velocity $3v/5$ (v = velocity of the incoming alpha particle).　By such experiments we compare the tracks due to the various particles at various kinetic energies.　For example, protons have much longer ranges than heavier particles of equal energy.　(This observation will be of importance in Rutherford's discovery of artificial transmutation.)

Two outstanding features of the tracks are noticed.　The average density of the track is characteristic of the type of the particle, *e.g.*,

50,000 ions per centimeter for alpha particles, about one-quarter of this value for protons, about 1/100 of the same value for beta particles.

It is true that at atmospheric pressure the density is so high that the droplets, each representing 1 ion, cannot be counted. But the counting is easily done at lower pressures, and the figure for 1 atm is computed as directly proportional to the pressure.

We may check the determination of the nature and velocity of any particle by applying a strong magnetic field in a direction perpendicular to its path.　Since we know the velocity (derived from the range), the magnetic deflection leads to a determination of e/m for the particle, which, in turn, reveals its nature and so provides a check on the argument.　Figure 17.6 shows the magnetic deflection of alpha particles by a magnetic induction of 43,000 gauss.

Fig. 17.6. Curved tracks of alpha rays in a magnetic field of 43,000 gauss. (*After Kapitza.*)

Excellent for demonstration is the continuously sensitive diffusion cloud chamber. In this instrument supersaturation is produced as follows.　Top and bottom of a large vertical, air-filled glass cylinder are closed by metal plates.　Alcohol evaporates continuously from a felt cushion that is mounted under the top plate, which may be electrically heated.　The alcohol is condensed at the bottom plate, which is placed on dry ice.　Thus the alcohol diffuses continuously from the top down to the bottom.　Above the bottom a considerable space is formed in which permanent supersaturation prevails and tracks due to cosmic rays or sources enclosed in the chamber are continuously produced.　Intense illumination makes them visible (see references in Appendix 2).

Summarizing, we notice the great variety of observations to be made with the cloud chamber.　It reveals the nature of particles, their velocities, and a great deal of detail of the collision processes between particles.

The processes by which X rays and alpha rays are losing energy when traversing matter are widely different, as is evident from the description of their absorption. The decay of intensity of X rays is described by an exponential law $I = I_0 e^{-\mu d}$ (Sec. 14.1d) which states that there is *no well-defined limit* of the thickness through which X rays may penetrate. On the other hand, Fig. 17.4 strikingly shows that all alpha rays emanating from the same element have about the same range; the absorber takes away all particles belonging to the ray *after they have traversed the same distance*. These contrasting observations are explained by the different processes. For X rays they are ionization or Compton effect. Within each centimeter path length either one of these processes has a certain probability and removes a certain fraction of all quanta from the ray (see Prob. 12.9). Thus the intensity of the X ray decays following an exponential law and never reaches exactly zero. Hence we describe the absorption by an *absorption coefficient*. On the other hand, the individual alpha particle spends its energy *in many processes*, in each one of them ionizing a molecule. Thus it gradually loses its initial kinetic energy, which is equal to several Mev. This is not noticeable on the photograph of Fig. 17.4 except by the sudden end of each track. The distance within which several hundred thousand ionization processes take place is about the same for all particles. This explains why we describe their absorption by *their range*, not by an absorption coefficient. The gradual loss of velocity of the individual alpha particle along its track becomes evident in a strong magnetic field deflecting the particle (Fig. 17.6). The radius of curvature R depends on the magnetic induction B by the relation $R = mv/eB$ (see Sec. 6.2a). In the experiment represented by the figure, e/m and B are constant. Hence the radius R is proportional to the velocity. The figure shows that the rays, coming from above, are increasingly curved, hence show smaller values of R, toward the ends of their ranges.

Another difference between X rays and alpha rays is obvious, considering their nature. The X-ray quantum when absorbed disappears. The alpha particle when slowed down picks up electrons and continues its life as a helium atom.

When studying light or X rays, we get used to the fact that the *observation* shows something *continuous*, like the light emitted from a lamp. Only an elaborate theoretical argument makes us believe that the process involved, the emission of light quanta, is *discontinuous*. In the Geiger counter, however, the discontinuity of radioactive radiation is strikingly evident by the discrete kicks of the loud-speaker. Still more striking is the aspect in the cloud chamber which shows the individual alpha-ray tracks, their lengths, their deflections by a magnetic field (Fig. 17.6) and, as we shall study in detail, the fate of the alpha particles in various collision processes.   The high energy of radioactive rays is required to produce these clearly visible tracks of individual particles.

b. Beta Rays.   Figure 17.1 illustrates an experiment that shows that alpha, beta, and gamma rays are all three present among the rays coming from a composite source.   When we apply chemical separation to a composite source, as was first done by the Curies, we find that each radioactive element emits either an alpha or a beta ray (with a very few minor exceptions in which both alpha and beta rays come from the same element).   This makes the separate study of beta rays simple.   As we shall see later, many beta emitters are produced by artificial transmutation. Gamma radiation is commonly associated with the emission of alpha or beta rays.

By magnetic deflection the beta ray indicates its negative charge.   The combination of magnetic and electric deflection enables us to determine its specific charge e/m and velocity.   The numerical value of the specific charge identifies the ray as consisting of free electrons.   Their velocities are high, in some cases even closely approaching the velocity of light. Beta rays of a sufficient density produce fluorescence of a screen, as is well known to everybody who has seen a cathode-ray oscilloscope. (The cathode ray is of the same nature as the beta ray, although the individual particles have lower kinetic energy, and it produces a bright fluorescence.)   However, *individual* beta particles, different from alpha particles, fail to show up by *individual* scintillations.   To determine the law of decay of a beta radiator (see Sec. 17.3) the *ionization chamber* and electroscope are used widely.

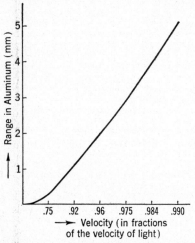

FIG. 17.7. Range of beta rays in aluminum as a function of their velocity.

Because of the high penetrating power of the beta ray, the chamber may be closed by a thin aluminum window.

The *penetrating power* of beta rays is not so well defined as that of alpha rays, as we shall see when observing their tracks in the cloud chamber.   Nevertheless one can determine rather well the thickness of the aluminum sheet that completely shields the ionization chamber from the effect of the beta rays coming from one or the other active element. Once the relation between this thickness and the velocity of the rays has been determined (Fig. 17.7), this is a convenient method for the determination of the maximum velocity of a bundle of beta rays.

Much more detail is revealed by a measurement of the velocities in a beta-ray spectrograph (Fig. 17.8). Its construction closely resembles that of a mass spectrograph. But here we know the specific charge e/m of the particles and want only to determine their velocities. A narrow bundle of beta rays, separated out by two slits, enters a magnetic field perpendicular to their path. The field turns each particle in high vacuum on a circular path of radius $R = mv/eB$ [Eq. (6.7)]. The formula shows that the magnetic field spreads the rays out according to their velocities v. After passing through half circles, the rays are recorded on a photo-graphic plate. The unexpected result is that, in many cases, the beta rays coming from an isolated active element have not all the same velocity, but, in most cases, show a *spread of velocity over a wide range* with a well-defined maximum limit, characteristic for the emitter. This is called the "continuous" beta-ray spectrum. Here beta rays differ from alpha rays, which, by their uniform range, show that they emanate

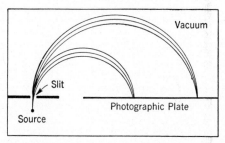

Fig. 17.8. Beta-ray spectrograph. The magnetic field bends the rays on circular paths.

from the same emitter all *with the same velocity*. Similarly gamma rays, emitted from the same element, have all the same energy quanta—in other words, a sharp-line spectrum (see Sec. 17.2c). Hence the *continuous* beta-ray spectrum is an unexpected observation.

This observed fact is opposed to our idea of sharply defined energy levels. Such levels are evident in the nuclei that are left after the emission of the beta rays, because the subsequent emission processes of alpha or gamma rays are sharply defined and bear no evidence of a continuous range of nuclear energy. This dilemma, the observation of a *continuous* spectrum leading to a *sharply defined* energy level, was tentatively solved by Pauli (1931), who postulated that the emission of a beta particle from the nucleus is accompanied by the emission of another particle which escapes direct observation. What could this particle be? It cannot be a particle of the mass of a proton or greater, because this would reduce the atomic weight of the product nucleus contrary to observation (see the displacement law, Sec. 17.4). Furthermore, the energy does not go into a gamma ray (Sec. 17.2c), because this would be observable. In this dilemma Pauli invented a new particle, the *neutrino*, assuming that the *total* energy emitted is sharply defined, but that its distribution between the beta particle and the neutrino varies over a continuous range. Thus the sharp high-energy limit of the continuous beta-ray spectrum repre-sents the *total* energy of each emission process; any beta emission of lower energy is accompanied by a neutrino emission which always brings the total energy emitted to the same amount. A great effort has been made to observe this elusive particle, but without positive result. All that is known is that the mass of the neutrino, if it has any, must be smaller than 2/1,000 of the mass of the electron. Although there is no direct evidence of the neutrino, its existence is generally accepted since otherwise we cannot account for the conservation of energy in the emission of electrons from nuclei.

A calculation leads to the startling result that the neutrinos emitted from a very small "nuclear reactor" (see Sec. 19.5) carry an energy as high as 50 kw. Although we have no shields protecting us from this powerful radiation, we need not fear ill effects since, presumably, the neutrinos travel through the human body as well as through all other substances without producing any noticeable effect at all.

There are other beta-ray spectra in which *sharply defined* electron velocities are observed. These beta emissions, however, are understood as secondary processes, due to the emission from the nucleus of a *gamma ray* which, in turn, ejects an electron from the K or L or M shell of the electronic structure by photoelectric effect. This more complex process is identified by an energy relation. Radium, for example, although an alpha emitter, emits also a beta-ray spectrum which consists of three sharp lines. The beta ray of lowest energy, called β_1, is ejected presumably from the most firmly bound shell, the K shell. If this is true, we expect the relation to apply:

Energy of gamma quantum = energy of β_1 + ionization energy of K shell

Correspondingly, to the next ray, β_2, the relation should apply:

Energy of gamma quantum = energy of β_2 + ionization energy of L shell

By subtraction we find

Energy of β_2 − energy of β_1 = energy of K limit − energy of L limit

The measurement of the beta-ray spectrum checks well with the difference between the K and L ionization limits, which are accurately known from the X-ray absorption spectrum. The corresponding relation holds for the beta rays β_2 and β_3 when compared with the L and M limits of the X-ray spectrum. These relations prove that the *sharp line* beta-ray spectra do not consist of electrons ejected from the nucleus but of K and L and M electrons ejected by gamma-ray quanta all of the same energy which, in turn, are emitted from the nuclei. This process is called "internal conversion" (Rutherford, 1917). When the lines of the beta-ray spectrum are assigned to the various X-absorption limits, the energy of the gamma-ray quantum can be computed (see Prob. 17.6).

This interpretation of internal conversion as a photoelectric effect needs a refinement. If it were exact, the yield of internal conversion would vanish for very thin layers of the emitter since such a thin layer would hardly absorb the gamma rays. Actually, however, the ratio of conversion electrons to gamma-ray quanta emitted does not diminish for very thin layers. Hence we must rather assume that a K or L or M electron may interact with the nucleus *of the same atom* and thus allow the nuclear energy, although ordinarily emitted as a gamma ray, to go into the ejection of the electron.

The Geiger counter responds well to beta rays. Its operation differs from that of the ionization chamber in that it exhibits a brief *self-maintained* electric discharge which is only *started* by the incoming particle.

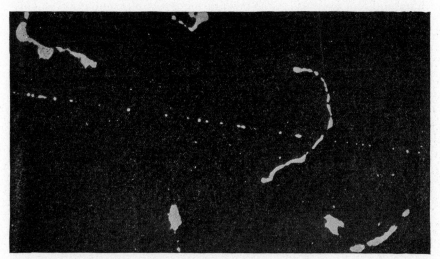

Fig. 17.9. Cloud-chamber tracks of beta rays. The curved, heavy tracks are due to slow beta particles; the straight, light track is due to a fast beta particle. (*Courtesy of C. T. R. Wilson.*)

Except by special devices, this discharge fails to give evidence whether it is started by an alpha or a beta particle. But by an aluminum window of proper thickness one can screen off the alpha rays and still transmit beta rays. Finally one can correct for possible gamma rays by inserting a heavier aluminum window, which stops all beta rays but has no noticeable effect on the much more penetrating gamma rays.

Cloud-chamber pictures show other properties of beta rays. Figure 17.9 shows slow beta rays ejected from gaseous molecules by gamma rays and, in addition, one straight track due to a fast beta ray. It is seen that slow beta rays are deflected by collisions much more readily than alpha rays. This has the effect that the range of a beta ray is less well defined than that of an alpha ray (see Fig. 17.4). Since beta rays have ranges much larger than those of alpha rays, it is convenient to measure them in aluminum instead of in air.   In spite of the numerous deflections suffered by beta rays once they slow down, one can reasonably well determine a distance beyond which no beta particle reaches; thus the curve of Fig. 17.7 has been obtained.   The straight track of the fast electron seen in Fig. 17.9 is less dense than the curved path of the slower electrons.   This indicates that the faster electrons have a smaller chance for energy losses. The high penetrating power of very fast electrons observed in cosmic rays (Chap. 20) is another manifestation of the same fact.

   c. Gamma Rays.   Gamma rays are similar to X rays and of a different nature from alpha or beta rays, which are the only *material* rays observed in natural radioactivity.   The penetrating power of gamma rays is equal to or greater than that of X rays, and, like the latter, they are studied by their effects on photographic plates or in ionization chambers or, most conveniently, with Geiger counters.   Since in all such devices both types of ray produce the same effects, we conclude that they are of the same nature.   The penetrating power of most gamma rays is the same as that of X rays generated by several million volts.   Frequently, the emission of an alpha or beta particle is associated with the emission of a gamma-ray quantum, indicating that alpha or beta emission may leave the nucleus in an excited level which gives away its energy by radiation.

   A difficult experimental problem is presented by the measurement of the wavelengths of gamma rays (or the energies of their quanta).   The following methods are used.   (1) The wavelengths of the less penetrating rays are measured by the Bragg crystal spectrometer.   These wavelengths have the same order of magnitude as those of X rays.   The spectrometer, however, requires a strong source and is not applicable to hard gamma rays because their wavelengths are too short as compared to the grating constants of crystals.   With an improved construction of the Bragg spectrometer, gamma-ray quanta up to about 0.5 Mev can be measured with great accuracy.   (2) In some cases the quanta are computed from the energies of associated beta rays which are due to internal conversion, as discussed in the preceding section.   (3) Systematic measurements of gamma rays are made by the photoelectric effect on thin metal foils.   The energies of the photoelectrons are measured in the beta-ray spectrometer or in the cloud chamber by magnetic deflection. (4) The Compton effect occurring in the gas of a cloud chamber can be used.   Figure 17.10 shows the trace of a bundle of gamma rays in air. Because of the high penetrating power of the rays, we are sure that most of their quanta pass through the chamber without producing any effect. The tracks observed are due to the few quanta absorbed; and these quanta show up only indirectly by the secondary electrons that they eject from the air molecules.   This effect of gamma rays in the cloud chamber is entirely different from the effect of alpha or beta rays; these latter rays produce tracks that show the paths of individual alpha or beta particles by continuous series of droplets.   On the other hand a gamma quantum when absorbed produces 1 high-energy electron whose path shows up by a cloud.   The aggregate of all these secondaries gives the impression of the gamma ray passing through the chamber.   But the track of the individual gamma quantum itself does not show up.   Therefore gamma rays are called a "nonionizing" radiation (see Sec. 18.2a). The high-energy secondary electrons observed in the cloud chamber may be due to photoelectric effect or Compton effect.   Although in many individual tracks no clear-cut decision can be made, a laborious statistical treatment of many tracks gives evidence of the energy quantum.   (5) Production of a positron-electron pair, discussed in the next chapter (Fig. 18.6), allows the measurement of quanta that are larger than 1.02

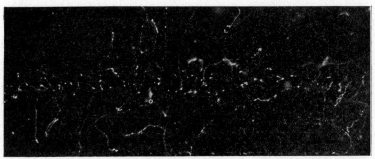

Fig. 17.10. Cloud-chamber tracks due to gamma rays.   The tracks show the secondary electrons ejected by the gamma rays.   (*Courtesy of C. T. R. Wilson.*)

Mev, the minimum energy required to produce a pair.   (6) Similarly, nuclear photoelectric effect on deuterium (Sec. 18.2c) can be applied to quanta larger than 2.15 Mev.

The various methods agree in showing that gamma rays have sharply defined wavelengths, characteristic for the emitting nucleus.   We compare the time-consuming and inaccurate methods for measuring one or two gamma-ray wavelengths with the ease with which optical wavelengths are determined.   On a photographic plate (see Fig. 11.3) many hundred sharp optical spectral lines are recorded and measured with high precision and without any ambiguity within a short time.   Great progress in our knowledge of the nucleus would result if we could construct a gamma-ray spectrograph as powerful as a Rowland grating for light.   There is no indication, however, that this can be achieved.

Our treatment of alpha, beta, and gamma rays is descriptive and does not lead to a theory of the nucleus as the description of optical spectra culminates in Bohr's theory.   There exists no theory of nuclear structure which would lead to so comprehensive a prediction of a simple nucleus as that given by Bohr's theory of the hydrogen spectrum (see Sec. 19.3).

The radioactive rays are compared with light and X rays in Table 17.2 given in the summary.

17.3. Half-life and Radioactive Equilibrium. After discussing the *nature* of the radioactive rays, we now study the *rate* at which they are emitted. For each radioactive element the rate of emission is directly proportional to the mass of the sample present. This simple observation indicates that the atoms do not affect each other, *e.g.*, in stimulating the emission of rays.

In most cases the decay of the emitter is conveniently traced by the gradual decrease of the emission. A familiar laboratory experiment is the measurement of the decay of thorium emanation. Here the quantity of the active element is measured by its activity, say, every 20 sec; this can well be done by once admitting a trace of thorium emanation into the condenser of an ionization chamber and next charging the condenser, say, every 20 sec to the same initial potential difference and measuring the rate of discharge by observing the leaf of an electroscope. (Here we disregard the fact that each individual reading covers a time interval of a few seconds during which we average the rate.)

The observation shows that a given radioactive element always takes the same length of time, called the "half-life," to lose one-half of its original strength, *i.e.*, to decay to one-half of its original amount. Mathematically, this law of decay is expressed in the plot of the activity N (on an arbitrary scale) against the time t. Here we obtain a curve (Fig. 17.11a) which is represented by an exponential law

$$n = n_0 \, e^{-\lambda t} \qquad (17.1)$$

where n = instantaneous activity
  n_0 = initial activity
  λ = empirical factor, called "decay constant"

In a few cases a very small effect of the chemical binding or high pressure on the decay constant has been found. The effect is of interest for the theory of radioactive decay (Segrè, Bainbridge).

Instead of plotting n, we rather plot $\log_e n = \log_e n_0 - \lambda t$ (or $\log_{10} n = \log_{10} n_0 - 0.434\lambda t$) against the time t, as in Fig. 17.11b. The eye can judge directly the straight character of a line, while it is unable to judge whether or not a curve is well represented by an exponential function. Moreover, the logarithmic scale readily represents a range much wider than that represented by a linear scale.

The constant λ represents the reciprocal of the time during which the activity n decreases to the fraction $1/e$ of its initial value. The decay constant λ is closely connected with the half-life T.   A simple computation, carried out in Prob. 17.9, gives

$$T = \frac{\log_e 2}{\lambda} = \frac{0.693}{\lambda} \tag{17.2}$$

Since n_0 does not enter into the expression for the half-life T, T does not depend upon the quantity of the element present.   Furthermore, the measurement of T is not affected by the efficiency of our counting device, which may register only a small but fixed percentage of all disintegration processes actually occurring.

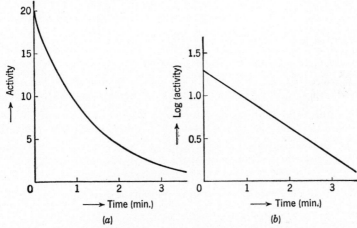

FIG. 17.11. Decay of thorium emanation. The exponential curve (a) is transformed into the straight line (b) by applying a logarithmic scale.

The observation described by Eq. (17.1) can be derived from the theoretical assumption that each atom has an intrinsic probability of disintegrating within any given time interval, irrespective of the disintegration of its neighbors.   On this basis we understand that in any fixed time interval *a certain fraction of the number of atoms* disintegrate.   In other words, when we consider a time interval Δt so short that within it the number n of atoms present is appreciably constant, then the number Δn decaying during Δt is proportional to n and Δt, the constant of proportionality λ being characteristic for the material and entirely independent of the physical conditions.   Hence,

$$\Delta n = -\lambda n \, \Delta t \tag{17.3}$$

In Prob. 17.18 it is proved that this fundamental assumption necessarily leads to the observed decay described by Eq. (17.1).   The quotient $\Delta n/\Delta t$ is called the "activity" of a radioactive sample.

In many observations of radioactive decay, the situation is complicated by the fact that the daughter substance in turn disintegrates and, therefore, does not accumulate without limit. This complication can be avoided completely in the case of radium if the daughter substance, the gas radon, is allowed to escape.

In the laboratory this situation must be carefully avoided, partly for reasons of health, partly because the escaping radon would deposit its daughter products on the walls of the laboratory and render them permanently radioactive.

We consider now the simple case in which the daughter substance is allowed to accumulate in the same container as the parent substance, say, radon (half-life, 3.82 days) with radium (half-life, 1,590 years). We start from pure radium; the daughter substance radon is generated at the same rate at which the radium decomposes. During the first minutes, the number of radon atoms is so small that their spontaneous decomposition (proportional to this number) is negligible as compared to the rate of their creation. However, when more radon accumulates, the uniform rate of its creation is more and more counterbalanced by the increasing rate of its decomposition. After a considerable length of time, these two rates become practically equal and so define the concentration of radon in "radioactive equilibrium" with radium. No larger concentration of the daughter substance can be created by the parent substance. This equilibrium is given by the equation stating that the rate of creation equals the rate of decomposition or, considering Eq. (17.3),

$$\lambda_p n_p \, \Delta t = \lambda_d n_d \, \Delta t$$

where the subscripts p and d indicate parent and daughter, respectively. The equilibrium concentration of the daughter element follows as

$$n_d = \frac{n_p \lambda_p}{\lambda_d} \tag{17.4}$$

This concentration goes down only very slowly with the decay of the parent substance radium. Hence an observer who paid attention only to the radon, disregarding the presence of the radium, would be misled into believing that radon decomposes with the long half-life of 1,590 years. The last equation is used for the determination of very long half-lives. For example, in uranium minerals radium is observed to be present in the constant relative concentration Ra/U = 3.4×10^{-7}, supposed to be the equilibrium concentration. Since the half-life of radium is 1,590 years, that of uranium is computed to 4.7×10^9 years.

We restricted our consideration of the radioactive equilibrium to the simple case of a parent and a daughter substance. In most cases the daughter substance in turn decomposes into products that are unstable and contribute to the activity observed. A good mechanical picture of radioactive equilibrium is given by several water containers, one placed below the other (Fig. 17.12). Any container except the first receives water in a stream more or less plentiful from its next upper neighbor and delivers it to its next lower neighbor. The last container is closed so that the water accumulates. It represents the stable end product of the decay (see Sec. 17.4). The case of radium and radon (long and short half-lives, respectively) is duplicated when we give a very narrow outlet to the top container and a much wider outlet to the next lower one. The experiment may begin with radium chemically purified, represented by all containers being empty except the highest. When we open its outlet, water will accumulate in its neighbor the water level of which will go up at a uniform rate because, to begin with, the rate of loss is small as compared with the rate of gain. But soon the rate of loss will become larger and slow down the rise of the water level. After some time, this level will reach a stationary state representing the radioactive equilibrium. The condition for this equilibrium states that the rate of gain equals the rate of loss.

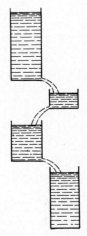

FIG. 17.12. Mechanical model of radioactive equilibrium.

Radioactive equilibrium between radium and radon enters into the original definition of the unit of activity, *i.e.*, the unit of $\Delta n/\Delta t$ [see Eq. (17.3)]. We simplify the definition as follows: One "curie" is the activity of any substance in which 3.7×10^{10} atoms disintegrate per second. (One curie gives the number per second of atoms disintegrating in 1 g of pure radium or in the equilibrium amount of pure radon.)

The two units, *curie* and *roentgen* (Sec. 14.1*d*), differ fundamentally. The *curie* defines a property of a specific radioactive sample; when its activity (in curies) and half-life are known, one can calculate the number of atoms present [see Eq. (17.3); the activity of short-lived daughter products, if there are any, must be taken into account]. Hence, when ordering radioactive material, the buyer states the number of curies desired of a substance whose half-life and type of activity he knows. On the other hand, the *roentgen* defines the biological effect of one exposure strictly speaking of air, implying that biological material suffers about the same effect. The unit roentgen per day is used to check to exposure of the operators of nuclear machines. For example, the "tolerance" of the human body (= permissible maximum exposure) is 0.1 roentgen per day assuming an exposure of the whole body. Here it is irrelevant whether the radiation consists of X rays, gamma rays, or neutrons (Sec. 18.2).

17.4. Radioactive Series. So far we have explored the *nature* of the radioactive rays by having them incident on the cloud chamber and other apparatus. Now we must discuss their *origin* and the *changes in the nuclei* connected with the emission processes. While it is easy for us to solve this problem since we are familiar with the nuclear atom, the original investigations (beginning about 1902), which are due to Rutherford, Soddy, and Fajans, were largely based on the chemical analysis of the parent and daughter substances.

In radioactive decay the atom whose nucleus emits an alpha or beta particle (= electron) changes its nuclear charge, hence its chemical nature. Our present knowledge of these particles and nuclei is so thorough that we can predict the change in the nucleus brought about by the emission. The *alpha particle* carries the mass 4 (in mass numbers) and the positive charge 2 (in electronic charges) away from the parent nucleus. Consequently the daughter nucleus is lighter by mass number 4 and is displaced 2 atomic numbers backward in the periodic table. The *beta particle*, emitted from the nucleus, has no appreciable mass but carries away the negative charge 1, hence leaves a daughter nucleus of unchanged mass number but displaced 1 atomic number forward higher in the periodic table. In both cases the change of packing fraction (the higher decimal places of the atomic weight) can be predicted only if we know the kinetic energy of the alpha or beta particle emitted. In this argument we presuppose that the electron is emitted from *the nucleus* and not ejected from an

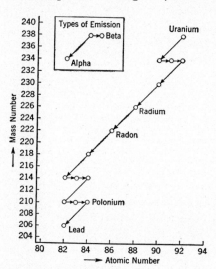

Fig. 17.13. Uranium series. The rare alternatives in two cases of branching are omitted.

outer shell by "internal conversion" (Sec. 17.2). The beta emission from the nucleus may be visualized as the spontaneous splitting of a neutron, contained in the nucleus, into a proton and an electron (see Prob. 18.4). While the electron is ejected, the proton stays in the nucleus and raises its atomic number by one.

The laws here stated, called the "displacement" laws, are represented in the diagram of Fig. 17.13. Here each element, characterized by its *atomic number*, occupies a certain place on the abscissa, while its various isotopes, characterized by their *mass numbers*, are displayed along the ordinate.   The emission of an alpha particle produces a new atom two places to the left and four places down.   (In the diagram only every second mass number is plotted.)   A beta emission shifts the nucleus only one place to the right.   The diagram shows the wide extension of this series of disintegration processes beginning with $_{92}U^{238}$ and ending with $_{82}Pb^{206}$, which we have mentioned before as one of the stable isotopes of lead (Sec. 16.5).

The facts represented in Fig. 17.13 are given in Table 17.1 which includes the half-lives of the various elements covering a range between 10^{-6} sec and 4.7×10^9 years.   (Very short half-lives have not been measured with a watch but estimated from an empirical relation between the half-life and the range of the alpha particle emitted.   We omit the discussion of this relation.)   Each isotope has its characteristic half-life and, in the great majority of cases, emits either an alpha or a beta particle.   There are two exceptional cases of "branching" in which a few hundredths of 1 per cent of the disintegrating atoms chose an alternative way down toward $_{82}Pb^{206}$ (omitted on the diagram and the table).

Our present knowledge of the nuclear charges and the nature of alpha and beta particles makes the displacement laws represented in this diagram quite obvious.   At the time of the discovery these laws, independently found by Fajans and Soddy (1913), represented great progress.   The experiments required to establish them consist largely of chemical analysis.   We have mentioned already the simplest case, the relation between radium and radon.   Radium was recognized by the Curies as an

Table 17.1.   *Uranium-Radium Series*
(Omitting two rare cases of branching)

Mass No.	Atomic No.	Element	Radiation	Half-life
238	92	Uranium I	α	$4.6 \times 10^9 y$
234	90	Uranium X_1	β	$24.1d$
234	91	Uranium X_2	β	$1.14m$
234	92	Uranium II	α	$2.7 \times 10^5 y$
230	90	Ionium	α	$8.3 \times 10^4 y$
226	88	Radium	α	$1,590y$
222	86	Radon	α	$3.825d$
218	84	Radium A	α	$3.05m$
214	82	Radium B	β	$26.8m$
214	83	Radium C	β	$19.7m$
214	84	Radium C'	α	$1.50 \times 10^{-4}s$
210	82	Radium D	β	$22y$
210	83	Radium E	β	$5.0d$
210	84	Polonium	α	$140d$
206	82	Lead		

alkaline earth. It was found that the emission of an alpha particle leads to a daughter element called "radon," previously unknown, chemically identified as a rare gas, hence, in the periodic table, preceding the parent element by two places. Another example is given by the beta emission from radium D, which is an isotope of lead and generates an element chemically identified as bismuth which follows lead in the periodic table. Thus chemical analysis led to the displacement law. Here an outstanding experimental problem of research in radioactivity appears, the chemical separation of neighbors or near neighbors in the periodic table. In modern research on the transmutation of elements, this chemical problem plays a major part, all over the periodic table of elements. In many cases this analysis is made difficult by the short half-lives of the elements, which prevent the accumulation of an appreciable quantity. The distinction of the element radium is due to the fact that it has a half-life sufficiently long to permit a weighable accumulation, and yet sufficiently short to make its radioactivity strongly noticeable. The results reported above, based on chemical analysis and the properties of alpha and beta particles, may be considered as another powerful confirmation of the law stating that the atomic number equals the nuclear charge.

We have introduced isotopes as the result of investigations with the mass spectrograph (Chap. 16; Aston, 1921). Historically, isotopes were discovered much earlier as the products of radioactive disintegration (Soddy). For example, $_{92}U^{238}$, by emitting an alpha particle, changes into $_{90}UX_1^{234}$, which is a heavy, short-lived isotope of the chemically known thorium $_{90}Th^{232}$. The occurrence of many isotopes among the heavy elements has been discovered by means of such relations. For example, Fig. 17.13 and Table 17.1 show that Ra B, Ra D, and lead are all isotopes of the element 82. A simple relation in which isotopes are predicted is evident in the disintegration of uranium $_{92}U^{238}$, the parent element of the whole series. By alpha emission it is transmuted into the element of atomic number 90 and mass number 234. The product emits 2 beta particles in succession and so brings the atom back to the atomic number of uranium but to an atomic weight smaller by 4. It follows that here an isotope of the parent element uranium is formed.

In addition to the *uranium-radium series* just discussed, two more such series have been known for many years. The *actinium series* begins with the rare uranium isotope $_{92}U^{235}$ and ends with lead $_{82}Pb^{207}$; the *thorium series* beginning with thorium $_{90}Th^{232}$ ends with the heavier lead isotope $_{82}Pb^{208}$. We shall not discuss the detail of these series, which follow the same principles as the uranium-radium series. Recently a fourth series was discovered which does not contain any element of half-life long enough to make it appear in nature. The series starts from artificially produced plutonium $_{94}Pu^{241}$ (see Sec. 19.1; this isotope originates from

$_{92}U^{238}$ by alpha, not by neutron, bombardment); the series ends with the stable bismuth isotope $_{83}Bi^{209}$. It is given the name "neptunium series" after the longest-lived member. These new results demonstrate that our knowledge of the radioactive series is limited by our technical ability to isolate short-lived radioactive elements. What we consider to be the first member of a series may well be the daughter of a short-lived element not found in nature.

All the radioactive isotopes contained in these four series belong to the heaviest elements. This agrees with our discussion of Aston's packing-fraction curve (Sec. 16.4). A large packing fraction, *i.e.*, a high location on the curve, is identified with large energy stored in the nucleus. All heavy, radioactive elements are located on the right, rising wing of the curve and so indicate the explosive tendency of their nuclei. It is a surprising exception that two lighter elements, the rare potassium isotope $_{19}K^{40}$ and the rubidium isotope $_{37}Rb^{87}$, show beta-ray emission. Both have very long half-lives; otherwise they would not be found in nature.

17.5. Report on the Theory of the Nucleus. What are the forces that keep the nuclei assembled? The only force we are sure of is the Coulomb repulsion, which tends to disrupt the nuclei. This repulsion explains satisfactorily the scattering of alpha particles even at approaches as close as about 10^{-12} cm (see Sec. 9.3). Hence, outside of this distance the Coulomb repulsion is the outstanding force acting between nuclei. In order to explain the existence of nuclei of positive charges larger than that of the proton, we must assume that for closer approaches of protons and neutrons new forces of attraction come into play, which are over-whelmingly larger than the Cou-lomb repulsion acting between the positive charges. Although we do not know these mysterious forces well enough to predict nuclear structures, we can describe some experimental facts by a simple curve of potential energy that may be visualized as a mechanical model.

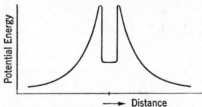

FIG. 17.14. Potential-energy diagram describing alpha emission.

Alpha rays are always emitted with a high kinetic energy characteristic of the radioactive element. (This differs from electron emission from a glowing filament, which occurs with negligible energy; see Fig. 15.2.) We accordingly picture a potential curve, remembering that the slope of the curve represents the force acting on a charged particle. The protons and neutrons constituting the nucleus (called by a common name "nucle-ons") may be partly lumped together as alpha particles. The particles are pictured as contained in a deep well (Fig. 17.14) within which they perform a random motion. One may attribute a temperature to the assembly of these particles, but this temperature bears no relation to the temperature of a body measured with a thermometer, since no energy exchange takes place between the particles within the nucleus and all the atoms constituting the body.   Occasionally, an alpha particle is pictured as thrown up to such a height that it escapes over the rim.   Outside the nucleus the alpha particle (unlike the electron ejected from a metal) is subjected to the Coulomb repulsion, which gives it the high kinetic energy observed.   The potential energy of the alpha particle with respect to the nucleus is highest near the rim of the well and decreases with increasing distance.

In Sec. 10.3 we computed this potential energy for the case of the electron and the nucleus as $-Ze^2/r$.   A similar expression applies to the alpha particle; but here repulsion takes place instead of attraction.

Graphically the potential energy is represented by a curve sloping down from the rim of the well (proportional to $1/r$).   Hence in the mechanical picture an ejected particle rolls down the slope and so acquires a high kinetic energy.   These slopes surrounding the well make the model appear like a volcano that occasionally erupts.

How high above the surroundings is the rim of the crater?   The kinetic energy of the alpha particles emitted seems to give a direct answer, because we visualize that a particle that is just thrown out of the crater "rolls down" the whole slope and, by the kinetic energy thus picked up, indicates the height of the crater over its surroundings.   For example, alpha particles from uranium U^{238} are ejected with a kinetic energy of 4.2 Mev.   Here, however, we encounter a vast discrepancy that indicates that our mechanical model is too simple.   In our discussion of the size of the nucleus (Sec. 9.3) we studied another method of measuring the height of the rim over the surroundings, *i.e.*, the observation of the scattering of alpha particles *coming from an outside source* and incident on uranium. This process is correctly described by the theory of scattering for energies of alpha particles as high as 8.8 Mev.   We must conclude that the *impinging alpha particles* when approaching the nucleus even with this high energy are repelled simply by the Coulomb force.   According to this argument, the height of the rim over the surroundings must be at least 8.8 Mev, hence much higher than indicated by the energy of the *alpha particles spontaneously ejected* from uranium.

This discrepancy is solved by wave mechanics.   Here, in contrast with Newtonian mechanics, a particle contained in the crater has a chance to escape even if its energy is not sufficient to lift it over the rim.   For any height of the particle *in the well* wave mechanics predicts a certain probability of finding the particle *outside the well*.   This is commonly referred to as the "tunnel effect."   An alpha particle contained in the well may collide very frequently with the walls without escaping. But there is a chance for an occasional favorable hit that leads to escape. These are the alpha particles we observe as emitted from uranium. (The same idea applies to the alpha particles bombarding the uranium nucleus from outside in the scattering experiment. Most of these alpha particles bounce off as a sphere would roll back from a slope like that of Fig. 17.14 and are recorded as scattered. In the same experiment it is not noticeable that a very few alpha particles penetrate as if through a tunnel into the interior of the uranium atom.) The quantitative application of wave mechanics leads to the prediction of a law correlating the half-life of the nucleus and the range of the alpha particle ejected. This law, which we shall not further discuss, agrees well with the observed facts (Geiger-Nuttall law).

The sharply defined energies of alpha and gamma rays and the sharp energy limit of beta rays give evidence of sharply defined energy levels in the radioactive nuclei. However, our knowledge of *nuclear* levels is very poor as compared with our detailed and accurate knowledge of energy levels of the *electronic system* (Chaps. 10 and 11). An example is as follows. When thorium C disintegrates by alpha emission into thorium C″, the alpha rays show a fine structure. There are five sharply defined rays with energies between 5.7 and 6.2 Mev. It is assumed that the final nucleus after the alpha emission, *i.e.*, thorium C″, may retain part of the total energy available in an excited level and emit it as a gamma-ray quantum almost instantaneously. Such gamma rays are observed, and their energies agree with the energy differences between the alpha rays.

We shall introduce a more detailed picture of nuclear forces in Sec. 19.3.

17.6. Applications. We shall discuss applications of radioactivity to geology, to medicine, and to the "tracer" method which solves widely different problems of many fields of science. This is a wide field which we can illustrate by only a few examples.

Suppose that in the earliest geological period a rock was formed with uranium present but no lead. The gradual decomposition of uranium slowly generates lead, and, since we know all decay constants, in particular the very low decay constant of uranium (Sec. 17.3), we can compute the amount of lead formed per year. Conversely, when we measure the amount of lead present in the mineral, we can compute its *age*. Here it is assumed that no ordinary lead, recognized by its isotopic constitution, is present but that all the lead present is of the isotope 206 and so manifests its radioactive origin (see Sec. 16.5). A typical result of a numerical computation (given as Prob. 17.13) is an age of rocks of about 650 million years.

In Sec. 17.3 dealing with the half-life we went through a related argument and computed the concentration of *radium* in the presence of uranium. In that case a certain equilibrium concentration is approached after a period of several times the half-life of the product because the latter is itself *unstable*. On the other hand, in the present case an unlimited accumulation takes place since we are concerned with the gradual accumulation of lead, the *stable* final product.

Generally known is the *therapeutic effect* of radioactivity. It was observed quite early that radium preparations have a slow, destructive effect on the skin, producing sores similar to burns. This effect, although vicious in many cases, proves beneficial in the treatment of tumors. Fortunately, it turned out that tumors are more susceptible to destruction than healthy tissue. Here *beta and gamma rays* are most effective while alpha rays have not sufficient penetrating power. Thus radium proper, being an alpha emitter, is not used. Radon, however, although itself an alpha emitter, has daughter elements which, after short half-lives, emit two beta particles and gamma rays (see Table 17.1). They are accordingly most useful for radiotherapy. This explains the use of radium at the hospital. Radium itself, the costly parent substance, in the shape of the chloride, is kept in a closed glass container from which the radon generated is taken off at regular intervals. The radon is collected in tiny "needles," glass tubes thin as needles, about $\frac{1}{4}$ in. long. While they are used on the patient, they lose their activity with a half-life of 3.82 days and are of no further medical value when, after one or two weeks, most of the radon has disintegrated into Ra D, which, in turn, has a half-life of 22 years. At the physics laboratory these old radon needles, although useless at the hospital, are still of considerable interest. For example, one may separate out the polonium, which has the distinction of being a pure alpha emitter, without generating daughter elements that would emit beta rays (see Table 17.1). For the application of radio cobalt, produced in the nuclear reactor, see Sec. 19.8.

During recent years the application of radioactive elements as "tracers" has developed into a field of major importance (Hevesy and Paneth, beginning 1913). This application of such elements is based on the fact that, with the help of the Geiger counter, they may be traced in exceedingly small quantities, very far below the limit of chemical detection. We shall discuss only one example. Bismuth exists as a stable element of considerable medical interest and, in addition, occurs in the various radioactive series. One isotope of bismuth, called Ra E, has a half-life of 5 days and lends itself well to biological investigations. Bismuth is prepared with a small addition of Ra E, which has exactly the same chemical properties. Thus the fate of the bismuth in the animal or human organism is traced by testing the radioactivity of the parts of the body. For example, it has been found that cancerous tissue retains larger amounts of bismuth than healthy tissue. The application of radioactive elements as tracers started from the use of natural radioactivity. This field has had a rapid development after the discovery of artificial radioactivity which made a great new variety of elements applicable. We shall come back to this field in Sec. 19.8.

SUMMARY OF CHAPTER 17

1. Uranium minerals emit radiations that blacken photographic plates and ionize air. The most active element of this kind is *radium*. The various rays are endowed with energies of several Mev. Radioactive elements are permanently generating small quantities of other elements. Radioactive disintegration is due to the large energy stored in the nucleus, released at a rate that depends on intrinsic properties of the nucleus, unaffected by almost anything we can do to it like heating or bombarding with electrons.

2. A magnetic field separates radioactive rays into three types: positively charged *alpha rays*, negatively charged *beta rays*, and uncharged *gamma rays*.

Alpha rays are helium nuclei of high velocity. They are counted in the *Geiger counter*. This is a special electric gas-discharge tube operated on a voltage slightly below the threshold required for a self-maintained discharge. Each individual alpha particle passing through the counter produces so much ionization that a discharge of brief duration is started and counted on a mechanical recorder. The rays are made visible in the *Wilson cloud chamber;* here the row of ions produced by an alpha particle in air causes the condensation of water from the supersaturated air; the cloud track so formed is visible under intense illumination. Each water droplet gives evidence of one ionization process. Each kink in an alpha-ray track shows that a collision with a nucleus, a much rarer event, has taken place.

Beta rays consist of fast electrons. They have a higher penetrating power than alpha rays. The beta-ray spectrograph, based on the magnetic deflection, shows that beta rays originating from nuclei have continuous ranges of energy with sharp high-energy limits. There is, however, a special class of beta-ray spectra of sharply defined energy; these consist of "secondary" electrons ejected by gamma rays from the K or L or M shell of the emitter. The cloud chamber shows that the tracks of beta rays are much longer and more crooked than those of alpha rays.

Gamma rays have a penetrating power very much higher than that of alpha or beta rays. They are identical with X rays of very short wavelengths.

A comparison of the various rays is given on Table 17.2.

3. The decay of a radioactive element is described by a simple exponential function, characterized by the *decay constant* λ or, instead, the *half-life T*. This is explained by the assumption that each element has an

Table 17.2. *Comparison of Light, X Rays, and Rays from Natural Radioactive Substances*

	Light or X rays	Alpha rays	Beta rays	Gamma rays
Character.	Quanta $h\nu$ (governed by waves of length c/ν)	He^{++} ions = He nuclei	Electrons	Same as X rays, same or shorter wavelength
Velocity...	Velocity of light c	Up to $1/15\,c$	Up to $99.8/100\,c$	c
Energy of particle or quantum	Visible light: several ev. Technical X rays: $10^4 - 10^6$ ev	Up to 8.8×10^6 ev	Up to 2×10^6 ev	Up to several 10^6 ev
Penetrating power		$1/100$ mm aluminum	Several $1/10$ mm aluminum	Several cm lead
Absorption, observed	$I = I_0 e^{-\mu x}$	Limited range; dense ionization over the full length of range; straight paths except very rare sharp deflections	Limited, not sharply defined range; less dense ionization than by α rays; crooked paths	$I = I_0 e^{-\mu x}$ good approximation
Absorption, theory	Each quantum when absorbed gives away total energy in one process; fraction of energy lost per cm path is constant	Each particle spends its energy on many ionization processes; no deflection in collisions with electrons because of large mass of α particle; very rare sharp deflection in collision with nuclei	Each particle spends its energy on many ionization processes; deflection occurs since β particle is light	Each quantum when absorbed gives away its energy in one of a few processes: ionization (photoelectric effect), Compton effect, or pair production
Relation to emitting atom	Wavelength sharply defined characteristic for electronic structure of emitting atom	Energy of α particle sharply defined, characteristic for emitting nucleus	*Continuous* β-ray spectra with sharp high-energy limit are characteristic for emitting nucleus; *sharp-line β-ray* spectra represent emission of K or L . . . electrons ejected by γ rays from nucleus	Wavelength of γ ray sharply defined, characteristic for emitting nucleus

intrinsic probability of disintegration, in other words, that the number Δn of atoms disintegrating during the short time interval Δt is proportional to the number of atoms n present.   If the daughter substance itself is active, it accumulates only to a limited equilibrium concentration.   The unit of radioactivity, 1 curie, is defined as the activity of any substance in which 3.7×10^{10} atoms disintegrate per second.

4. The emission of alpha or beta particles is responsible for the *spontaneous transmutation of elements*.   Thus uranium $_{92}U^{238}$ is gradually transmuted into $_{88}Ra^{226}$ and, in many further steps, finally into the stable lead isotope $_{82}Pb^{206}$.   The emission of an alpha particle produces a new element with an atomic number smaller by 2 and a mass number smaller by 4.   The emission of a beta particle increases the atomic number by 1 and leaves the mass number unchanged (displacement laws). These transmutations have led to the discovery of *isotopes* before the mass

spectrograph.   There are three more radioactive series, the actinium, the thorium, and the neptunium series, all following the same principles.

5. The emission of an alpha particle is represented by a *mechanical model* resembling an erupting volcano.   Wave mechanics predicts the tunnel effect, *i.e.*, the occasional passing of the alpha particle through the thin wall of the volcano.

6. *Radioactivity is applied* to the determination of the age of minerals. For medical applications beta and gamma rays are most important. Usually they are applied as coming from daughter substances of radon which is sealed into tiny glass needles.   Radioactive isotopes serve as tracers.

PROBLEMS

17.1. *Deflection of alpha rays.*   Radium emits alpha rays of a velocity $v = 1.519 \times 10^9$ cm/sec.   How large a magnetic induction B (in gauss) is needed to bend them in a circle of radius $R = 50$ cm?   How large an electric field E (in volts/cm) must be superimposed on the magnetic field (as in Fig. 6.2) to compensate for this magnetic deflection?

17.2. *Avogadro's number.*   A microgram (10^{-6} g) of radium (which is not separated from its products) emits 14.8×10^4 alpha particles per second.   One gram of radium produces 172 mm^3 of helium gas under standard conditions per year.   Compute Avogadro's number.   Density of helium gas under standard conditions $= 1.77 \times 10^{-4}$ g/cm^3.

17.3. *Energy consumed by ionization process.*   Alpha particles of 4.2 Mev energy have a range in air of 2.6 cm.   The track has a density of about 50,000 ions/cm. Calculate the average energy consumed by each ionization process.

17.4. *Total ionization by single alpha particle.*   An ionization chamber (capacitance 50×10^{-12} farad) is charged to 1,000 volts and then disconnected.   By what percentage is the original charge reduced when a single alpha particle passing through the chamber generates 200,000 ion-electron pairs?

COMMENT: The result shows that the effect can be measured only with the help of an amplifier.

17.5. *Alpha-particle impacts.*   Using the result of Prob. 9.1, calculate the velocities of the two emergent particles when a 2.1-Mev alpha particle makes a head-on elastic impact on (a) $_1H^1$; (b) $_2He^4$; (c) $_8O^{16}$.   These nuclei are supposed to be at rest before the impact.

17.6. *Internal conversion.*   The element $_{83}$Ra C emits a gamma ray of sharply defined quanta which, by internal conversion, liberates electrons of the energies 36.74, 37.37, 39.63, and 48.85 kev, respectively.   The X-ray absorption limits of the element 83 have the energies 16.34, 15.67, 13.38, 3.99 kev.   Calculate the energy of the gamma ray (in kev).

17.7. *Wavelength of gamma ray.*   Wavelengths of gamma rays may be measured by the Compton effect.   The rays when passing through a cloud chamber eject "Compton electrons."   We select only those electrons that are ejected in the direction along which the gamma ray is aimed ($\theta = 0$).   Then the impinging quanta are scattered backward [$\phi = 180°$; see Eq. (III) of theory].   Suppose that the range of the ejected electron indicates a kinetic energy of 18.0×10^{-10} erg.   Calculate the wavelength of the gamma ray.

17.8. *Determination of half-life.*   The activity of thorium emanation is measured at intervals of 1 min by the rate of discharge of an electroscope as follows: 100, 47,

22, 10. (This means that each measurement of the rate is performed in a period small as compared to 1 min.) (a) Plot these counts as a function of the time. (b) Plot the $\log_{10}$ of these counts as a function of the time. (c) From your diagram determine the half-life. Notice that for the measurement of the half-life the type of instrument used and the unit of activity are immaterial.

17.9. *Relation between half-life and decay constant.* A radioactive substance is decaying according to Eq. (17.1). (a) Compute the time T during which the initial number n_0 of molecules is reduced to half its value. (b) Compute the time T' during which the initial number N_0 is reduced to 90 per cent of its value.

17.10. *Number of particles emitted.* Radium has a half-life of 1,590 years. (a) What fraction of the radium disintegrates within 1 sec? (b) How many alpha particles are emitted per second from 1 mg of radium? Disregard the alpha particles emitted by the disintegration processes succeeding in the radioactive series. (c) What fraction disintegrates within 300 years? (d) What fraction is left after 5 half-lives?

17.11. *Concentration of K^{40}.* The present abundance of the radioactive potassium isotope K^{40} is 0.011 per cent. Calculate its abundance as of the time of the origin of rocks, say 10^9 years ago. Half-life of $K^{40} = 4 \times 10^8$ years.

17.12. *Current emitted from radium.* (a) How large a number of alpha particles is emitted per second from 1 g pure radium? (b) Calculate the electric current represented by this emission. (c) Answer question (a) for radium that contains all daughter products in the equilibrium concentration (see Table 17.1).

17.13. *Age of rocks.* In a uranium mineral, lead is found predominantly of the isotope 206, indicating the radioactive origin of the lead. The mineral contains 0.093 g lead to 1 g uranium. Calculate the age of the mineral. Given: half-life of $_{92}U^{238} = 4.5 \times 10^9$ years. All other elements of the uranium series have much shorter half-lives.

HINT: (a) Calculate the decay constant λ. (b) Calculate $n =$ present number of uranium atoms and $n_0 =$ initial number of uranium atoms = present number of (uranium + lead) atoms. Calculate the time t from Eq. (17.1).

17.14. *Equilibrium concentration of radon.* Compute the number of atoms and the mass of radon in equilibrium with 1 g of radium called "1 curie of radon." Given the atomic weights and half-lives (Ra^{226}, 1,590 years; Rn^{222}, 3.82 days).

17.15. *Half-life of uranium.* The very long half-life of $_{92}U^{238}$ is determined by measuring the equilibrium concentration of $_{88}Ra^{226}$, which is always found associated with uranium in a relative concentration by weight $= 3.31 \times 10^{-7}$. Calculate the half-life of $_{92}U^{238}$, taking that of Ra from Table 17.1.

17.16. *Activity expressed in curies.* After a certain nuclear reaction (see Chap. 18) radioactive sodium $_{11}Na^{24}$ is found with an activity of 0.01 millicurie and a half-life of 14.8 hr. Compute the disintegration constant λ, the number N of sodium atoms present, and their total mass.

17.17. *Thorium series.* Enter the thorium series into the diagram of Fig. 17.13, beginning with $_{90}Th^{232}$ and continuing with the following sequence of emission processes: alpha, 2 beta, 4 alpha, beta, alpha, beta. What is the final product of the series?

17.18. *Radioactive disintegration (calculus problem).* Suppose that a radioactive substance decays spontaneously, *i.e.*, with a certain *intrinsic probability.* This has the effect that the number Δn of atoms disintegrating in the short time interval Δt (counted with the Geiger counter) is proportional to Δt, the number n present at the time t, and nothing else. The factor of proportionality λ, called the "disintegration constant," is characteristic of the substance. Calling n_0 the number of atoms present at $t = 0$, express the number n present after the long time interval t in terms of t and n_0. Compare with the empirical equation 17.1.

HINT: Apply the same method as in Prob. 12.9.

17.19. *Growth of a daughter substance (calculus problem)*. Starting with chemically pure radium at the time $t = 0$, consider the growth of the daughter substance radon. Radon is *generated* at a *constant rate* (because of the very long half-life of radium) and *consumed* at *a rate proportional to the instantaneous number of its atoms*. (a) Calculate the number n of radon atoms, in terms of the time t, the (constant) number of radium atoms N, and the decay constants λ_1 and λ_2 of radium and radon, respectively. There is no radon present at $t = 0$. (b) From your general result derive the special equation expressing n for $t = \infty$ (the "equilibrium concentration").

HINT: The differential equation must express the fact that, in any time interval dt, the change of n equals the gain (coming from the radium) minus the loss (due to decomposition of the radon). Introduce $y = \lambda_1 N - \lambda_2 n$ as a new variable.

17.20. *Operation of a radium plant*. Suppose you are asked to remove the radon from the radium plant of a hospital whenever it has reached $\frac{1}{2}$ of its equilibrium concentration. How often must you remove it? Start from the result of the preceding problem. Use Table 17.1.

CHAPTER 18

ARTIFICIAL TRANSMUTATION AND RADIOACTIVITY

During the Middle Ages the search for gold was an outstanding incentive for research in chemistry. The conversion of a common metal into gold was the chief aim of many medieval alchemists. This problem has been solved within the past decades, though at a scale too small to satisfy the fantastic hopes of the alchemists and with an effort and technical development far surpassing anything they could imagine. In the present chapter we shall follow the historical development and begin with discoveries made without the modern machines for the production of high-energy particles. Then we shall describe these machines and the wealth of new results obtained by their application until, finally, in uranium fission, we shall come to the controlled production of nuclear energy.

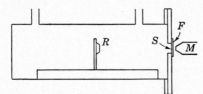

Fig. 18.1. Rutherford's discovery of the artificial transmutation of nitrogen; chamber filled with nitrogen. S, silver foil; F, fluorescent screen; M, microscope; R, sliding holder of radium sample.

18.1. Discovery of Artificial Transmutation. The observation of the well-defined range in air of alpha particles (Sec. 17.2a) led to the systematic exploration of their ranges in various gases. During such measurements (1919) Rutherford found a very rare type of scintillation when the chamber was filled with nitrogen (Fig. 18.1). As the source R, emitting alpha rays, is gradually moved away from the fluorescent screen F, the *abundant* scintillations stop abruptly at the well-defined distance of 7 cm (which includes the air equivalent of the silver foil). Nevertheless some *very rare* scintillations continue for a distance as large as 40 cm. Cloud-chamber pictures, too, show occasional tracks of abnormal lengths generated by alpha particles impinging on nitrogen nuclei (Fig. 18.2).

What is the *nature* of these rays of long range and what is their *origin?* The standard procedure (Sec. 6.2) for a determination of the specific charge and velocity cannot be applied to these rays because it applies only to rays that originate from a well-defined spot like a glowing filament, while these new rays start anywhere in the volume of the chamber.

Therefore, a less straightforward line of argument must be used. The rays are recognized as consisting of *fast protons* (1) by their long range and (2) by their cloud-chamber tracks, which are less dense than those of alpha rays (Sec. 17.2a). By experiments with artificially produced fast protons a relation between the range of protons and their initial velocity has been found (Sec. 17.2a). Hence the range observed in Rutherford's experiment can be taken to indicate the velocity. This complicated argument is confirmed by the deflection of the rays in a strong magnetic field. Here the cloud-chamber tracks indicate the positive charge of the particles and confirm the value of e/m as that of protons when their velocity is derived from their range as just mentioned. Thus there is no doubt about the *nature* of the rays; they consist of fast protons generated somehow by alpha rays passing through nitrogen.

Regarding the *origin* of the rays, one may suspect that the nitrogen contains traces of gaseous hydrogen as an impurity and that these rays of long range are due simply to impacts of alpha particles on hydrogen nuclei (similar to that shown in Fig. 17.5a). This trivial explanation, however, cannot be correct for two reasons: (1) The same alpha rays when passing through *hydrogen* produce proton rays of much shorter range, only up to 28 cm instead of the 40 cm characteristic of the new rays observed here (both figures for rays ejected forward). (2) The ordinary elastic collisions, like collisions between billiard balls, necessarily cause the particle to be ejected with a *forward* component, whereas the cloud chamber shows the surprising fact that in nitrogen some of the protons are ejected *sideways* and even *backward* (Fig. 18.2). These arguments prove that the protons ejected are not due to hydrogen present as an impurity but to a fundamentally new process.

We continue by quoting Rutherford's paper (1919):

From the results so far obtained it is difficult to avoid the conclusion that the long-range atoms arising from collisions of alpha particles with nitrogen are not nitrogen atoms but probably atoms of hydrogen . . . . If this be the case, we must conclude that the nitrogen atom is disintegrated under the intense forces developed in a close collision with a swift alpha particle, and that the hydrogen atom which is liberated formed a constituent part of the nitrogen nucleus . . . . The results as a whole suggest that, if alpha particles—or similar projectiles—of still greater energy were available for experiment, we might expect to break down the nuclear structure of many of the lighter atoms.

Since the proton is observed with considerably higher kinetic energy than it could receive in an ordinary collision with an alpha particle, one must assume that the alpha particle and the nitrogen nucleus form a "complex" containing, as internal energy, most of the kinetic energy of the impinging alpha particle. (Not all the kinetic energy of the alpha particle is transferred to internal energy because of the conservation of momentum; see Prob. 18.15.) This energy content immediately breaks up the complex. Since the probability of this process is very small indeed, the amount of hydrogen produced is far below the chemically detectable limit. Only one alpha particle in a million gives rise to the ejection of a proton.

What happens to the alpha particle and the nitrogen nucleus in this collision? The cloud-chamber picture gives the answer (Fig. 18.2). It shows only two tracks after the collision process: the light track of the proton and a heavy track that must be attributed to the other nuclear

FIG. 18.2. Cloud-chamber photograph of the artificial transmutation of a nitrogen atom by an alpha particle. (*Courtesy of P. M. S. Blackett and Proceedings of the Royal Society.*)

masses sticking together. Simple arithmetic shows that $_7N^{14}$ combining with $_2He^4$, after losing $_1H^1$, forms $_8O^{17}$, *i.e.*, the nucleus of a rare isotope of oxygen. For the sake of computation it is convenient to introduce an intermediate particle called the "compound nucleus" which would result if the projectile $_2He^4$ and the target $_7N^{14}$ should actually stick together. This would be the rare fluorine isotope $_9F^{18}$, which, instead of having a stable nucleus, would have a nucleus endowed with high energy and thus would immediately split into $_1H^1$ and $_8O^{17}$. The nuclear reaction here described is conveniently written

$$_7N^{14} + _2He^4 \rightarrow (_9F^{18}) \rightarrow _1H^1 + _8O^{17}$$

or, shorter, $_7N^{14} (\alpha, p) _8O^{17}$, stating in brackets first the projectile, next the particle knocked out.

In summary then we have the result that a fast *helium* nucleus colliding with a *nitrogen* nucleus may produce a transmutation, knocking out a *hydrogen* nucleus and combining itself with the residual to form *oxygen* $_8O^{17}$. Rutherford made this great discovery also with a strikingly simple technique involving the painstaking scrutiny of scintillations.

Rutherford and his collaborators extended the search for nuclear transmutations to other elements which they subjected to bombardment by alpha particles. Most of the lighter elements show corresponding effects. It is easily understood why the effect cannot be obtained with heavier elements. Their nuclei, because of the higher positive charges, repel the alpha particle, itself a positively charged body, so strongly that the approach is never close enough to lead to a nuclear reaction. This is a general limitation on the effect of charged projectiles on nuclei, the heavy nuclei being protected by high but not insurmountable electrostatic barriers.

18.2. Neutrons. *a. Discovery of Neutrons.* In 1932 and 1933 four important discoveries, initiating a new epoch in nuclear research, followed each other within a short period. They are the discoveries of the neutron, the positron, artificial radioactivity, and nuclear transmutations by high-energy particles generated in machines.

Rutherford's discovery of the nuclear transmutation caused by alpha-particle bombardment of N atoms initiated the systematic search for other cases of transmutation. The prospect for such transmutations should be best among the light elements because their small nuclear charges allow sufficiently close approaches of the impinging alpha particles. In such experiments it was discovered that beryllium, $_4Be^9$, when bombarded by alpha particles, gives off a highly penetrating radiation (Bothe, 1930). At first this was believed to be gamma radiation, which, in 1930, was by far the most penetrating radiation known. In the following year Irène Curie-Joliot and F. Joliot made the striking observation that the ionization chamber in which the "beryllium rays" are recorded shows an *increased* effect when paraffin or other matter containing hydrogen is placed, like an absorber, in front of the window of the ionization chamber. They interpreted this effect by assuming that the beryllium rays have the unexpected power of ejecting fast protons from the paraffin and that these, in turn, enhance the ionizing effect observed in the chamber. For the process of ejection they assumed that gamma-ray quanta constituting the beryllium ray exert a Compton effect on the protons contained in the paraffin. It is true that the original theory of the Compton effect has been introduced for a different problem, the collisions of quanta and *electrons*. But there is no reason why the same theory should not apply to the collisions of quanta and *protons*.

However, Chadwick pointed out an intrinsic contradiction to which this interpretation leads. The difficulty becomes evident from quantitative considerations as follows. The "recoil protons" are given the highest possible energy when they are ejected in the direction in which the incident radiation is traveling (see Fig. 18.3). In this case their kinetic energy, inferred from their range in air, amounts to 5.7 Mev. How large, then, is the gamma-ray quantum which, by Compton effect, would transfer so much energy to the proton? The answer is derived from the theory of the Compton effect simplified by the special assumption of a head-on collision—in other words, of a collision in which all motion occurs in a straight line. This computation (see Prob. 18.1) gives the energy of the hypothetical quantum $h\nu$ in terms of the measured velocity v of the recoiling nucleus (mass m) as

$$h\nu = \frac{mv}{4}(2c + v) \cong \frac{mvc}{2}$$

For our special case the energy of the quantum $h\nu$ is computed as 55 Mev. The numerical value of this energy is unexpectedly large and difficult to reconcile with the energies stored in light nuclei according to Aston's curve of packing fractions.

An intrinsic contradiction, however, becomes manifest when we perform the same experiment for the case of *nitrogen* instead of hydrogen. Here the range of the nitrogen "recoil nuclei" produced by the beryllium radiation indicates their kinetic energy as about 1.2 Mev. The corresponding energy of the hypothetical impinging gamma-ray quanta is computed as 90 Mev. These are the same quanta which when passing through *hydrogen* seem to contain only 55 Mev. This discrepancy proves that the basic idea, explaining the "beryllium rays" as hard gamma rays, is wrong. Chadwick introduced an entirely different hypothesis about their nature, writing as follows:

If we suppose that the radiation is not a quantum radiation, but consists of particles of mass very nearly equal to that of the proton, all difficulties connected with the collisions disappear, both with regard to their frequency and to the energy transfer to different masses. In order to explain the great penetrating power of the radiation we must further assume that the particle has no charge. We may suppose it to consist of a proton and an electron in close combination, the "neutron" discussed by Rutherford in his Bakerian Lecture of 1920.

Next, on the basis of the observation just cited, Chadwick computed for this hypothetical neutron the mass and velocity that would give the observed energy transfer in the two collisions reported. The result of the computation (to be performed by the reader, see Prob. 18.2) is

Mass of neutron = 1.16 × mass of proton

This result, although not claiming high accuracy, satisfactorily proves that the contradiction mentioned above is removed when the highly penetrating "beryllium radiation" is assumed to consist of neutral par-

ticles of nearly the mass of the proton.   This, then, was the discovery of
the neutron.   (A precise determination of its atomic weight will be discussed in Sec. 18.2c.)

The great penetrating power of the neutron is explained by its lack of
charge, which makes it wholly insensitive to the close approach to an
electron or any nucleus, in contrast to the alpha particle, which, near

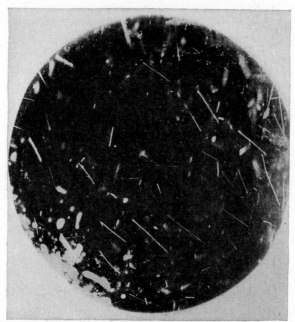

Fig. 18.3. Tracks of recoil protons.   The protons are hit by neutrons coming from a
source at the lower right corner.   (*Courtesy of P. I. Dee and C. W. Gilbert.*)

a heavy nucleus, is deflected by the strong Coulomb repulsion (Chap. 9).
In our schematic way, the production of neutrons is written as

$$_4Be^9 + {}_2He^4 \rightarrow ({}_6C^{13}) \rightarrow {}_6C^{12} + {}_0n^1 \qquad \text{or} \qquad {}_4Be^9 \, (\alpha, \, n) \, {}_6C^{12}$$

As in a preceding example the "compound nucleus" $_6C^{13}$ is not observed
but only computed as the unstable particle which immediately splits up.

The cloud-chamber photograph (Fig. 18.3) confirms the assumption
that the neutrons kick the protons, and the proton tracks cause the
ionization measured.   When the cloud chamber is filled with CH_4 and
subjected to neutron bombardment, the short, straight tracks of recoil
protons show up and their preference for a forward velocity is noticeable.
(The neutrons come from the lower right corner.)

Comparison of cloud-chamber photographs shows a striking contrast between the various types of radiation.   Alpha and beta rays, protons, all other nuclei, and electrons form "ionizing radiations"; for these the whole track of the individual particle is visible.   On the other hand, neutron rays and gamma rays are called "nonionizing radiations" since most of them pass unnoticed through the cloud chamber.   Gamma rays will only occasionally ionize a molecule and are then noticed by the crooked tracks of the secondary electrons so produced (Fig. 17.10). Very different is the picture produced by a beam of neutrons passing through a hydrogen (or methane)-filled cloud chamber (Fig. 18.3).   Only the tracks of the recoil protons appear, while the neutrons, kicking the protons and bouncing off, do not leave tracks.

In surveying the discovery of neutrons, we remark that Chadwick's argument is more involved than any preceding argument we have dis-- cussed, in that it presupposes cloud-chamber measurements and their interpretation, the laws of impact as applied to atoms, and the theory of the Compton effect.   Chadwick's discovery turned out to be very fruitful.

b. Neutrons as Building Blocks.   The ejection of neutrons from nuclei suggests the hypothesis that the neutron is one of their common con- stituents.   If so, all nuclei may be thought of as consisting of protons and neutrons, the number of protons being identical with the atomic number and the sum of protons and neutrons representing the mass number.   (Other arguments leading to the same hypothesis are con- cerned with the spins of the constituent particles, which we shall not discuss.)   The alpha particle, because of its great stability (Sec. 16.3), presumably plays the part of an intermediate building block in which 2 protons and 2 neutrons are firmly bound together.   This picture agrees well with the nuclear reaction that has led to the discovery of the neutron; $_4\text{Be}^9 + {}_2\text{He}^4$ may form 3 alpha particles sticking together as $_6\text{C}^{12}$ and 1 neutron, which is thrown out.   "Nucleon" is the common name given to protons and neutrons as representing building blocks of the nuclei.

The isotopes of all elements are conveniently represented in a diagram in which the number of protons (atomic number) is plotted against the number of neutrons (mass number − atomic number).   Figure 18.4 shows this diagram for the light elements.   Many stable, light nuclei are located on the 45-deg line, indicating equal numbers of neutrons and protons, like $_1\text{H}^2$, $_2\text{He}^4$, $_6\text{C}^{12}$, $_8\text{O}^{16}$, $_{10}\text{Ne}^{20}$.   The heavier elements, how- ever, contain more neutrons than protons.   The most common isotope of the heaviest element occurring in nature, $_{92}\text{U}^{238}$, has 146 neutrons and only 92 protons.   One may suppose that here the strong electric repulsion tending to break up the protons is overcome by a binding force due to the neutrons (see Sec. 19.3).   This diagram is commonly used for repre- senting the results of artificial transmutations.   The reader will easily find on the diagram the steps representing spontaneous alpha or beta emission.

   c. Atomic Weight and Binding Energy.   How can we determine the atomic weight of the neutron more accurately than it was crudely done above on the basis of collision experiments?   The chemical methods and the method of electric and magnetic deflections fail.   Instead, the atomic weight has been determined by a thorough examination of the deuteron, *i.e.*, the heavy-hydrogen nucleus, in which 1 proton and 1 neutron are

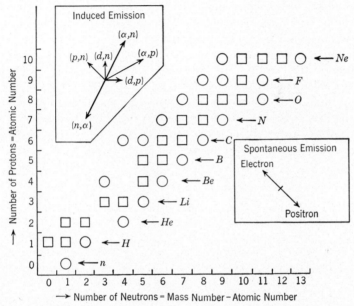

Fig. 18.4. Isotopes of the light elements.   □ stable isotope; ○ unstable isotope. The unstable isotopes *above* the stable ones are *positron* emitters; those *below* the stable ones are *electron* emitters.   A complete diagram is published by the General Electric Company (November, 1952).

bound together.   The atomic weight of the deuteron and the proton are known with very high accuracy by Bainbridge's analysis carried out with the mass spectrograph.   The difference between the two gives the value of *nearly one* for the neutron; but this value is inaccurate because the mass of the separate particles, $_1H^1$ and $_0n^1$, is larger than that of the deuteron, $_1H^2$, by the mass D/c^2, where D is the energy required to disintegrate the deuteron.   In other cases we calculate the energy D from the masses of the partners and the combined nucleus; here, however, the mass of one partner is unknown, and what we need is an independent determination of the energy of disintegration of the deuteron.

This is supplied by a new observation. It has been found that hard gamma rays when passing through a cloud chamber filled with deuterium produce characteristic single tracks of a well-defined length. These tracks are explained as follows. The deuteron consists of a proton and a neutron bound together. Assuming that the gamma-ray quantum separates the deuteron into its constituents by "nuclear photoelectric effect" we expect to see the track of the proton only since the neutron is nonionizing (see Sec. 18.2a and Fig. 18.3). Nevertheless, the track of the proton gives evidence of the neutron which shoots away invisibly in the opposite direction. (Only these two particles must be considered in the conversion of momentum, since the momentum $h\nu/c$ of the gamma quantum is negligible.) The numerical data are as follows: The energy of the gamma-ray quantum (2.65 Mev) is partly consumed for the disintegration of the deuteron; in addition, it produces a proton track in the deuterium-filled cloud chamber which, by a calibration of its range, indicates a proton of kinetic energy $W_k = 0.25$ Mev. Since the neutron has about the same mass, it carries the same energy, for, by conservation of momentum, it moves off with the same speed. These data are used to state first the conservation of energy:

$$h\nu = D + 2W_k$$

D results to 2.15 Mev. Next we state the conservation of mass, keeping in mind that the energy D is just sufficient to dissociate the nucleus without imparting kinetic energy to the fragments:

$$\text{Mass of } {}_1\text{H}^2 + \frac{D}{c^2} = \text{mass of } {}_1\text{H}^1 + \text{mass of } {}_0n^1$$

It is convenient to rewrite the same equation in terms of atomic weights, remembering that 931 Mev is the energy equivalent to 1 atomic-weight unit. This equation contains only one unknown, the atomic weight of the neutron, which is found to be 1.00898. This figure indicates that the neutron contains more mass than the combination of a proton and an electron, and, in fact, the neutron is found to be unstable, tending to disintegrate into a proton and an electron (see Prob. 18.3).

Once we know the atomic weight of the neutron, we can compute the energies of its combination with other nuclei from the packing fractions of the various isotopes (see Prob. 18.4). The energy with which a neutron is bound to any heavy nucleus is of the order 5 to 8 Mev.

18.3. Positrons. Before studying neutron reactions and artificial radioactivity, we continue our survey of the elementary particles. We study next the discovery of the positron, which originated from an entirely different group of experiments. In Chap. 20 we shall discuss cosmic rays. These are highly penetrating rays of unknown origin traveling through the cosmos, producing secondary particles in air and, in particular, in heavy materials like the wall of a cloud chamber. Figure 18.5 shows a famous cloud-chamber photograph from which C. D. Anderson (1932) inferred the existence of a new particle. When the picture was taken, there was a magnetic field perpendicular to the face of the chamber bending the tracks of the particles. The new particle traverses a 6-mm-thick lead plate placed across the chamber, and so gives evidence of an extraordinary energy. The photograph also shows that the magnetic field curves the track more strongly above than below the lead plate. This indicates that the particle above the plate is slower than below.

FIG. 18.5. The discovery of the positron. (*Courtesy of C. D. Anderson.*)

Since the lead plate can only slow down the particle, this must be assumed to come from below and to be a secondary liberated from the bottom of the cloud chamber by a cosmic ray. The density of the cloud track and the penetrating power through metals are the same as for very fast electrons.

FIG. 18.6. Production of two positron-electron pairs in the wall of the cloud chamber. (*Courtesy of C. D. Anderson and S. H. Neddermeyer.*)

The strangest feature of the track is that the sense of its curvature combined with the direction of the magnetic field (directed into the paper) indicates a *positive charge*. Thus this simple picture represents the important discovery of a positively charged particle having the same ionizing power as the electron. This particle is called the "positron." When we attribute to it the specific charge of the electron, its initial kinetic energy amounts to 63 Mev. Another very significant photograph is shown in Fig. 18.6; here a cosmic ray ejects both electrons and positrons from the same spot of the wall, both producing tracks of equal density but oppositely curved. As a final convincing proof of the existence of positrons, it was soon found that artificial transmutation generates radioactive isotopes of many elements, which give rise to a copious supply of positrons (see Sec. 18.4).

Since we have unambiguous evidence for positrons and electrons, we may ask, for the sake of symmetry, whether the well-known proton has its counterpart in a *negative proton*. No conclusive experimental evidence of such a particle has been published.

18.4. Artificial Radioactivity; Neutron Reactions. Artificial radioactivity has been discovered by the same type of experiment that Rutherford performed to produce the first artificial transmutation, *i.e.*, bombardment of light elements with alpha particles. Later the experiments were vastly extended by using as projectiles neutrons, which themselves were produced by alpha-particle bombardment. At about the same time the machines to be discussed in the next sections produced a wealth of new radioactive isotopes, partly by the use of other projectiles, partly by the use of projectiles with higher energies than those available in natural radioactivity. Here we shall describe at some length examples of the methods for analyzing these reactions and their products. Later, in discussing the work done with the cyclotron, we shall only summarize the results.

Irène Curie-Joliot and F. Joliot (1934) discovered that several light elements, after being bombarded with alpha particles, remain radioactive after the bombardment; their activities follow the same exponential law of decay as those of natural radioactive elements. An example is aluminum $_{13}Al^{27}$ which, *at the time of alpha-particle bombardment*, gives off neutrons (observed in a boron-lined ionization chamber, see below). Simple arithmetic suggests the following nuclear reaction:

$$_{13}Al^{27} + {_2}He^4 \rightarrow (_{15}P^{31}) \rightarrow {_{15}}P^{30} + {_0}n^1$$

where the compound nucleus $_{15}P^{31}$ serves only for an intermediate step of the computation. But here, in contrast with the bombardment of beryllium (Sec. 18.2a), it is found that *the piece of metal remains radioactive after the bombardment* and decays with a half-life of 2.5 min. The magnetic deflection of the particles emitted shows that they are positrons. Chemical separation of aluminum and phosphorus leads to a fraction containing the phosphorus in which all the activity is concentrated and so confirms the reaction scheme suggested.

Here we meet again the chemical problem that plays so great a part in nuclear research, the separation of neighbors or near neighbors in the table of elements. Special techniques had to be developed because only an exceedingly small fraction of the atoms of the original element suffer transmutation.

The emission of positrons from the radioactive isotope $_{15}P^{30}$, which is produced here, changes it into a stable isotope, namely $_{14}Si^{30}$. The

Joliots, discovering more processes of the same kind, produced several artificially radioactive isotopes of the light elements.

A much greater variety of such isotopes covering the whole periodic table has been produced by neutron bombardment (Fermi and collaborators, 1935). Instead of giving the long list of all neutron reactions, which may be found in special treatises, we shall discuss one reaction in detail in order to make clear the observations and arguments that lead to the final reaction scheme.

Pure aluminum, $_{13}Al^{27}$, is bombarded by neutrons generated in a radium-beryllium source as described in Sec. 18.2a. The electroscope shows that the piece of metal stays radioactive when the neutron source is removed and that it decays with a half-life of 14.8 hr. The activated metal is subjected to various chemical separations which separate any adjacent element from aluminum. Thus it is found that the active element is not aluminum itself but sodium. Since sodium has an atomic number (11) smaller by 2 than that of aluminum (13), we infer the ejection of an alpha particle. This process must be connected with a loss of mass number by 4, thereby leading to the mass number 24 of the active sodium. Now we are able to write the nuclear reaction introducing, for the sake of convenience, the compound nucleus as an intermediate body

$$_{13}Al^{27} + _0n^1 \rightarrow (_{13}Al^{28}) \rightarrow _{11}Na^{24} + _2He^4 \qquad \text{or} \qquad _{13}Al^{27} (n, \alpha) _{11}Na^{24}$$

The process is called a "neutron-alpha reaction."

A separate problem is presented by the properties of the radioactive $_{11}Na^{24}$. With a half-life of 14.8 hr it emits electrons and so changes into the element with a nuclear charge larger by one, $_{12}Mg^{24}$. This final product is known as a stable magnesium isotope. In all later investigations of the neighbors of sodium, a half-life observed as 14.8 hr (combined with electron emission of a certain penetration) served, without further chemical analysis, as an unambiguous test for the presence of $_{11}Na^{24}$.

The neutron-alpha reaction does not necessarily generate a *radioactive* isotope. For example, the reaction $_5B^{10} (n, \alpha) _3Li^7$ results directly in the formation of a *stable* isotope. This reaction, having a high yield, is of practical interest since it is commonly used as a test for neutrons. A "boron-lined" ionization chamber responds to neutrons by the emission of alpha particles which, in turn, produce ionization. This device is particularly effective for slow neutrons (see below).

In another type of neutron reaction a proton is ejected instead of an alpha particle. In the same experiment one or the other reaction may be induced by neutron bombardment. In aluminum just considered, under neutron bombardment, the alternative reaction is

$$_{13}Al^{27} (n, p) _{12}Mg^{27}$$

The probabilities of the various reactions depend upon the neutron velocity. The product nucleus is heavier than all stable magnesium isotopes. After a certain half-life it changes by electron emission into the stable $_{13}Al^{27}$.

Figure 18.7 shows typical cloud-chamber tracks due to neutrons impinging on nitrogen. The neutrons themselves, coming from below,

do not leave tracks. Nevertheless their momenta show up in the fact that the two particles produced in the nuclear reaction have upward components of momentum. (If the imping-ing neutron should have no momen-tum, the two particles formed in one reaction would part along a straight line.)

FIG. 18.7. Disintegration of a nitrogen nucleus by a neutron (no track) into an alpha particle (long track) and a boron nucleus (short track). (*Cour-tesy of N. Feather and Proceedings of the Royal Society.*)

The most important neutron reac-tion is *neutron capture*. Here simply an isotope of higher mass number is generated, which may be stable or unstable. This reaction, which is most probable for slow neutrons, may occur with aluminum, too. By the capture of the neutron, its binding energy becomes available and thus provides energy for the emission of a gamma ray. Hence the reaction is written

$$_{13}Al^{27} \ (n, \ \gamma) \ _{13}Al^{28}$$

The product nucleus $_{13}Al^{28}$ is radioactive, emitting an electron and so changing into the stable silicon isotope $_{14}Si^{28}$. Electron emission is typical for the product of neutron capture if the nucleus so produced has a neu-tron in excess of a stable number. One may visualize that in this unstable nucleus a neutron, after a certain lifetime, spontaneously changes into a proton by ejecting an electron that is observed.

A special case of this type is given by the natural radioactivity of potassium, which stands isolated among the lighter elements, not being a member of one of the radio-active series (Sec. 17.4). It may have been induced in preterrestrial times by the neutron reaction

$$_{19}K^{39} \ (n, \ \gamma) \ _{19}K^{40}$$

The product $_{19}K^{40}$ is an electron emitter of such a long half-life (of the order 10^9 years) that a very small abundance has survived up to the present time.

In many other cases the product of neutron capture fails to show any radioactivity. Then one must conclude that one stable isotope has been transformed into another stable isotope of the same element with an increase of mass number by one.　In such cases the binding energy of the neutron which is made available by its capture is emitted as a gamma-ray quantum.

Neutron capture differs from other neutron reactions in that *slow neutrons* are most effective.　We can predict how to produce slow neutrons. The discovery of neutrons (Sec. 18.2a) is based on the fact that the neutrons, ejected with high speed from the radium-beryllium source, readily transfer their kinetic energy to protons.　Hence, when passing through a thick layer of water, the neutrons finally slow down to the average kinetic energy associated with room temperature.　Such "thermal neutrons" are still effective for neutron capture and in most cases even much more effective than fast neutrons.　For example, neutron capture by silver is 40 times as effective for thermal as for fast neutrons.　Uranium fission will present another example of the high activity of thermal neutrons (Sec. 19.2).

Neutron capture may serve to remove free neutrons that are produced in large quantities in the cyclotron or the nuclear reactor (see below). The protons, *e.g.*, in water, which effectively *slow down* neutrons, may finally *capture* them in the reaction $_1H^1$ (n, γ) $_1H^2$, producing deuterons and emitting a gamma ray.　This process, however, has only so small a probability that the neutron, after being slowed down, may make, say, a hundred collisions with protons before capture occurs.　The most efficient trap for thermal neutrons is cadmium.　Its technical importance will be mentioned in the discussion of the nuclear reactor (Sec. 19.5).

After discussing the outstanding neutron reactions [schematically called (n, α), (n, p), and (n, γ)], we compare the two processes by which we have learned to induce radioactivity, alpha and neutron bombardment. Neutrons are much more efficient projectiles because, even when slow, they are able to approach any nucleus, light or heavy, without having to overcome the Coulomb repulsion.　Alpha particles, on the other hand, are so strongly repelled by the heavier nuclei that particles emitted from naturally radioactive sources (energy < 9 Mev) fail to produce reactions in elements heavier than calcium (atomic number, 20).　Another difference is due to the type of radioactivity induced.　Neutron bombardment produces *electron* emitters (except if the impinging neutron knocks out two of the bound neutrons), while alpha bombardment leads in some cases to *electron* emitters, in other cases to *positron* emitters.　What is the general rule predicting the type of emission?　The tendency is the same as mentioned before, *i.e.*, toward the most stable configuration.　On this basis we predict as follows: In the diagram of Fig. 18.4 the stable nuclei which are indicated by squares represent the targets.　Neutron capture leads to a nucleus shifted to the right.　This unstable nucleus is an electron emitter because this emission (visualized as replacing a neutron contained in the nucleus by a proton) brings the nucleus upward to the left, *i.e.*, back to the stable configuration. In general, the unstable nuclei located *below* the stable ones are *electron* emitters, whereas the nuclei located *above* the stable ones are *positron* emitters. For example, $_1H^3$ and $_6C^{14}$ emit electrons, whereas $_6C^{10}$ and $_6C^{11}$ emit positrons. Also in the numerous cases of artificial radioactivity induced in the cyclotron or other machines (Sec. 18.6), the alternative between electron or positron emission is decided by the tendency toward the stable configuration.

The emission of a *positron*, however, may be replaced by another process. A nucleus that tends to lose a positive electron may instead *capture one of the external electrons*, presumably one of the K electrons, which are the ones closest to the nucleus. By either of these processes, positron emission or "K-electron capture," the nuclear charge is reduced by one unit, *i.e.*, to a stable nuclear configuration. K-electron capture is evident from the subsequent X-ray emission caused by the vacated place in the K shell. This X-ray emission differs from the ordinary emission only by the process of excitation. While ordinarily a K electron is knocked out, here it is swallowed by the nucleus. Heavy nuclei show K-electron capture in preference to positron emission, since their large nuclear charges are responsible for close approaches of the K electrons.

Here let us summarize the wealth of discoveries made by investigations of alpha particles and their effects: (1) natural transmutation of elements such as radium; (2) the nuclear atom; (3) artificial transmutation such as that of nitrogen; (4) artificial radioactivity such as that of P^{30}; (5) positrons as emitted from artificially radioactive nuclei; (6) the neutron and its effects (transuranic elements, uranium fission; see Chap. 19).

18.5. Annihilation of a Pair; Pair Production. One may ask: Why are not positrons observed more often? The answer is that they readily combine with electrons when passing through matter. In this process a large amount of energy becomes available, and one may guess that this energy will be transformed into radiation. The energy available is simply computed on the basis of Einstein's principle assuming that, in addition to the kinetic energy of the two particles, twice the mass of the electron is exchanged into energy. This "annihilation" contributes an energy of 1.02 Mev. Theoretically, however, one should not expect to observe only one gamma-ray quantum of this energy for the following reason. Suppose that 1 positron and 1 electron, both with negligible kinetic energy, come together. Since they do not have any appreciable linear momentum, their exchange into a gamma-ray quantum, which has a momentum $h\nu/c$, would violate the law of conservation of momentum. However, the momentum is conserved when the total energy available is divided up into *two equal quanta emitted in opposite directions*. What appears to be a bold speculation leads here finally to the prediction of a gamma radiation that can easily be checked by observation.   Actually, when positrons are incident on matter, gamma-ray quanta of just 0.51 Mev are observed.   This observation proves that the hypothesis of annihilation is valid.   The energy of 0.51 Mev, which is equivalent to the electron mass, is called the "self-energy of the electron."

The observation shows a *sharply defined* gamma ray at 0.51 Mev and thus indicates annihilation without an appreciable contribution of kinetic energy.   We conclude that fast positrons, which would produce gamma rays shifted to higher energies, are much less effective in the annihilation process than slow ones.

Another experimental test of this speculation lends itself to a demonstration or laboratory experiment.   It is based on "coincidence counting," the essential idea of the apparatus being the combination of two Geiger-Müller tubes in series, as in Fig. 18.8.   When only one tube is made conducting by a gamma-ray quantum, the other tube still blocks

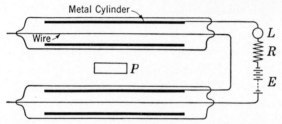

Fig. 18.8. Coincidence counter; schematic diagram of two Geiger-Müller counters connected in series.   *L*, loud-speaker; *R*, high resistance; *E*, source of 4,000 volts; *P*, positron emitter.   Coincidences are due to two gamma-ray quanta emitted by the annihilation of a positron-electron pair.

the current.   Only when both tubes are made conducting simultaneously will the loud-speaker or the mechanical recorder respond.   (This may be accomplished, for example, by a cosmic ray that is hard enough to shoot through both counters; see Sec. 20.1.)   In order to demonstrate the fact that the two quanta generated simultaneously by the annihilation process travel *in opposite directions*, we place a positron source between two counters connected in a coincidence circuit.   Annihilation takes place within the positron source itself, and the pairs of quanta simultaneously generated produce coincidence counts.   When we shift the source outside any straight line connecting the two counters, the counting stops.   The result fully agrees with the theoretical prediction.

While, in the annihilation process just described, mass is transformed into radiation, in the reverse process radiation is transformed into mass. This process, the *production of a positron-electron pair* by a gamma-ray quantum, is also observed.   It does not happen without the presence of matter, and it turns out that heavy matter is most effective in pair production.   According to the preceding argument, the gamma ray must have a minimum energy of 1.02 Mev.   An example is given by the cloud-chamber tracks of Fig. 18.9.   They are caused by a hard gamma-ray quantum, itself nonionizing, which in the air of the chamber produces a positron-electron pair.   The momentum of the quantum coming from below is responsible for the upward momenta of the two particles generated.

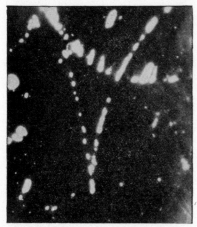

Fig. 18.9. Pair production in the gas of the cloud chamber; gamma ray coming from below. (*Courtesy of F. Joliot.*)

When gamma rays are passing through heavy matter, say, lead, pair production removes quanta from the ray and so is partly responsible for the absorption of gamma rays.   Let us now survey the processes that cause absorption of gamma rays in heavy material like lead.   The *photoelectric effect* (removal of a K electron, see Sec. 14.2d) is most effective for X-ray quanta of an energy just above the limit of the K series which, for lead, is at 89,500 ev (or at a wavelength of 0.138×10^{-8} cm).   The contribution of this effect to the absorption coefficient *decreases* with increasing energy of the quanta, hence is much smaller for gamma rays of higher energy.   The *Compton effect* (Sec. 14.3) attenuates and scatters gamma-ray quanta as well as X-ray quanta, again with *decreasing* effectiveness when the energy of the quanta is increased.   Finally, *pair production* begins to be effective for gamma-ray quanta at 1.02 Mev; this is the only effect that is *increasingly probable* for increasing energy of the quantum. As an example, Fig. 18.10 analyzes the absorption coefficient of lead into the various contributions.   It shows that the *total* absorption coefficient has a minimum for gamma-ray energies of 3.5 Mev.   The right branch of this curve, which goes up for high energies, is of importance for cosmic-ray research (Chap. 20).

We are used to the idea that energy stored in a particle, *e.g.*, a nucleus, increases its mass according to Einstein's principle (Sec. 16.4).   Our present result, however, represents a still more radical violation of the age-old principle of conservation of *matter*.   Here we explain certain observations by the *complete annihilation* of two particles creating radiation or, vice versa, the *production of particles* from radiation.   All such processes are in accord with the principle of conservation of *energy*, provided the change of mass is taken into account according to Einstein's principle.

18.6. Machines for the Production of High-energy Particles. Natural radioactivity generates particles and quanta up to about 10 Mev energy. The effects of alpha bombardment, including artificial transmutation, artificial radioactivity, and the production of neutrons, opened up so profound a view into nuclear structure that it appeared desirable to extend the energy range of fast ions. This is the purpose of the machines we shall discuss presently. Since 1932 they have led to an amazing progress by producing new phenomena and new particles and increasing our

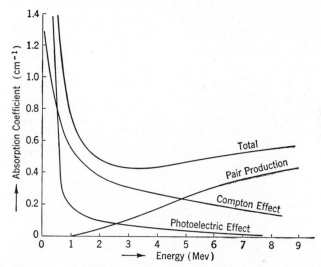

Fig. 18.10. Absorption of gamma rays in lead; comparison of the various processes.

insight into nuclear structure. The machines are generating particles of energies that reach into that of cosmic rays.

a. Production of High Potential Difference. The first artificial transmutation performed with a machine was the breaking up of the lithium nucleus by Cockroft and Walton (1932). They used high voltages generated by a transformer and doubled by an ingenious system of condensers and rectifiers to provide a d-c supply of 700,000 volts.

Another powerful tool, described in elementary textbooks, is the Van de Graaff electrostatic generator which generates up to about 12 Mev. Although it does not give energies so high as those provided by the machines discussed below, it is of importance because it generates relatively large currents of electrons or ions with sharply defined energies which are used for an accurate determination of threshold energies in nuclear reactions. This technique meets with the difficulty that the insulating property of the air breaks down at high voltages. However, this difficulty has been partly overcome by the use of higher pressure of air or, preferably, some other gas (air mixed with Freon CCl_2F_2) which shows better insulating properties.

But energies of an entirely different order of magnitude are given to ions by machines in which the ions are accelerated *many times in succession* by the same moderate potential difference before they are made to hit the target. We shall describe six types: the linear accelerator, the fixed-frequency cyclotron, the synchrocyclotron, the betatron, the electron synchrotron, and the proton synchrotron.

b. Linear Accelerator. In the *linear accelerator* (Fig. 18.11) ions are shot in high vacuum down the axis of a long row of coaxial metal tubes. The tubes are connected alternately with one or the other terminal of a high-frequency generator. Suppose an ion, emerging from an electric discharge (not on the diagram) arrives at the first gap between two tubes at a moment when the potential difference between these two tubes produces maximum acceleration of the ion. After this initial impulse, the

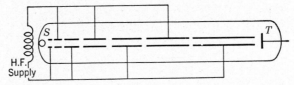

Fig. 18.11. Schematic diagram of a linear accelerator. The ions emitted from the source S are accelerated between the coaxial tubes in steps toward the target T.

ion takes a certain time to travel from the first to the next gap along the axis of the metal tube, *i.e.*, through a field-free region where its speed remains constant. During this time interval the polarity of the alternating current is reversed. Now if the tube's length is chosen properly, the ion will arrive at the second gap simultaneously with a potential difference, which again gives it an acceleration. This proper length, which increases along the path of the ion, is readily determined for a particle of a given specific charge from the frequency of the alternating current. It was with an accelerator of this type that Lawrence and Sloan (1931) succeeded in generating mercury ions of 205,000 volts while applying high-frequency alternating current of only 10,000 volts. Present machines of this type have been vastly improved by the application of the microwave techniques developed for radar since the beginning of the Second World War.

c. Fixed-frequency Cyclotron. Lawrence and Livingston (1932) overcame the difficulty inherent in the linear accelerator by the construction of the cyclotron. They describe their method as follows:

The present experimental method makes use of the same principle of repeated acceleration of the ions by a similar sort of resonance with an oscillating electric field, but has overcome the difficulty of the cumbersomely long accelerating system by causing, with the aid of a magnetic field, the ions to circulate back and forth from the interior of one electrode to the interior of the other.

Consider a closed, round, and flat pillbox that is cut in halves along a diameter. In a cyclotron there are two such halves made of metal and called "dees" because of their resemblance to the letter D. Their diameter in an early cyclotron was about 12 in., but in the largest present cyclotron they are about 14 times as large. Like the pillbox, the dees are closed all around except at the diameter along which the box has been

Fig. 18.12. The vacuum chamber of the cyclotron, open (see Fig. 18.13).

cut. Insulators support the dees, with a narrow gap between them, in a large high-vacuum chamber (Figs. 18.12 and 18.13). An auxiliary small device (not visible in the figure) inserted at the center of the chamber, generates protons, deuterons, or helium ions. At a certain moment, the high-frequency voltage (say, 50,000 volts) connected to the dees accelerates the ions across the gap. Within the dee, as within a space free of an electric field, the ions would travel in a straight line with uniform velocity. However, the whole vacuum box containing the dees is set in a strong, uniform magnetic field perpendicular to the plane of the dees. This field turns the path of the ions within each dee into a half circle, which brings the ions back to the gap.   If the time required to travel one half circle just equals one half-period of the alternating current, the ions are accelerated again, when passing through the gap.   This play continues several hundred times and makes the ions accumulate a high kinetic energy.

In order to select the proper frequency of the alternating current, we compute the time t required to traverse one half circle.   We have solved the same problem in our discussion of the determination of e/m of elec-

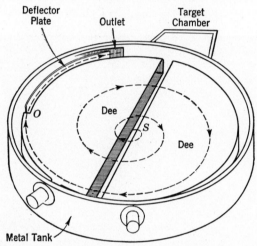

Fig. 18.13. Cyclotron open (see Fig. 18.12).   The positive ions emitted from the source S (not shown on the diagram) are accelerated in steps between the D-shaped hollow electrodes, are bent in half circles by an axial magnetic field, leave the left dee at the opening O, and, finally, are pulled out from their circular path by the negatively charged deflector plate so that they hit the target.

trons by the helical method (Sec. 6.2c).   Using the same notation, we compute

$$t = \frac{\text{distance}}{\text{velocity}} = \frac{\pi r}{v}$$

Introducing the expression for the velocity $v = Ber/m$ we find

$$t = \frac{\pi m}{Be} \qquad (18.1)$$

We adjust the a-c half-period to be equal to the time t of one-half revolution to make sure that the ions meet an accelerating potential difference when arriving at the gap.   It is of outstanding importance for the instrument that r and v drop out of the last equation, because, for a larger radius r, the linear velocity v is larger in proportion so that the time t is independent of both.   Hence, the *same frequency of alternating current* is as appropriate for the small inner half circles slowly traversed as for the large outer ones traversed with high speed.   Thus after passing any half circle, when arriving at the gap, the ion is accelerated again. This is the principle that enabled Lawrence to wind up the path of the ions and so construct the cyclotron with only two electrodes. The last equation gives the condition for tuning. For a given projectile, *e.g.*, deuterons, the time t, identical with one half-period of the alternating current, bears a simple relation to the magnetic induction B. Hence for a given frequency of alternating current the magnetic field strength must be accurately adjusted. The ion, starting near the center, spirals out in several hundred half circles. When approaching the rim, it escapes through an opening in the cylindrical wall of one of the dees, where it is pulled slightly out of its circular path by a negatively charged "deflector plate" and hits the target.

A considerable group of cyclotrons, designed largely according to the plans of Lawrence, Livingston, and their coworkers, have been built with pole pieces of about 36 in. diameter supplying a deuteron (heavy hydrogen ion) beam of about 8 Mev and 50 microamp. Fortunately, this small value of the current is compensated for by the high energy because the yield of many disintegration processes increases rapidly with the energy of the projectile. Many difficult engineering problems come up in the construction of the cyclotron. For the size just referred to, a power supply of about 10 megacycles and 100 kw is needed. The construction of the magnet, weighing not much less than 100 tons, the vacuum system, the safety devices, all present innumerable problems. The beam produces penetrating radiations, gamma rays, and neutrons, of vicious intensity. The operating crew is protected from neutrons by a 3-ft-thick water tank. Since, during the operation, nobody is allowed near the cyclotron, the control table is placed at a distant corner of the building.

d. Synchrocyclotron. In the cyclotron (Sec. 18.6c) ions are accelerated in steps between the half circles of their paths, provided that the a-c frequency is tuned to the frequency of the ionic rotation ($t = \pi m/Be$). The same resonance condition, which is based on Newtonian mechanics, may be expressed in terms of the angular velocity $\omega = 2\pi/2t$:

$$\omega = \frac{Be}{m}$$

During the development of large cyclotrons a limit to the kinetic energy accessible was forecast, since as soon as the velocity of the ions becomes comparable to that of light, their mass increases and their gain of velocity during each step of acceleration becomes smaller. Hence they tend to fall out of step. Although the *linear velocity* of a particle is limited, there is no such limit for its kinetic energy. The difficulty is overcome by the *synchrocyclotron*. Considering its great importance, we must explain its principle at some length. We shall discuss first frequency modulation, next the phase stability given to the ion in the relativistic velocity range, and, finally, the practical application of these principles to the operation of the synchrocyclotron.

The purpose of *frequency modulation* is qualitatively understood as follows. Since in the relativistic range the ions gain linear velocity at a lesser rate than at lower velocities, resonance may be maintained if during the acceleration process the frequency of the potential difference is gradually reduced. Technically the machine *modulates* the frequency of the accelerating potential difference by introducing a periodically variable condenser into the circuit. Thus the frequency is made to vary periodically about its average value. The modulation is adjusted so that during a fraction of each period, while the frequency is *decreasing*, ions are accelerated far into the relativistic velocity range. The rest of the period is useless. Therefore, the machine furnishes high-energy ions in surges, one surge during each period of modulation.

It may seem too optimistic to hope that we shall adjust the rate of decrease of the frequency so accurately that the ions always hit an *accelerating* potential difference when reaching the gap between the two dees. This requirement, however, is automatically met by the new *principle of phase stability* discovered independently by Veksler and McMillan (1945). We start from the effect of relativity on the condition for tuning $\omega = B \times e/m$. This equation shows that in *Newtonian mechanics* the angular velocity ω is independent of the kinetic energy of the ions. *In relativistic mechanics, i.e.,* for linear velocities approaching that of light, the same equation holds with only the modification that the mass m of the ions increases with the linear velocity (see Sec. 6.4). Let us start from a case which differs from the ordinary operation of the cyclotron. Let us assume that the ion passes through the gap when the potential difference between the dees *goes through zero* and is *changing from the accelerating to the decelerating* half-period. (Apparently this case has no interest, since the ion is not accelerated when passing through the gap.) Let us also assume that B and ω have values obeying the condition $\omega = Be/m$, where m depends on the velocity, and that, on the average, the frequency of the alternating current is tuned to the angular velocity ω. In order to prove that the orbit is stable, we apply the conventional criterion of stability. We assume an incidental small decrease of the a-c frequency so that between two passages of the ion the accelerating potential difference lags behind a little. Does this change throw the ion out of step or is the ion automatically brought back into step? When the a-c frequency *decreases* a little, the ion arrives at the gap *before* the potential difference is reversed; hence the potential difference *accelerates* the ion, which, due to its increased linear velocity, acquires a *higher* mass m. The *angular velocity* ω, which determines whether the ion remains in step, goes down.   Hence the particle automatically follows the *decrease* of the a-c frequency.   This is the meaning of "phase stability."

This principle is applied to the practical operation of the machine as follows.   We assume that small *decreases* of the a-c frequency (each small step *accelerating* the ion) occur continuously; in other words, we assume a gradual slow decrease of the a-c frequency.   The phase stability will permanently keep the ions in step with the a-c frequency and allow an unlimited gain of energy.   Since at each crossing of the gap the gain of

Fig. 18.14. Large cyclotron of the University of California.   (*Courtesy of E. O. Lawrence.*)

energy is small, a very high vacuum is required to prevent scattering of the ions.

In actual operation the ion will start the race by the ordinary cyclotron action.   (This is so rapid a process that, in spite of frequency modulation, the tuned frequency is available for a sufficient length of time.) After the relativistic range is reached, the decrease of the angular velocity ω is taken into account by the gradual reduction of the modulated frequency.   Gradually the operation changes to the principle just discussed which keeps the ions in step.   It is true that the ions when passing the gap do not find the maximum potential differences but a considerably smaller value.

In the large synchrocyclotron (Fig. 18.14) which has been in operation in California since 1946, the diameter of the pole pieces is 184 in. and the magnetic induction about 15,000 gauss. The machine was built to generate 190 Mev deuterons or 380 Mev alpha particles (about 100 times as energetic as the alpha particles produced in natural radioactivity). Later the machine was changed over to generate 350 Mev protons. Each ion performs about 10,000 revolutions in a period of about 1/1,000 sec. The frequency modulation produces about 100 such surges of ions per second.

e. Betatron. The *betatron*, constructed by Kerst in 1940, is used for the production of high-energy electrons. These electrons, attaining energies as high as 300 Mev in the largest betatron in operation, are used largely for the production of very hard X rays. The betatron is essentially a transformer whose secondary coil has only one single turn, a ring-shaped high-vacuum tube. The change of flux accelerates free electrons around this tube, much as if it served as the secondary coil of the transformer. Figure 18.15 shows the evacuated glass chamber built in the shape of a giant doughnut and placed between the pole pieces of a powerful electromagnet which is designed for alternating current, in contrast to the cyclotron magnet.

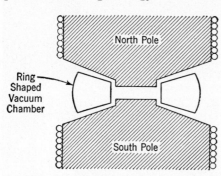

Fig. 18.15. Betatron. Magnet is laminated for use with alternating current. Ring-shaped vacuum chamber serves as a secondary coil of one turn. Electron source and target are omitted.

Free electrons emanate from a glowing filament and are accelerated by the sinusoidal emf.

We report briefly on the theory, which is based on relativistic mechanics. We consider electrons that start their journey with the velocity zero at the instant at which the alternating flux ϕ goes through zero. Here its rate of change $\Delta\phi/\Delta t$ and hence the induced emf have their maximum values. (The emf is determined by $\Delta\phi/\Delta t$ where ϕ is the flux cutting the whole cross section.) This emf exerts a *tangential* mechanical force on the electrons, which, in high vacuum, are free to be accelerated (different from their situation in the copper coil of a transformer).

What force constrains the electrons on their circular path in the vacuum tube? The same magnetic induction whose rate of change accelerates the electrons exerts a centripetal, *i.e.*, *radial* mechanical force throughout the accelerated motion. With increasing velocity, starting from $v = 0$, the electrons need a proportional increase of the magnetic induction B. When these two functions of the magnetic induction (the acceleration and the deflection on a circular path) are mathematically expressed, the result is that the magnetic induction B at the periphery must have half of the average it has over the cross section. This is the tuning condition for the betatron.

By the operation described we utilize only that fraction of each period near zero flux ϕ, when its rate of increase $\Delta\phi/\Delta t$ is largest and causes the most rapid acceleration of electrons. Hence in the betatron a group of electrons are accelerated continuously to very high speed (not in many discrete steps as the ions in the cyclotron); but these groups come in surges, one in each period of the alternating current that feeds the electromagnet. At the end of the acceleration period, a magnetic field, produced by a sudden condenser discharge through an auxiliary coil, deflects the stream of electrons to a target which then emits X rays.

f. Electron Synchrotron and Proton Synchrotron. The most recently constructed machines operate on so complicated a combination of the various principles discussed that only a brief survey can be given.

In the *electron synchrotron* electrons are accelerated to the relativistic velocity range by the betatron effect. When their velocity approaches that of light, further acceleration is achieved by letting the electrons pass through a gap (as in the cyclotron) to which a high-frequency electric field is applied. Throughout their race the electrons are forced on their circular paths by a magnetic field.

Very successful is the application of essentially the same idea to the acceleration of protons in the *proton synchrotron.* Figures 18.16 and 18.17 demonstrate the growth of nuclear machines within twenty years, 18.16 showing one of the first cyclotrons (1932) and 18.17 the proton synchrotron of the Brookhaven National Laboratory, called "cosmotron" (1953). It generates protons of nearly 3 Bev. Initial acceleration is given by an auxiliary machine, a 4-million-volt Van de Graaff electrostatic generator. The machine applies both the simultaneous increase of B and decrease of the a-c frequency. The ions, while traveling several million times around the huge track with nearly the velocity of light, cover a distance of 100,000 miles in about $\frac{1}{2}$ sec.

18.7. Types of Nuclear Reactions. In a preceding section we first discussed the nuclear reactions caused by *alpha particles*, which led to the discovery of artificial radioactivity, and then those caused by *neutrons*, which produced numerous, new radioactive isotopes all over the periodic table. A wealth of new processes and new radioactive isotopes has been discovered by the application of projectiles accelerated in the machines just described. The first progress in this field was made by Cockroft and Walton (1930), who used a proton beam. Their apparatus is described briefly in Sec. 18.6a. Since protons cannot easily approach heavy nuclei because of the Coulomb repulsion and since the proton has no effect on other protons or helium nuclei, the authors used lithium, the third ele-

FIG. 18.16. Second oldest cylotron, 1932; 11-in. vacuum chamber. (*Courtesy of E. O. Lawrence and M. S. Livingston.*)

FIG. 18.17. Cosmotron, 1953.   (*Courtesy of Brookhaven National Laboratory.*)

ment of the periodic table, as a target.　As products of the nuclear reaction, they found two alpha particles, recognized by their cloud-chamber tracks.　Hence they attributed the effect to the heavy lithium isotope transformed by the proton in the reaction

$$_3\text{Li}^7 + {_1}\text{H}^1 \rightarrow (_4\text{Be}^8) \rightarrow {_2}\text{He}^4 + {_2}\text{He}^4$$

We are interested in the energy relation observed in this experiment, considering that in the present book we introduced the equivalence of mass and energy as a *principle*, *i.e.*, as a statement that requires proof by further experiments (Sec. 6.4).　The first experimental proof we found for this principle consisted of the mass increase of very fast cathode rays. We have taken the principle for granted when discussing the mass defects of isotopes.　Here, finally, the experiments of Cockroft and Walton, in conjunction with Bainbridge's accurate determination of atomic masses, permit another check of the principle.　Cockroft and Walton observed that bombardment by protons of 0.3 Mev kinetic energy causes the $_3\text{Li}^7$ nucleus to disintegrate into two helium nuclei of 8.4-cm range.　This range indicates a kinetic energy of 8.6 Mev for each particle.　The total kinetic energy so observed (17.2 Mev) is so much larger than the share supplied by the impinging proton (0.3 Mev) that most of the total (as much as 16.9 Mev) is supplied by energy stored in the nuclei.　On the other hand, knowing all nuclear masses (see Appendix 5), we predict the contribution of the nuclear energy on the basis of Einstein's principle as 17.2 Mev.　The agreement with the experimental value of 16.9 is well within the limit of the experimental error.

An important problem is whether a reaction *releases* or *consumes* energy. If it *releases* energy, the product nuclei have *more* kinetic energy than the projectile used.　They have *less* kinetic energy if the reaction *consumes* energy.　This is conventionally expressed, as in chemistry, by the sign of the "energy of the reaction" called Q, a positive value indicating *release* of nuclear energy into kinetic energy.　For example, in the proton bombardment of Li^7 just discussed, Q ($=$ kinetic energy of products minus that of projectile) $= +16.9$ Mev.　Here the proton impact triggers an explosion.　In chemistry this type of reaction is called "exothermic." In the discovery of artificial transmutation, $_7\text{N}^{14}$ (α, p) $_8\text{O}^{17}$, the atomic weights show that the final pair contains more energy stored, hence has less kinetic energy than the initial pair.　This makes the value of Q negative ($Q = -1.09$ Mev; endothermic reaction).　For more examples see Prob. 18.12.　In general, initial and final states are correlated by an equation stating that (mass $+$ mass equivalent of kinetic energy) is the same for the initial and the final partners.

· With *deuteron* bombardment of lithium Cockroft and Walton again found a pair of alpha particles and correspondingly explained the effect as due to the light lithium isotope

$$_3Li^6 + {}_1H^2 \rightarrow ({}_4Be^8) \rightarrow {}_2He^4 + {}_2He^4$$

Having discussed in detail the kind of argument used in the pioneer work of Cockroft and Walton and in the interpretation of alpha and neutron reactions (Sec. 18.4), we now refrain from giving more detail on individual reactions and only summarize the results obtained, principally with the cyclotron. The projectiles inducing nuclear reactions are protons, deuterons, alpha particles, neutrons, or gamma rays, abbreviated as p, d, α, n, and γ respectively. Nuclei of higher charge are less effective because of the Coulomb repulsion. The principal types of nuclear reactions, including those we have already discussed, are arranged according to the projectile as follows:

p, d	d, p	α, p	n, p	γ, n
p, α	d, α	α, n	n, α	$\gamma, 2n$
p, n	d, n		n, γ	
p, γ			$n, 2n$	

Important examples of nuclear reactions are summarized in Table 18.1, which, however, is far from complete. Many product nuclei are stable,

Table 18.1. *Important Examples of Nuclear Reactions*

Transmutation of elements	$_7N^{14} (\alpha, p) {}_8O^{17}$	Stable isotopes produced
Artificial radioactivity	$_{13}Al^{27} (\alpha, n) {}_{15}P^{30}$	$_{15}P^{30} \rightarrow {}_{14}Si^{30} + {}_{+1}e^0$
Neutrons	$_4Be^9 (\alpha, n) {}_6C^{12}$	The fast neutron produced may transfer its kinetic energy to protons (paraffin) or cause transmutation of nuclei
Proton reactions	$_3Li^7 (p, \alpha) {}_2He^4$	2 fast α particles observed
Deuteron reactions	$_3Li^6 (d, \alpha) {}_2He^4$ $_{11}Na^{23} (d, p) {}_{11}Na^{24}$	2 fast α particles observed $_{11}Na^{24} \rightarrow {}_{12}Mg^{24} + {}_{-1}e^0$
Photodissociation of nucleus by γ rays	$_1H^2 (\gamma, n) {}_1H^1$	Binding energy of deuterium and mass of neutron
Slow neutron capture	$_{13}Al^{27} (n, \gamma) {}_{13}Al^{28}$	$_{13}Al^{28} \rightarrow {}_{14}Si^{28} + {}_{-1}e^0$
Fast neutron reactions	$_{13}Al^{27} (n, \alpha) {}_{11}Na^{24}$	$_{11}Na^{24} \rightarrow {}_{12}Mg^{24} + {}_{-1}e^0$
Fission by slow neutrons	$_{92}U^{235} (n \rightarrow \text{various fragments})$	Uranium fission; energy released is about 200 Mev

many others unstable, generally emitting electrons or positrons *after a characteristic half-life;* only heavy nuclei may emit alpha particles. This contrasts with natural radioactivity, in which only electrons or alpha particles are emitted.

Although neutrons are not repelled by the target nucleus, all charged projectiles are. This partly explains the fact that the yields of all nuclear reactions induced by charged projectiles increase rapidly with the energy of the projectiles. The cloud-chamber photographs of alpha rays (Figs. 17.4, 17.5, and 18.2) show that nuclear collisions are exceedingly rare as compared with ordinary ionization processes evident by cloud formation. Hence the projectiles are most likely to lose energy before making a nuclear hit. If they do not have an ample excess energy to start with, they have a very poor chance for an effective nuclear collision.

The reaction of a deuteron impinging on another deuteron requires the lowest energy of all nuclear reactions induced by charged particles, because the Coulomb repulsion has the smallest value; here an effect is observed with an energy as low as 0.02 Mev. Of interest are the product nuclei of this reaction. The reaction $_1H^2$ (d, p) $_1H^3$ leads to a heavy hydrogen isotope of mass 3, called "tritium," which is an electron emitter with a half-life of 12.4 years. An alternative is $_1H^2$ (d, n) $_2He^3$, which gives a light helium isotope known as a stable isotope, occurring in nature with an extremely low abundance.

The probability of a nuclear reaction is not so large that for every impact of a projectile on a target nucleus a reaction would ensue. By definition the "cross section of the reaction" attributes to the target nucleus only so large an area that every impact *on this cross section* leads to the reaction. To express this definition mathematically, we visualize that a uniform beam of high-energy particles is incident on a target which is so thin that most particles traverse it without loss of energy. We define the cross section by the following equation: number of reactions occurring per cm² and sec = number of projectiles incident per cm² and sec × number of target nuclei per cm² × cross section. The cross section so defined differs widely for different reactions and, for any one reaction, depends on the energy of the incident particles (see Prob. 18.13).

There are several cases in which two different nuclear reactions generate the same radioactive isotope *with two different values of half-life.* For example, $_{35}Br^{80}$ has two such values, 18 min and 4.2 hr. Here it must be assumed that the nucleus $_{35}Br^{80}$ can exist in two states with different energy contents. (We ascribe sharply defined energy levels to nuclei since the gamma-ray spectra show sharply defined frequencies.) Furthermore, we assume that the level endowed with higher energy has a very small probability of radiating its energy content as a gamma ray and, in this respect, resembles the metastable levels known in electronic systems (Sec. 11.1d). This long half-life gives the excited nuclear level a chance of exhibiting its own disintegration. These two states of $_{35}Br^{80}$

are called "nuclear isomers." (Isomers are known in chemistry as compounds that are built of the same constituents but differ in properties because of different arrangements of the constituents.) A few cases of nuclear isomers show up in natural radioactivity. For example, $_{83}RaC^{214}$, although principally a beta emitter, shows a few alpha emissions (4 out of 10,000).

The detailed investigation of all possible nuclear reactions has involved an enormous effort, since each reaction presents its individual problems to be solved with a special technique. The result is a system of radioactive isotopes, an addition to the well-known system of stable isotopes. At present about 670 radioactive and 276 stable isotopes are known.

In many cases, the same new isotope is being produced by various types of nuclear reaction. For example, the radioactive aluminum isotope $_{13}Al^{28}$, characterized by its half-life of 2.3 min and the penetrating power of the electrons it emits, is generated in the following five reactions:

$$_{13}Al^{27}\ (n,\ \gamma)\ _{13}Al^{28};\ _{15}P^{31}\ (n,\ \alpha)\ _{13}Al^{28};\ _{13}Al^{27}\ (d,\ p)\ _{13}Al^{28};$$
$$_{14}Si^{28}\ (n,\ p)\ _{13}Al^{28};\ _{12}Mg^{25}\ (\alpha,\ p)\ _{13}Al^{28}$$

These various reactions leading to the same, well-identified product present an important cross check for the validity of our argument.

Such cross checks are particularly valuable with regard to the effects of neutrons because the evidence of neutrons is based on an argument much more indirect than that for charged particles. Here let us pause and look back over the long chain of experiments and their theoretical interpretations leading to the present picture of the neutron and "neutron chemistry." We begin with Chadwick's discovery of the neutron and keep in mind that his argument, in turn, presupposes a great deal of information, experimental and theoretical, regarding various rays and their absorption by matter, in particular regarding atomic collisions and the Compton effect. Next come the discovery of deuterium and the precise determination of its atomic weight, after this the photodissociation of the deuteron, explained by its splitting into a proton and a neutron, and then the determination of the frequency threshold of this process. This figure, interpreted on the basis of the equivalence of mass and energy, leads to the atomic weight of the neutron, for which an accuracy of six significant figures is claimed. Finally, we come to neutron chemistry, an elaborate field by itself. We *observe* that radium, beryllium, and aluminum, when brought close together for a while, affect the aluminum by giving it the power to discharge an electroscope. We *hypothesize* that alpha particles emerging from radium eject neutrons from the beryllium nuclei and that these neutrons, in turn, cause a certain reaction in the aluminum. The results of such lengthy arguments are cross-checked with the results of so many other nuclear reactions caused by protons, deuterons, alpha particles, and gamma rays that we cannot doubt the validity of the whole elaborate picture.   In conclusion, the explosion of the atomic bomb may be cited as a fact that gives convincing evidence of neutrons.

The modern alchemist who attempts to make gold may survey the possible nuclear reactions in order to select the proper target element to be bombarded with the proper projectile.   Thus he has a choice, keeping in mind that it may be worthwhile first to produce the next lighter or heavier element which by electron or positron emission will change into gold.

18.8. Mesons and Other Fundamental Particles.   The 184-in. cyclotron has led to fundamentally new results.   When deuterons are used, a well-collimated beam of high-energy neutrons emerges from the target. Here it is assumed that, when a deuteron strikes a target nucleus, the proton, which is a part of the deuteron, may be broken off while the residual neutron continues its path.   At the very high energies involved, which far surpass the binding energies of the individual nucleons, our picture of the *compound nucleus* (= target + projectile; Sec. 18.1) becomes useless.   More useful is the picture of a projectile directly hitting *one of the nucleons* whose binding in a heavy nucleus may be disregarded.

Of fundamental interest are the new particles, called "mesons," which are generated in the same powerful machine.   In 1936 C. D. Anderson, in his systematic cosmic-ray work, examined the density of cloud-chamber tracks and their magnetic curvature.   Thus he discovered the rare occurrence of particles of a mass intermediate between those of the electron and proton (see Secs. 19.3 and 20.3).

A systematic investigation of the new particles became possible after they were produced in the high-energy cyclotron.   Here we summarize the results obtained by the cyclotron and cosmic-ray investigations.

While cloud chambers provide important results, outstanding progress is due to the application of a very simple technique, the observation of tracks produced by fast particles in photographic emulsions, *i.e.*, the sensitive layers of photographic plates (Powell).   These tracks have lengths of a small fraction of a millimeter.   They are photographed through a microscope which reveals the density of the grains.   Thus the following properties of the tracks are measured: (1) grain density; (2) range; (3) scattering (*i.e.*, occasional small deflections caused by electric fields near nuclei); (4) magnetic deflection which is produced in the chamber of the cyclotron and admits only selected particles to the emulsion.   On the basis of theory and empirical calibrations two such measurements serve for the determination of the two unknowns, the specific charge e/m and the velocity v of the particles, where e is assumed to be the electronic charge.   (Grain density, range, and scattering are well observable in Figs. 20.5 and 20.8.)

The results are unexpectedly complicated. The mesons originally discovered in cosmic rays, called "mu mesons," have no direct bearing on nuclear structure but are only a decay product of heavier mesons called "pi mesons," which are generated by the bombardment of nuclei with photons or protons. Pi mesons were originally discovered in the upper atmosphere, where they are produced by the primary cosmic rays (Powell, 1947). Positively or negatively charged pi mesons are observed. Their charges are supposed to equal the electronic charge, positive or negative. (The evidence for *neutral* pi mesons is much more indirect, since they do not produce tracks.)

The masses of the charged pi mesons amount to 277 electron masses; the mass of the neutral pi meson is slightly smaller. Thus the pi mesons meet Yukawa's theoretical prediction. The mu meson has a mass of 212 electron masses and may carry a positive or a negative charge.

Tracks in photographic emulsions demonstrate the decay of the mesons. The photograph (Fig. 20.5) shows the abrupt end of the heavy track attributed to the pi meson and, starting at the end, the thinner track of the lighter mu meson, which, in turn, comes to an abrupt end and is followed by the track of an electron. (The theory predicts the simultaneous emission of neutrinos, which are not evident in the emulsion picture.)

Meson physics is a field in which our knowledge is rapidly progressing.

Here let us survey our present knowledge of fundamental particles, disregarding the fact that decay processes may make the fundamental character of one or the other particle questionable.

The situation seemed simple after the discovery of the neutron (1932). It seemed evident that nuclei are built of *protons* and *neutrons* and surrounded by *electrons*. This picture was only slightly marred by the hypothetical neutrino.

Cosmic-ray research revealed the existence of other particles which soon were produced and systematically explored at the laboratory. They are the positron and the different types of meson. In cloud-chamber photographs of cosmic rays there seems to be evidence of several other particles of intermediate mass. Occasionally heavier particles are observed, called "*V* particles," after a peculiarity in their tracks. They are more massive than protons, since protons are products of their decay.

It is evident that our present information on fundamental particles is far from complete.

SUMMARY OF CHAPTER 18

1. Artificial transmutation was discovered by Rutherford, who observed that nitrogen when bombarded with alpha particles gives off protons, first recognized by their long range, later identified by their cloud-chamber tracks.

2. Beryllium, when bombarded by alpha particles, gives off an exceedingly penetrating radiation which knocks protons out of paraffin or water. Chadwick identified this radiation as consisting of neutrons $_0n^1$. All nuclei are supposed to consist of a combination of protons and neutrons, the number of protons defining the atomic number, the number of both particles together defining the mass number. The atomic weight of the neutron is accurately determined by the atomic weights of the proton and the deuteron and the energy required for the splitting of the deuteron into its constituents. This energy is measured by photodissociation of the deuteron.

3. The positron has been discovered on a cloud-chamber photograph as a secondary particle ejected by a cosmic ray. The positron has the same absolute charge and mass as the electron but carries a charge of the opposite sign.

4. Bombardment of various light elements with *alpha rays* causes nuclear reactions that lead to new, radioactive isotopes. An example is the reaction $_{13}Al^{27}$ (α, n) $_{15}P^{30}$. The resulting $_{15}P^{30}$ is a positron emitter with a half-life 2.5 min. A great variety of nuclear reactions, many of them leading to radioactive isotopes, are caused by *neutron* bombardment. In particular, neutron capture leads to stable isotopes or electron emitters. In most cases of artificial radioactivity, the particle ejected is a positron or an electron; in any case the particle emitted has such a sign that the nucleus reverts to a stable configuration.

5. The life of a positron ends by its combination with an electron leading to the emission of two gamma-ray quanta of 0.51 Mev each (annihilation of a pair). One gamma-ray quantum of an energy above 1.02 Mev incident on matter may generate a positron-electron pair (pair production).

6. The outstanding machines for the production of high-energy particles are the voltage doubler of Cockroft and Walton, the Van de Graaff generator, the linear accelerator, the cyclotron, the synchrocyclotron, the betatron, the electron synchrotron, and the proton synchrotron.

7. The projectiles that may cause nuclear reactions written in the conventional way are p, d, α, n, and γ. Ionizing particles (p, d, and α) produce nuclear reactions with a yield rapidly increasing with their energy, as contrasted with neutron capture, which is most efficient for slow neutrons. In many cases the same radioactive nucleus can be produced by various reactions starting from various elements. This gives important cross checks for the interpretation of the individual reactions. Some important nuclear reactions are summarized in Table 18.1. Some reactions consume kinetic energy of the projectile (negative Q); others release nuclear energy (positive Q).

8. Mesons are particles (positive, negative, or neutral) of two distinct

masses intermediate between the masses of the electron and proton. Mesons were discovered in cosmic rays and later abundantly produced in synchrocyclotrons. Mesons decay spontaneously.

PROBLEMS

18.1. *Beryllium radiation interpreted as gamma radiation.* Irène Curie-Joliot and F. Joliot discovered that the mysterious radiation from a radium-beryllium source knocks protons out of paraffin with a kinetic energy of 5.7 Mev. The authors tentatively supposed that this energy is given to the proton by very hard gamma rays originating in the radium-beryllium source and producing Compton effect. (1) Calculate the energy $h\nu$ that this gamma-ray quantum must have in order to eject a proton in the forward direction with an energy of 5.7 Mev. (The scattered quantum $h\nu'$ is bouncing straight back.) (2) Following Chadwick, calculate the energy of the gamma-ray quantum which gives a forward motion with the observed energy 1.2 Mev to a *nitrogen nucleus*.

HINT: (*a*) State the fundamental equations of the Compton effect for the special case $\phi = 180°$; $\theta = 0$. (*b*) Since the scattered quantum $h\nu'$ is not observed, eliminate $h\nu'$. (*c*) Express $h\nu$ in terms of m and v. (*d*) Introduce numerical values.

18.2. *Discovery of the neutron.* In this problem the reader is asked to go through an essential part of Chadwick's argument leading to the discovery of the neutron. Chadwick wanted to identify the particles which, by elastic impacts, produce "recoil protons" and "recoil nitrogens" of measured energies. A particle of the unknown mass m_1 and velocity u_1, when hitting a proton (mass m_H) head on, transfers to it the velocity $v_H = 3.3 \times 10^9$ cm/sec, inferred from the range of the cloud-chamber track. When hitting a nitrogen nucleus (mass m_N), it transfers the velocity $v_N = 4.7 \times 10^8$ cm/sec. Compute m_1 and u_1. Use the results and the notation of Prob. 9.1, "elastic collisions."

HINT: In the problem "elastic collisions," the velocity given to the target particle is expressed in terms of the velocity of the projectile. Write this equation once for the proton as representing the target and once for the nitrogen. From these two equations compute m_1 and u_1 as the unknowns.

18.3. *Lack of stability of the neutron.* We imagine that a neutron, upon giving off an electron, changes into a proton. You are asked to calculate the energy Q which is consumed or liberated by this process.

COMMENT: The result shows that the neutron is *unstable*. There is experimental evidence for electron emission by neutrons.

18.4. *Binding energy of the neutron.* (*a*) Calculate the energy *required* to separate 1 neutron from $_8O^{17}$ and so produce a free neutron and $_8O^{16}$. (*b*) Answer the same question for the separation of $_8O^{18}$ into $_0n^1 + _8O^{17}$.

18.5. *Mass number versus atomic number.* On the basis of Fig. 18.4 draw a similar diagram with the *mass number* as ordinate and the *atomic number* as abscissa for all isotopes of the elements 1 through 6.

18.6. *A vicious circle.* The argument of the text (Sec. 18.2c) seems to contain a vicious circle. First we assume that the photodisintegration of the deuteron imparts equal kinetic energies to the proton and the neutron. This implies that we *presuppose* equal masses of proton and neutron. Next we *compute* these masses and do not come out with exactly equal masses. Satisfy yourself that the result is not spoiled by this circle. Assume the atomic weights as given by our final result, *i.e.*, differing slightly. The deuteron is disintegrated by a quantum of 2.65 Mev. Calculate the energy given to the proton and that given to the neutron by writing the two equations expressing conservation of energy and momentum. (Neglect the momentum of the gamma-ray quantum.) Satisfy yourself that these energies are equal with much higher accuracy than the measurement of the energy of the proton (0.25 Mev) implies.

18.7. *Mean binding energy per nucleon.* While Aston's curve of "packing fractions" (Fig. 16.5) gives the arbitrary value zero to $_8O^{16}$ atoms (atomic weight 16.00000), you are asked to draw an equivalent curve using as arbitrary zero the total mass of the separated protons and neutrons which are assembled in the nucleus. The total energy required to analyze a nucleus into the constituent protons and neutrons divided by the mass number gives the "mean binding energy per nucleon." Plot this energy against the mass number, using the atomic weights of $_1H^2$, $_2He^4$, $_6C^{12}$, $_8O^{16}$, $_{15}P^{31}$, $_{36}Kr^{86}$, and $_{92}U^{235}$ (see Appendix 5 and the data of Prob. 19.4).

18.8. *Tuning of cyclotron.* (a) A cyclotron that is tuned for deuterons will be used for alpha particles. While keeping the frequency of the alternating current constant, how must we readjust the magnetic induction B? (b) The cyclotron originally tuned for deuterons will be used for protons. While keeping the magnetic induction B constant, how must we readjust the frequency of the alternating current?

18.9. *Total number of revolutions in cyclotron.* (a) How many half revolutions does an ion perform in a cyclotron? Given: e/m, B, accelerating potential difference V, and radius R of the dees. The ion, starting near the center, is given the same additional energy eV by each step from one to the other dee. (It is irrelevant whether in the first step only a fraction of eV is given to the ion.) (b) How do the total number of half revolutions N of the ion and the final kinetic energy W depend on the potential difference V? (c) Introduce figures assuming deuterons revolving in a pair of dees of $R = 45.0$ cm in a magnetic induction $B = 15,000$ gauss; $V = 10,000$ volts. (d) Replace the deuterons by alpha particles.

HINT: For the largest half circle write the equation: centripetal force = force exerted by the magnetic induction. Calculate v, $\frac{1}{2} mv^2$, and the number N of transitions from one to the other dee required to produce this energy.

18.10. *Diagram of nuclear reactions.* Supplement the arrows given on Fig. 18.4 by arrows representing the following reactions: (p, d); (p, γ); (d, α); $(n, 2n)$.

18.11. *Nuclear reactions.* Write the complete schemes of the following nuclear reactions as in Sec. 18.2, including the compound nucleus and the product nucleus. In all reactions given here the product nuclei are either stable or emitters of electrons or positrons. (These particles are indicated as $_{-1}e^0$ and $_{+1}e^0$, respectively.) In each case state which is true (see Sec. 18.4) and, if the nucleus is active, state what the final *stable* nucleus is (see Fig. 18.4 and Appendix 5. You may extend the figure on the basis of the Appendix). (a) $_5B^{10}(\alpha, p)$; (b) $_4Be^9(\alpha, n)$; (c) $_7N^{14}(\alpha, n)$; (d) $_{11}Na^{23}(p, \alpha)$; (e) $_3Li^7(p, n)$; (f) $_3Li^6(d, p)$; (g) $_6C^{12}(d, n)$; (h) $_1H^2(\gamma, n)$; (i) $_5B^{10}(n, \alpha)$; (j) $_{11}Na^{23}(n, \alpha)$; (k) $_7N^{14}(n, p)$; (l) $_{13}Al^{27}(n, \gamma)$; (m) $_{15}P^{31}(n, 2n)$.

18.12. *Energies of nuclear reactions.* Calculate the energies Q of the following reactions: $_7N^{14} (\alpha, p) {}_8O^{17}$; $_4Be^9 (\alpha, n) {}_6C^{12}$; $_3Li^7 (p, \alpha) {}_2He^4$; $_3Li^6 (d, \alpha) {}_2He^4$. Use Appendix 5. (Since in all cases the initial and the final particles have the same numbers of external electrons, you may use the atomic weight of Appendix 5 without correcting for the external electrons.)

18.13. *Cross section of a reaction.* A deuteron beam (12 microamp) incident on a thin carbon target (area 3.0 cm^2; thickness 2.5×10^{-3} cm; density 1.9 g/cm^3) produces the reaction $_6C^{12} (d, n) {}_7N^{13}$. The activity produced indicates that, in the target, the bombardment generates 18×10^7 active nuclei $_7N^{13}$ per second. Compute the cross section of the reaction.

18.14. *Instability of triton.* The $_1H^3$ nucleus emits an electron of 18 kev energy. Calculate the difference of the atomic weights of $_1H^3$ and the product, both as neutral particles. Use Appendix 5.

18.15. *Nuclear activation energy (difficult problem).* In the text the statement is made that the energy required to produce a certain proton reaction is measured by the minimum kinetic energy of the impinging proton (0.125 Mev) which is needed to produce the reaction. This statement requires a correction. When a proton impinges on a lithium nucleus, the law of conservation of momentum predicts that the *common center of gravity* will continue its path with unchanged velocity. This law is independent of any detail of the collision process (elastic or inelastic, nucleus or bullet of a gun). Hence in the inelastic collision here considered, we are bound to assume that the compound nucleus $_4Be^8$ just formed takes up a part of the kinetic energy which, before the collision, is all concentrated in the fast proton. Compute this kinetic energy given to the compound nucleus. For its excitation only the balance is available. This balance, strictly speaking, is the energy of activation. (This problem is related to Prob. 17.4, "inelastic collisions.")

HINT: (*a*) Compute the velocity v_c of the center of gravity when the proton (mass m, velocity v_p) approaches the lithium nucleus (mass M) which is at rest before the collision. (*b*) Compute the *kinetic* energy given to the compound nucleus. (*c*) Compute the balance available as *excitation* energy of the compound nucleus in terms of m, M, and v_p. This is the activation energy. (*d*) Introduce numerical values.

CHAPTER 19

FISSION AND FUSION

Einstein's theory of relativity (1905) gave the first indication of the vast energy that would be made available if we could fuse 4 hydrogen atoms to form 1 helium atom; to use our present vocabulary, it predicted the energy stored in nuclei. A third of a century elapsed before a prospect opened up of our gaining access to nuclear energies at will. This is the significance of the most widely known nuclear reaction, uranium fission. Fusion of hydrogen atoms takes place in the interior of the sun. Only to a very limited extent are we able to achieve a closely related reaction at the surface of the earth. These reactions will be discussed in the present chapter.

19.1. Transuranic Elements. We shall best understand uranium fission by tracing the historical development of its discovery, which was an unexpected by-product of a systematic investigation aimed at a different problem. Why is the periodic table limited to 92 elements, the last element being uranium? The fact that the heaviest elements are radioactive suggests the answer, namely, that elements heavier than uranium may well exist but decay with shorter half-lives and therefore do not occur in nature. If this is true, uranium is not the absolutely first element of the "uranium-radium series" (Sec. 17.4) but, within a more extended series, is the first element with so great a half-life that it has not vanished. Indeed, uranium is commonly considered to be stable, since its half-life is so long (of the order 10^9 years) that even a heavy chunk of pure uranium metal can be handled without the precautions required for the handling, say, of radium. This idea opens up the prospect of making elements of higher atomic number. Fermi and his collaborators, in their first extensive work on neutron reactions (1934), succeeded in doing so by the following method. They had found that *slow neutron capture*, with subsequent electron emission, transforms an element into its neighbor of *higher atomic number*, e.g., $_{13}Al^{27}$ into $_{14}Si^{28}$ (Sec. 18.4). They applied this method to uranium in order to produce "transuranic elements."

The bombardment of uranium with neutrons leads to a great variety of products that are difficult to analyze because some of them are unknown to the chemist. There is no doubt that the predicted process takes place. Here neutron capture is even followed by two consecutive electron emissions.   These processes are written as follows:

$$_{92}U^{238} (n, \gamma) \; _{92}U^{239}$$

The nucleus $_{92}U^{239}$ is an electron emitter of half-life 23 min and spontaneously produces a new element called "neptunium," Np:

$$_{92}U^{239} \rightarrow _{-1}e^0 + _{93}Np^{239}$$

Neptunium, in turn, is an electron emitter of half-life 2.3 days.   It spontaneously leads to a new element called "plutonium," Pu:

$$_{93}Np^{239} \rightarrow _{-1}e^0 + _{94}Pu^{239}$$

Plutonium, finally, is an alpha emitter (half-life 24,100 years) and so spontaneously goes back to uranium, forming the rare isotope which occurs in nature:

$$_{94}Pu^{239} \rightarrow \alpha + _{92}U^{235}$$

(For many years, Uranus was considered to be the most distant planet, as uranium the last element of the periodic table.   More recently, the planets Neptune and Pluto were discovered at still greater distances. Hence the names given to the new elements.)   The two processes of electron emission occur rather rapidly, so that the atoms U^{239} and Np^{239} do not accumulate. Pu^{239} has a half-life long enough for an accumulation during our lives, but not long enough to make the element occur in nature in noticeable quantities; only recently have traces of plutonium been found in uranium minerals.

Four elements of still higher atomic numbers have been produced in the cyclotron (Seaborg).   They are called "americium," $_{95}Am$; "curium," $_{96}Cm$; "berkelium," $_{97}Bk$; and "californium," $_{98}Cf$.   Various processes lead to as many as eight isotopes of plutonium, eight of neptunium, and eleven of uranium, including those occurring in nature.   Furthermore, the elements with the atomic numbers 43, 61, 85, and 87, which are not found at the surface of the earth, are manufactured in the cyclotron. They are called technetium, prometheum, astatine, and francium, respectively.   The elements 99 and 100 have been briefly reported.

19.2. Uranium Fission.   So far we have discussed the work that follows the program of Fermi, *i.e.*, the production of elements of atomic number higher than that of uranium.   In these experiments an unexpected discovery was made.   In 1939 Hahn and Strassmann investigated a certain product of the bombardment of uranium by neutrons.   This product had been chemically identified as an alkaline earth.   In 1939 it seemed well established that in artificial transmutation only light particles, not heavier than alpha particles, are knocked out (as is evident from the survey of nuclear reactions given in Sec. 18.7).   Therefore, at first the new product was assumed to be the heaviest alkaline earth, *i.e.*,

$_{88}$Ra.   The results of later observations contradicted this assumption.
(1) Hahn and Strassmann (1939) carried out an exhaustive chemical test
and thus identified the new product as barium, $_{56}$Ba, rather than Ra.
(2) They found that this is a radioactive variety of barium and, by
measuring its half-life as 85 min, identified it as a well-known barium
isotope, $_{56}$Ba^{139}.   (3) Soon afterwards Lise Meitner, who had collabo-
rated in many preliminary experiments, and Frisch called attention to
the vast amount of energy made available by the process.   It generates
bursts in an ionization chamber much stronger than those due to any
other known atomic projectile.   (These bursts lend themselves to a
demonstration experiment.)   Correspondingly heavy tracks are observed
in the cloud chamber.   The energy liberated is estimated to be 200 Mev,
i.e., 50 million times as much as 1 carbon atom generates by combustion.
(4) By separation in the mass spectrograph it was found that the rare
isotope U^{235} (abundance 0.7 per cent) is responsible for the process.
(5) The process, which is started by neutrons, generates more free neutrons than it consumes.

These observations lead to the following picture of the new process.
We must assume that $_{92}$U^{235} when bombarded with neutrons splits into
nuclei that belong to the middle of the periodic table.   Its discoverers,
Hahn and Strassmann, called this new process "fission."   Although later
many other nuclei of medium atomic weight were identified as fission
products, let us consider in particular $_{56}$Ba^{139}.   It is plausible to assume
that the balance of the positive charge available in $_{92}$U goes into another
fragment of atomic number 36, which belongs to krypton, $_{36}$Kr.   This
assumption, however, fails to take account of all neutrons contained in
the initial complex (U^{235} + n).   Since the heaviest stable isotope of Kr
carries only 86 neutrons, there are at least 11 more neutrons available.
This result explains the fact that free neutrons occur among the fragments of the fission process.   But we do not claim that we can predict
their number since the first fission fragments are strongly radioactive
because of excess neutrons and are stabilized only by successive emission
processes.   Later it was found that each fission process liberates an
average of approximately 2½ neutrons.

The high energy liberated by uranium fission is not accounted for by
the kinetic energy of a fast-impinging neutron, since neutrons that are
slowed down by their passage through water are most effective.   Furthermore, the capture of a slow neutron by any heavy nucleus makes available
an energy of only about 5 Mev, i.e., only a small fraction of the energy
actually liberated by fission.   Hence the neutron acts largely as a trigger
for releasing the large energy stored in the uranium nucleus.   The
explosive character of this nucleus agrees with the fact that in Aston's
curve of packing fractions (Fig. 16.5) the heaviest nuclei, by their loca-

tion above the bottom of the curve, indicate the storage of large energies.

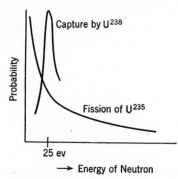

(A quantitative statement requires a detailed knowledge of the fission fragments; see Prob. 19.4.)

Finally we consider the *probabilities* of the reactions discussed. The outstanding (not the only) processes produced by neutrons in uranium are "fission capture" by U^{235} and "nonfission capture" by U^{238}, the latter leading to U^{239} and, after two electron emissions, to Pu^{239}. Their probabilities, as functions of the kinetic energy of the incident neutrons, are schematically given by Fig. 19.1.

Fig. 19.1. Schematic diagram of the probabilities of the reactions of neutrons with uranium.

Nonfission capture has a distinct preference for neutrons within a narrow energy range near 25 ev, while fission capture is most probable for slow neutrons.

Which other nuclei are subject to fission? Fission is produced by *slow* neutrons in $_{94}Pu^{239}$. Furthermore, thorium, $_{90}Th^{232}$, an element as abundant as uranium, is subject to nonfission capture and so generates U^{233}, another uranium isotope, which, in turn, is fissionable by slow neutron capture. It is hoped that this process will make the nuclear energy stored in thorium technically available. In certain nuclei lighter than thorium, fission is produced by high-energy projectiles, in tantalum, *e.g.*, by 400 Mev alpha particles. This energy barrier seems so high that one does not expect to utilize the energies of these nuclei as readily as those of uranium.

We summarize the unique features of fission which are responsible for the preeminent importance of this process:

1. Fission is a new type of nuclear reaction.

2. The energy liberated far exceeds that due to any other reaction although it may be started by very low-energy, "thermal," neutrons.

3. The reaction is not spontaneous, as radioactive disintegration is, but can be started at will by neutrons shot into uranium.

4. Uranium is much more abundant than radium.

5. Since the reaction itself reproduces the same particle, the neutron, that starts the reaction, we may expect that in a large body of $_{92}U^{235}$ the reaction will perpetuate itself because the first nucleus going into fission will cause one or several others to do the same, and the process will continue. Hence, in the ideal case, 1 neutron may burst the whole block of uranium. In chemistry this is called a "chain reaction."

We keep in mind, however, that this picture is idealized by the imagination of an optimist who forgets that neutrons may easily fail to continue the chain because they may escape from the block of uranium or be caught by nuclei other than U^{235}.   How these difficulties are overcome will be discussed below.

19.3. Report on the Theory of the Nucleus.   In the chapter on *stable isotopes* we discussed evidence on the "shell structure" of nuclei inferred from the marked stability of certain nuclei, supported by properties of the nuclear spins and nuclear volumes (Sec. 16.8).   In the following chapter, dealing with *natural radioactivity,* we interpreted the finite half-lives of an alpha emitter by a potential curve which shows the alpha particles imprisoned in a well so deep that the kinetic energy of the particles does not enable them to climb to the rim.   However, a particle rarely is able to shoot through the wall as if there were a tunnel (Sec. 17.5).   In this discussion the nature of the forces that are responsible for the shape of the potential well, *i.e.*, the forces that keep the particles assembled in the nucleus, remains unknown.   Furthermore, natural radioactivity reveals the existence of nuclear energy levels by certain energy relations between alpha particles and gamma-ray quanta, both emanating from the same nucleus.   There are other, rather complicated arguments on energy levels of light nuclei that are inferred from the energies of the projectiles causing transmutations.   We shall not discuss this complicated evidence, which is less convincing than the evidence on electronic levels.

In the present section we shall further develop the theory of the nucleus by discussing the forces acting within the nucleus and, at the same time, giving a picture of fission.   We shall start from a summary of the experimentally known nuclear properties that are to be explained.   Second, we shall discuss the nature of the forces that keep the nucleons together to form a stable nucleus.   Finally, we shall discuss the problem of nuclear stability in order to judge which nuclei, light or heavy, offer the best prospect of our gaining access to their energies.

From the measurements of the radii (Sec. 9.3) we derive the volumes of the nuclei.   They turn out to be nearly proportional to the masses so that the nuclear *densities* are nearly constant.   The value is as high as 10^{14} g/cm^3 (Prob. 9.3).   This result differs widely from the corresponding result for neutral atoms, which have, very crudely, all the same *volume* (diameter a few times 10^{-8} cm).   Hence our picture of the nucleus does not resemble that of the cloud of external electrons surrounding the nucleus of a neutral atom.   The constant high density rather suggests a tight packing of protons and neutrons.   Hence a *drop of liquid* appears to present a better model of the nucleus than a planetary system (Gamow, 1930).

The energy with which the nucleons are kept together is known from nuclear reactions and packing fractions (Prob. 18.7).   Except for the lightest nuclei it amounts to 6 to 8 Mev per nucleon.

The only nuclear force of which we are sure is the Coulomb repulsion that acts between the protons and tends to explode the nucleus.   There must exist a force of attraction which, at nuclear distances, overwhelms the Coulomb repulsion.   The dependence of this force on the distances and, possibly, the spins of the nucleons is explored by proton-proton scattering or neutron-proton scattering.   Proton-proton scattering at low kinetic energies (up to a few hundred kev) is completely explained in terms of Coulomb repulsion.   Here we are only interested in the deviations from this simple behavior at higher kinetic energies, which allow so close an approach that the force of attraction comes into play.   For neutron-proton scattering there is no repulsion to be overcome by high kinetic energy.   (This process is explored, $e.g.$, by having neutrons scattered by liquid hydrogen.)   We refrain from discussing details of the results as their correlation with the theory is complicated.

The experimental results just mentioned suggest that a strong force of attraction comes into play at very close approaches, $i.e.$, at distances of the order of magnitude 10^{-13} cm.   This force diminishes with increasing distance so rapidly that for a pair of protons at 4×10^{-13} cm it has only the value of the Coulomb repulsion.   The new force is $much$ larger at smaller distances.   It is surprising that the new force of attraction seems to have the same dependence on distance for the pairs p-p, p-n, and n-n.

The potential well which we postulated to explain alpha emission and the long lives of some emitters (Sec. 17.5) fits well into our picture of nuclear forces.   The alpha particle that, within the nucleus, comes close to its surface is ordinarily pulled back by the overwhelming new force just described.   This explains the steep $inside$ wall of the well which hinders the escape.   At a certain distance from the nucleus, however, the Coulomb repulsion dominates and is responsible for the $outside$ slope of the well.   The combination of the two forces is responsible for the high but thin potential wall of Fig. 17.14.

What is the $nature$ of the force of attraction whose $strength$ we just discussed?   In the discovery of its nature theory was ahead of experiment. Yukawa (1935) argued as follows.   Let us take it for granted as a result of wave mechanics that a rapid, random exchange between two particles produces a binding force that has the desired dependence on the distance. Yukawa found that the high binding energy and close approach of particles make it necessary to assume the $exchange\ of\ a\ new\ particle$ of mass 100 to 200 times the electronic mass and of either positive or negative electronic charge.   Later this new particle was called a "meson" because of its intermediate mass.   The exchange may be visualized either by supposing that the proton gives a positive meson to the neutron or that the neutron gives a negative meson to the proton.

A year later such particles were experimentally discovered as free particles, constituents of cosmic rays (Anderson and Neddermeyer, 1936;

see Sec. 20.4). This result, however, was soon modified. Again in cosmic-ray research it was found that there are two types of meson, light and heavy, called mu mesons and pi mesons or pions (Powell, Occhialini, and Lattes, 1948; see Sec. 18.8). Furthermore, it was found that a large cyclotron allows the artificial production and systematic investigation of such particles. The heavy meson, or pion, has a very short life, partly because of its chance of spontaneous disintegration into a light meson, partly because of its strong interaction with matter. This interaction indicates that here we are dealing with the particle that was predicted by Yukawa as reponsible for the force of attraction between nucleons. On the other hand, the light meson, because of its much longer life, is much commoner in cosmic rays, in particular at sea level, and therefore was discovered much earlier than the theoretically more important heavy meson, the much-investigated pion. The discovery of free particles with nearly the same properties as those theoretically predicted by Yukawa gives us confidence in his theory of nuclear forces.

Next we shall explore the relation of this theory to fission. Here Gamow's comparison of the nucleus to the drop of a liquid is helpful. In a drop, the molecules are kept together by forces of mutual attraction. The molecules in the *interior* feel *no average force* because on all sides they are surrounded by neighbors. The *surface* molecules, however, have neighbors only on one side and hence are pulled *toward the body* of the droplet. The forces so described exert the same effect on the droplet as if it were wrapped in an elastic envelope, an effect mathematically described as "surface tension." This tension determines the most stable shape of the drop as a *sphere*, which is the body with the smallest surface for a given volume.

This picture of a nucleus as a drop helps us to visualize the various nuclear events. In ordinary liquids the surface tension is not strong enough to prevent parts of the drop from flying off. Parts may be lost by either one of two events: (1) Molecules that are given sufficient energy by random thermal motion may *evaporate* from the surface. (2) The drop as a whole may vibrate about its stable, spherical configuration and thus occasionally *split* into two parts of more or less equal size. Large drops are especially subject to this splitting. This is why raindrops never exceed a certain size. Correspondingly the nucleus, if endowed with sufficient energy, may either *shoot off particles* or vibrate as a whole and thus split, *i.e.*, *go into fission*. In particular, the largest molecules are subject to fission.

The forces effective in the two cases compared are of entirely different natures, intermolecular forces in the liquid, and nuclear forces in the nucleus. These forces have in common the property that they provide "cohesion."

Aston's curve of packing fractions (Sec. 16.4) gives information on the energies liberated or consumed when nuclei, light or heavy, are broken up or assembled.   As an example, we computed the energy liberated when 2 protons and 2 neutrons *combine* to form 1 helium nucleus (Prob. 18.7). We can compute the enormous energy that would be liberated if $(_{92}U^{235} + n)$ were *broken up* into $_{56}Ba^{139}$, $_{36}Kr^{86}$, and 11 neutrons (Prob. 19.4).   This process does not actually occur, since it has been found that some fission fragments carry excess neutrons.   Without knowing the atomic weights of the fragments immediately produced, we are unable to calculate the exact energy balance.   Nevertheless from Aston's curve we derive the general conclusion that the nuclei around the middle of the curve of Fig. 16.5, near atomic number 60, exhibit the highest binding energies per nucleon and are therefore the most stable.   However, the nuclei of the right and left wings of the curve indicate by their smaller binding energies per nucleon that they may possibly change to the more stable elements of the middle portion *with release of energy*.   Hence Aston's results indicate that the lightest nuclei may release energy by *fusion*, the heaviest nuclei by *fission*.

Why do not these processes, the combination of light atoms and the fission of the heavy ones, occur spontaneously in nature, following the general tendency toward the most stable configuration?   This question is answered by the analogy with certain chemical reactions.   For example, a mixture of hydrogen and oxygen is explosive; nevertheless, at room temperature, the mixture seems completely stable, as if there were a barrier separating any hydrogen molecule from any oxygen molecule. It takes a high temperature, *i.e.*, thermal collisions of particularly high energy, to overcome this obstacle.   Then explosion takes place and suddenly liberates an energy far exceeding that of any thermal collision.

Such a system as this mixture is called "metastable," like certain excited states of atoms (Sec. 11.1*d*) which contain stored-up energy but are prevented from going down to their stable states.   Carbon and oxygen represent another familiar example.   In chemistry this barrier or obstacle is described as an "energy of activation."   At high temperature the mixture of hydrogen and oxygen explodes.   Here thermal motion *supplies* the energy of activation and so *liberates* the larger energy of the reaction.   A mechanical picture is that of a rock located in a groove high on the slope of a mountain, *i.e.*, in a metastable position.   A small amount of energy, the energy of activation, must be *supplied* in order to make the rock roll down the slope and so *liberate* its larger potential energy.

Aston's curve of packing fractions gives only the *energies liberated*, not the *energies of activation* by which nuclear reactions may be retarded or even prevented.   The energies of activation were explored by Bohr and Wheeler (1939) on the basis of Gamow's picture representing the nucleus as a droplet.   When a particle, *e.g.*, a neutron, is caught by a nucleus, its energy of condensation (estimated to be about 5 Mev for a neutron, see Sec. 18.2c) becomes available and produces a violent commotion within the nucleus, which may be described as heating.   (The hypothetical "temperature" of the particles constituting a heavy nucleus bears no relation to the temperature of the whole body measured with a thermometer.)   This energy, exchanged at random among the particles of the nucleus, may, after an immeasurably short time interval, give so much energy to one particle that it is able to leave, like a molecule evaporating from a drop of an ordinary liquid.   This is the picture of a reaction in which one particle is caught and another ejected.   Alternatively, the excess energy may be emitted from the nucleus as a gamma ray.   One or the other of these events stabilizes the nucleus.   In this theory the "compound nucleus," introduced above in Sec. 18.1 for the convenience of the computation, is an essential part of the reaction although of so short a life that it cannot be observed.

A very different process, fission of the heaviest nuclei, is well represented by the same idea.   Instead of the evaporation of one particle, a vibration within the whole drop about the spherical shape of equilibrium may be induced by a collision or neutron capture. It is true that, by the effect of the surface tension, a spherical drop is stable against a small deformation.   However, if the impact or capture causes a violent vibration, the drop may be elongated to the shape of

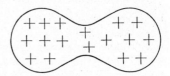

Fig. 19.2. The vibrating droplet as a model of nuclear fission.

a dumbbell to such an extent that fission occurs (Fig. 19.2).   This picture illustrates the limited stability of the nucleus with respect to vibration. A well-defined energy of activation must be *supplied* to initiate fission; this energy, however, is much smaller than that *liberated* by fission.

In the case of fission, the energy of activation is supplied by the incoming neutron, partly by its kinetic energy, partly by its energy of capture, estimated to be of the order 5 Mev.   Thermal neutrons are of outstanding importance because their capture has a much higher probability than that of fast neutrons.   However, fission by thermal neutrons is restricted to those nuclei whose limit of stability is low, say 5 Mev.   This requirement is met by only a few of the heaviest nuclei, U^{235} and Pu^{239}.   From the point of view of the mechanical picture, it is satisfactory that the largest nuclei, like the largest drops, are the least stable.   There is a much wider range of heavy nuclei in which *fast* neutrons may cause fission. Such processes, however, although energetically possible, occur only with low probability.

On the other hand, as anticipated above from the packing-fraction curve, *light* nuclei may deliver large energies by *fusing*. Here again an activation energy is necessary—otherwise all light nuclei would have changed to the most stable configuration. In this case the activation energy is explained by a more obvious picture. Such an energy exists for all *charged* projectiles because charged particles are prevented by the Coulomb repulsion from approaching each other so closely that the nuclear forces of cohesion, whatever they are, can come into effect.

The energy of activation is measured separately in the experiment of Cockroft and Walton (Sec. 18.7). In the reaction $_1H^1 + _3Li^7 \rightarrow _2He^4 + _2He^4$, the energy liberated is as large as 17.2 Mev. But in spite of the large energy liberated, the reaction does not occur when a slow proton approaches the lithium atom because the Coulomb repulsion prevents a sufficiently close approach. It has been observed that the reaction occurs only when protons are shooting into the lithium target with an energy of at least 0.125 Mev. This value represents the energy of activation. (Strictly speaking, this energy is not wholly available because the laws of conservation of energy and momentum require that a part of this energy be preserved as kinetic energy; this correction is computed in Prob. 18.15.) The lightest nuclei offer the best chance for overcoming the Coulomb barrier because they carry the smallest electric charges.

We summarize the outstanding result. The curve of packing fractions gives evidence of the fact that the *light* nuclei may liberate large amounts of energy by *fusion;* the *heavy* nuclei by *fission*. This argument refers only to the energies of the reaction but not to the barriers protecting the nuclei from the reactions. These barriers, *i.e.*, the activation energies, have been estimated by Bohr and Wheeler. For *heavy* nuclei the energy of activation is identical with the minimum energy of vibration that must be given the nuclear droplet to cause fission; this energy is lowest for the largest nuclei. On the other hand, for *light* nuclei the Coulomb repulsion provides a similar barrier, which is lowest for the lightest nuclei. According to this theory, it is not a mere coincidence that the heaviest atom occurring in nature, uranium (Sec. 19.1), and the lightest atom, hydrogen (Sec. 19.6), play outstanding parts in the liberation of nuclear energy. These are the atoms whose energies are fenced in by the lowest barriers.

19.4. Atom Bombs. The fact that energy is produced by nuclear processes has been known for decades. Radium *spontaneously* generates energy by alpha-particle emission; but we have to wait 1,590 years until one-half of our radium supply has gradually liberated its energy content. Rutherford's discovery of artificial transmutation and the discovery by Cockroft and Walton of lithium disintegration led to the controlled liberation of energy in many nuclear reactions (see Secs. 18.6 and 18.7); but this occurs only for a few lucky nuclear hits that are associated with many energy-consuming misses. It was early recognized by Fermi and his collaborators that uranium fission might have the unique quality of perpetuating itself, like a chemical chain reaction, since any one neutron consumed in fission *liberates several new neutrons* in the same process in which, in addition, it liberates a vast amount of energy. Hence uranium fission lends itself to large-scale controlled energy production; it can even lead to an explosion.

We shall summarize the nuclear reactions of uranium that are of outstanding practical importance. Slow neutrons or, less effectively, fast neutrons cause fission of the rare isotope U^{235} into two heavy fragments of nearly equal mass and, in addition, several fast neutrons. Neutrons, preferably of about 25 ev, *i.e.*, with energies above the thermal range, transform the abundant isotope U^{238} into U^{239} by neutron capture; U^{239} spontaneously and rapidly disintegrates by the emission of 2 successive electrons and so forms plutonium $_{94}Pu^{239}$. Plutonium, in turn, which has a very long life, is susceptible to fission by neutrons, slow or fast, like the rare uranium isotope U^{235}. In this summary we disregard the pitfalls that threaten the survival of the neutrons before they do their useful work. They may react with impurities or may escape from the uranium. The whole picture is so complex and the probabilities of the individual reactions, desired or undesired, vary over so wide a range, depending on the speed of the neutrons, that the prediction of the outcome is very complicated.

Everybody has heard of the development that culminated in the explosion of the atomic bomb. Following the official report by H. D. Smyth,* we shall discuss how the nuclear reactions have been utilized. The Smyth Report is highly recommended for everybody who wants to study the method of research, which is closely associated with large-scale technical development. In the early days of the Second World War, the ultimate aim was the construction of the *uranium bomb*, which is simple in principle although its production is difficult. It is hoped that the "*nuclear reactor*" will ultimately be of greater significance for the future of humanity.

The *uranium bomb* consists of a certain quantity of the "fissionable" isotope U^{235}, in which the fission of 1 atom causes the fission of more atoms by the chain reaction described, until the whole body is consumed by fission or dispersed by the explosion. For this purpose U^{235} is separated from the much more abundant U^{238}. We may imagine that mass spectrographs which are specially constructed for the handling of large quantities (not for precise measurements) perform the separation. At present the diffusion of gaseous uranium compounds is the most successful method used (see Sec. 16.6). The uranium used in the bomb must be extremely pure, since impurities are likely to consume the neutrons

---

* Smyth, H. D., "A General Account of the Development of Methods of Using Atomic Energy for Military Purposes," Superintendent of Documents, U.S. Government Printing Office, Washington, D.C., 1945.

which are needed for the continuation of the chain reaction. Since the great majority of these neutrons would escape from a small bomb, the explosion occurs only if the bomb is larger than a "critical size." No experimenting with small-scale explosions is possible.

The nucleus of U^{235} is more susceptible to slow than to fast neutrons. Although the neutrons due to fission have a great excess of energy beyond the most favorable value, no provision is made for slowing them down by elastic collisions (as it is done in the nuclear reactor; see Sec. 19.5) for two reasons: (1) Extra material added for this purpose would make the bomb too heavy; (2) the slowing down of the neutrons would take so much time (counted in microseconds) that the explosion would lose its extreme suddenness. Hence the explosion relies upon fission of U^{235} by fast neutrons.

The bomb is *detonated* by bringing together several *subcritical* masses of U^{235} to form one *supercritical* mass. This assembly must be done extremely suddenly. Otherwise, *i.e.*, if several subcritical masses should gradually come together, the explosion would start when the critical size is just barely reached and would blow off and waste the uranium pieces arriving later. Hence, it would be ideal to throw together the parts within a time interval that is short compared to the duration of the explosion.

The "duration of the explosion" may be estimated as follows. How much time elapses between the initiation of the chain reaction by 1 neutron and the fission of an appreciable quantity of uranium? We disregard losses of neutrons. A neutron of 1 Mev (velocity $v = 1.3 \times 10^9$ cm/sec) travels through uranium, at random, colliding with nuclei. Its mean free path l is estimated in Prob. 19.2 to be about 1.5 cm. Hence the time between consecutive collisions with nuclei is $l/v = 1.1 \times 10^{-9}$ sec. Only a fraction of these collisions are actually causing fission. If we arbitrarily assume that 1 collision in 1,000 is effective, the time between *effective* collisions is about $t = 10^{-6}$ sec. Furthermore, let us simply assume that 1 neutron when consumed by fission creates 2 neutrons. Let us estimate how much time is needed until a chain reaction starting from 1 single neutron leads to the fission of a sizable quantity, say, 1 gram atom ($= N_0$ atoms) of uranium. An elementary calculation shows that a chain of 80 consecutive links, each lasting $t = 10^{-6}$ sec, is required. Hence the total time required for the fission of 1 gram atom is of the order of magnitude $80 \times t$ or 10^{-4} sec. This crude estimate, which starts from arbitrary assumptions, is intended only to demonstrate that a very sudden assembly of the supercritical mass is required. The assembly may be accomplished by shooting several parts, which are originally mounted on a circle, along the respective radii toward the common center.

In order to reduce losses of neutrons by escape, the bomb is surrounded by an envelope, called the "tamper," which consists of a material that reflects many neutrons back into the bomb. Furthermore, the inertia of the envelope delays the early expansion of the reacting uranium. The first bombs were detonated at a certain height above ground to give the maximum blasting and heating effect.

Plutonium offers the chance of the easier production of a bomb. The uranium bomb requires the thorough separation of the rare uranium isotope, which presents an exceedingly difficult practical problem because of the small relative mass difference between the two isotopes (see Prob. 16.12). It was mentioned in Sec. 19.2 that Pu^{239}, which originates from U^{238}, is as susceptible to fission as U^{235}. The Pu^{239} is produced in large quantities in the uranium pile (see Sec. 19.5). Here, however, no *isotope separation* is needed but, instead, a *chemical separation* which, although difficult, lends itself to mass production much better than isotope separation. The plutonium so produced is assembled into a bomb according to the same principles that underlie the construction of the uranium bomb.

19.5. Nuclear Reactor. In the "uranium pile," or "nuclear reactor," fission takes place at a relatively slow, carefully controlled rate. The reactor far surpasses the cyclotron by the concentration of generated neutrons.

a. History and Purpose. While during the war the "nuclear reactor" was built and used for purposes of the atomic bomb, after the war other purposes came into the foreground. The first nuclear reactor was built before the first uranium bomb because the slower process in the reactor permitted the experimentation which was needed before the construction of the bomb could be undertaken. Later during the war, large nuclear reactors were built to transform U^{238} into Pu, one of the materials needed for the bomb. Such reactors were called "breeders." In addition to plutonium they produce vast amounts of energy which during the war went to waste. It has been estimated that the production of 1 kg of plutonium per day requires the dissipation of an energy of the order 10^6 kw (see Prob. 19.5) and, for cooling, the equivalent of the water supply of a fair-sized city. In the Smyth Report, this estimate is combined with the statement that a single bomb will require between 1 and 100 kg of plutonium.

For the future the great problem, which may affect the economic and political history of mankind, is the utilization of these vast nuclear energies which may be applied partly to general industrial consumption, partly to special purposes like the propulsion of ships and planes. From the point of view of engineering these two purposes differ widely. The energy produced for general consumption must be sufficiently inexpensive to compete with the energy provided by the common sources, coal, oil, etc. On the other hand, for the propulsion of a submarine over long distances the cost of the energy will be an unimportant factor. There is one more important purpose for which nuclear reactors are now in very successful operation: the production of artificially radioactive elements used for medical purposes and as tracers for all kinds of research.

We summarize the various purposes of the nuclear reactor: (1) research; (2) breeding of fissionable material; (3) large-scale economic energy production; (4) special energy production, *e.g.*, for the propulsion of a submarine; (5) production of artificially radioactive elements. One nuclear reactor may, at the same time, serve several purposes. We shall describe one reactor in some detail and then give a brief outline of other constructions. The reader must keep in mind that the accessible information is limited.

b. Principles of Construction and Operation. The first *large* reactors had the purpose of breeding, *i.e.*, transforming the abundant isotope U^{238} into the fissionable Pu^{239}. The nuclear reactor requires a construction widely different from that of the bomb. While in the bomb the greatest possible preference is given to fission, the designer of the reactor must strike a balance between the various processes that may happen to neutrons. Neutrons may (1) cause fission of U^{235}; (2) be captured by U^{238} and so generate Pu^{239}; (3) be captured by impurities; and (4) escape from the reactor. Only the first two processes are desired, whereas neutron losses by the two latter events must be avoided by extreme purification of all materials and by building large reactors whose shape minimizes the chance of escape.

Since the fast neutrons originally generated by fission are less effective than slow ones, the neutrons are first slowed down by providing many *elastic* collisions (collisions without nuclear reactions). For this purpose the uranium, which contains its two isotopes in their natural relative abundance, is embedded in large quantities of a medium, called the "moderator," which provides elastic collisions without reacting. What is the best material for the moderator? Since, according to the laws of mechanics, the most effective energy transfer in elastic collisions takes place between bodies of equal masses (see Prob. 9.1), ordinary hydrogen, $_1H^1$, apparently meets the requirement. Unfortunately, however, $_1H^1$ occasionally swallows neutrons to form deuterons (Sec. 18.4) and hence must be excluded. Deuterium provides the best combination of all desirable qualities. Unfortunately, it is not so readily available that during the war it could be used in quantity. Actually the first piles used pure carbon (graphite), which, although heavier than is desirable, undergoes almost no reaction with neutrons. It is estimated that slow neutrons must diffuse through 40 cm of graphite in order to slow down to thermal speed. Rods of pure uranium are inserted into the moderator.

The two desired processes, fission of U^{235} and plutonium production from U^{238}, must be balanced by the proper quantity of the moderator (see the schematic diagram of Fig. 19.1). Plutonium production has a pronounced maximum probability near a neutron energy of 25 ev, while fission has its highest probability at very low energies. If a *very large quantity* of the moderator is used, the initially fast neutrons are effectively slowed down before they collide with a uranium atom. Hence most neutrons have no chance of generating plutonium (near 25 ev), but they do produce plenty of fission of U^{235} and so continue the chain reaction. Such a reactor would be ineffective as a "breeder" of plutonium. On the other hand, when only a *small quantity* of the moderator is used, the neutrons have a much better chance of colliding with uranium during their gradual slowing down. Then, near the critical energy range around 25 ev, U^{238} will consume most of the neutrons and so produce plutonium. This process, however, although in itself desirable, would starve the chain reaction since it fails to generate new neutrons by fission. Consequently this reactor, too, would be an ineffective breeder. Hence there is an intermediate quantity of the moderator that is suitable for maximum plutonium production.

The activity of the reactor is adjusted by pushing in or pulling out cadmium strips; here we remember that cadmium has great ability to trap slow neutrons (Sec. 18.4). Hence, when introduced into the reactor, it has the same effect as an adjustable escape for neutrons.

The activity of a reactor (determined by its size, the relative amount of the moderator, and the insertion of cadmium strips) is measured by the "reproduction factor" k. It measures the average fertility of the neutrons. A neutron may perish by various events or generate new neutrons by the fission process. The reproduction factor k is defined as the average number of new neutrons generated by any existing neutron in its next nuclear reaction. The significance of the factor is understood by comparison with the "net reproduction rate" of human beings. If this rate is unity, each human being produces an average of one offspring before he or she dies and a stationary population results. Similarly a stationary level of operation of the reactor is described by the value $k = 1$, while $k < 1$ indicates discontinuance of the chain and $k > 1$ denotes an approach to explosion. However, one must not conclude that a reproduction factor only slightly larger than unity will cause a prompt explosion. Fortunately, it has been found that some of the neutrons liberated are delayed and thus give the operator a chance of adjusting the activity by the cadmium strips.

To start the chain reaction, it is not necessary to introduce neutrons, since a few stray neutrons are available everywhere, possibly because of cosmic rays, possibly because of rare spontaneous fission processes occurring in the reactor.

We summarize the processes by considering the life history of a group of neutrons just generated by fission. By elastic collisions with nuclei of the moderator they gradually slow down. Some of them, before reaching thermal speed, are captured by U^{238} and so produce plutonium. Others pass the critical range (near 25 ev) without performing this reaction and go down to thermal speed where they cause fission and thus keep the chain reaction going. Some neutrons are lost by escape or by reactions with impurities. A very few neutrons while still fast cause the rare fission reaction of U^{238}.

The cooling is much more difficult than in conventional machinery. Water is not allowed in the reactor since hydrogen is a neutron consumer. Therefore a liquid metal (sodium-potassium alloy) or a gas (helium) is used as an intermediary, receiving heat in the reactor and delivering it in the "heat exchanger" to water.

From time to time the rods of uranium are taken out for the removal of the plutonium and of fission products which may absorb neutrons. Plutonium has so long a half-life (2.4×10^4 years) that it does not noticeably decompose. However, its removal is complicated by the unavoidable presence of all fission products, *i.e.*, the fragments into which U^{235} splits. We mentioned barium and krypton only as examples. Actually many different elements of medium atomic weight are produced, most of them viciously radioactive. Their disposal or their utilization for other processes presents difficult problems. The chemical separation of plutonium is especially difficult, and the atomic bomb requires material of the highest purity obtainable. Because of the strong radioactivity all chemical operations must be performed by remote control.

The mechanism of the "breeder" reactor described makes it evident how difficult it is to gain access to the large energy stored in the isotope U^{238} (abundance 99.3 per cent). Each atom U^{238} must consume a neutron. However, each fission of the rare U^{235} generates only a few neutrons, between two or three in the fission process itself and in addition a few more "delayed neutrons." For our estimate let us arbitrarily assume that the total number of neutrons liberated by one fission process is 4, transmuting less than 4 U^{238} atoms into plutonium. Hence for a total of 1,000 atoms of natural uranium the seven atoms U^{235} which are naturally present will cause less than 28 atoms of U^{238} to be transmuted while the other atoms of U^{238} (about 965) are not affected. If now, after we have consumed all fissionable atoms, we remove the plutonium in order to use it for a bomb, all the residue, in this case about 96.5 per cent of all initial U^{238}, remains unaffected. This example, although based on arbitrary figures, demonstrates that we gain access to the large energies stored in U^{238} and Th^{232} only by sacrificing considerable quantities of the fissionable U^{235}. Our great success in utilizing nuclear energy depends entirely on the lucky coincidence that there exists one type of nucleus, although a rare one, U^{235}, that occurs in nature and is fissionable by slow neutrons.

c. Description of Nuclear Reactors. The first pile in Chicago was gradually assembled. From step to step the *neutron density* was measured, and its increase, as the critical size was approached, was watched. The cadmium strips provided safety by destroying neutrons. We quote the report of Fermi:

On the morning of December 2, 1942, the indications were that the critical dimensions had been slightly exceeded and that the system did not chain react only because of the absorption by the cadmium strips. . . . Actually, when about seven feet (of cadmium strip) were removed the (neutron) intensity rose to a very high value but still stabilized after a few minutes at a finite level. It was with some trepidation that the order was given to remove one more foot and a half of the strip. This operation would bring us over the top. When the foot and a half was pulled out, the intensity started rising slowly, but at an increasing rate, and kept on increasing until it was evident that it would actually *diverge*. Then the cadmium strips were again inserted into the structure and the intensity rapidly dropped to an insignificant level.

This experiment marks the beginning of a new epoch in the history of energy production by human beings. It was the first time that a self-maintaining nuclear chain reaction had been initiated.

Considering the sudden explosion of the atomic bomb, it seems strange that the Chicago physicists, starting the operation of the pile, dared to watch the automatic rise of the neutron intensity by their instruments and, before the pile exploded, had time to stop it. This delay of the threatening explosion is explained by the action of "delayed neutrons." Not all the neutrons liberated by the fission process go off instantaneously; about 1 per cent of them are delayed by periods up to 1 min. Near the critical stage of the pile this delay of a small group retards the development of the chain sufficiently to permit the control by cadmium strips. On the other hand, in the explosion of the atomic bomb these delayed neutrons cause only an insignificant energy loss.

After the first experiments in Chicago, a pile of intermediate size was built at Clinton, Tenn., operating on a power level of 1,000 kw. The main production plant was erected in a more isolated location, at Hanford, Wash. Here in the early summer of 1945 several piles were in operation "producing plutonium and heating the Columbia River." The radioactivity built up in a pile is estimated to be the equivalent of about a million tons of radium.

The following detailed information was released by the Atomic Energy Commission. The Chicago reactor was moved to the Argonne National Laboratory. It is 30 ft wide, 32 ft long, and 21 ft high. Its weight is 1,400 tons of which 52 tons consist of uranium (partly as metal, partly as oxide) divided into 17,700 rods. Each rod is enclosed in an airtight aluminum container which prevents the diffusion of the fission products. The intensity of the chain reaction increases with increasing size of the reactor. The reactor is finally enclosed in heavy shields of graphite, wood, lead, and concrete. There are five cadmium control rods, each 5 ft long.

The Argonne Laboratory has another reactor that uses deuterium (in the form of heavy water, D_2O) as a moderator. Because of the high efficiency of deuterium in slowing down neutrons this reactor is smaller than the graphite reactor. It contains

$6\frac{1}{2}$ tons of heavy water, in which 120 uranium rods, each protected by aluminum, are immersed.   The cooling system keeps this reactor at a temperature as low as 95°F.

In another reactor, the "water boiler" at Los Alamos, the uranium is distributed uniformly as a uranium salt dissolved in heavy water.   Its uranium content is "enriched," *i.e.*, it contains about 17 per cent of the fissionable U^{235} instead of 0.7 per cent, as in natural uranium.   The liquid is contained in a 1-ft stainless steel sphere.

The reactors here described are early types which provided the foundation for modern constructions.   No description of more recent reactors is available.   It is known, however, that the construction of two submarines to be propelled by atomic energy is well under way.

We can visualize some of the difficulties with which these constructions are confronted.   Apart from the problems of remote control, health protection, cooling, and waste disposal, an outstanding difficulty for the economic utilization of nuclear energy is presented by the decay of materials.   The nuclear energy must be converted into electric energy to

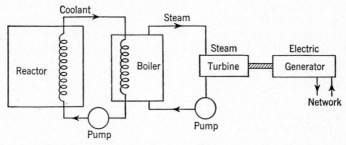

FIG. 19.3. Energy transfer from the nuclear reactor to the electric network.

be distributed over a wide area.   The heat generated in the reactor is carried away by a "coolant" which must not consume neutrons.   The liquid sodium-potassium alloy serves this purpose.   In the "heat exchanger" or "boiler" (Fig. 19.3) the coolant boils water.   The steam, in turn, drives a steam turbine which is coupled with an electric generator. It is well known that any heat engine, to be efficient, must operate between one heat reservoir of as high a temperature as possible, say, 700 to 1000°F, and another reservoir of low temperature, *i.e.*, cooling water.   Hence for the purpose of efficient energy production the nuclear reactor itself must be operated at as high a temperature as possible. Here the properties of materials cause trouble.   Although materials are well known that keep their strength at high temperature, the nuclear reactor adds another requirement since the same material must be able to withstand the violent bombardment by fast and slow neutrons.   It is not publicly known to what extent the problem has been solved.   This difficulty should not prevent the utilization of the large amounts of energy generated in reactors which are primarily built as *breeders*, although when considered as *energy producers* they are uneconomical.

While the *uranium reactor* serves two purposes, the production of plutonium and the generation of power, a *plutonium* reactor seems to offer the best chance of a relatively small atomic power plant. Since plutonium is sufficiently susceptible to fast neutrons, a plutonium reactor, called a "fast reactor," has been built without a moderator or, possibly, with a small amount of heavy water as a moderator. This seems to be the most compact type. At Los Alamos a fast reactor of this type is in operation. This least bulky type of reactor will presumably serve for the propulsion of ships. It is evident, however, that the energy produced by a fast reactor is exceedingly expensive. We explained above why, at present, energy production in the ordinary reactor is uneconomical. However, energy produced in the fast reactor should be very much more expensive since this reactor consumes as fuel not natural uranium but plutonium, which itself has been produced in a breeder pile at the expense of a great deal of uranium.

The cost of a small nuclear reactor is given as between 1 and 5 million dollars, that of a large one as between 25 and 50 million.

In our discussion of the pile and the bomb we considered only the few desired processes and how to produce them. This by no means gives an adequate picture of the difficulties that had to be overcome. The problems of chemistry were as great as those of physics. It is easy to require that "pure uranium" be used or that plutonium be separated from uranium. As a matter of fact the concentration of some impurities in the uranium and the graphite used in the pile had to be reduced to a value as low as a few parts in a million. This requirement recalls the fact that, up to 1940, only a few grams of moderately pure uranium metal had been produced. Furthermore, the separation of plutonium from uranium is obviously not described in any handbook of chemistry; all the chemical properties and reactions of plutonium must be worked out.

It is evident here how rapid the technical progress has been. Before the Second World War, the quantities of most elements produced by artificial transmutation were unweighably small. In cyclotron work it was a great success that gold was transformed into mercury in a quantity sufficient for a spectroscopic analysis, presumably of the order of a milligram. A few years later the new element plutonium was manufactured in a quantity that may be gauged from its power to destroy part of a city.

d. Prospect for Industrial Use. Can we expect to utilize the energy of other heavy nuclei, predecessors of uranium in the periodic table? The best prospect is offered by thorium, $_{90}Th^{232}$, which by neutron capture (after several steps) is transmuted into the fissionable U^{233}. The abundance of thorium in nature is large enough to make this process important. Aston's curve of packing fractions (Fig. 16.5) gives evidence of large energies stored in all heavy nuclei. We do not know, however, whether these energies are fenced in by "activation energies," so high that they prevent chain reactions. Fission has been observed for a few lighter elements. But here projectiles of very high energy (400 Mev alpha particles generated in the cyclotron) are required for the fission process. We cannot therefore expect chain reactions, which are needed for the large-scale liberation of nuclear energies, to occur. Hence our great success in the exploitation of the nuclear energy of uranium has not opened the door to the energies of many other nuclei. The energy stored in hydrogen nuclei will be discussed in the next section. For the time being we do not see a way of making available the nuclear energies of any but the heaviest elements.

How great is the *economic importance* of power production from uranium compared with that from other fuels such as coal, oil, and natural gas? (Water at present supplies only about 4 per cent of the power consumed in the United States.) All known deposits of uranium may represent a total amount of energy of the same order of magnitude as the energy available from the combustion of fuel. In this estimate the energy of U^{238} is included. Hence the energy famine threatening the human race within a few thousand years may be postponed but will not be averted by industrial applications of uranium fission.

Is there any prospect of an ample supply of energy from another source? Unless abundant energy is gained from other nuclei, light or heavy, the power of *solar radiation* far surpasses any other supply available for our rapidly increasing needs. This follows from the "solar constant," which gives the power arriving per square centimeter at the position of the earth (1.96 cal min^{-1} cm^{-2}). Assuming that only half of this power penetrates through the atmosphere, we compute the power of solar radiation incident on 1 sq mile, placed perpendicular to the rays, as 1.7×10^6 kw. This is comparable to the capacity of a large hydroelectric power plant. It has been stated that the total power of the solar radiation incident on the roof of a factory, if efficiently harnessed, would drive all its machinery which now receives energy ultimately from combustion of coal or water power. "Enough energy falls on about 200 square miles of an arid region like the Mohave Desert to supply the United States" (quoted from C. C. Furnas, 1941). We utilize only the very small fraction of the incident solar energy which is responsible for the growth of plants and, in addition, the other fraction which is consumed by the evaporation of water, which returns to the surface of the earth as rain and ultimately drives hydroelectric power plants. The industrial, direct utilization of solar energy meets great technical difficulties since it is *too dilute*, arriving in quanta of a few electron volts, distributed over the surface of half the earth. This difficulty is in contrast to that encountered in the exploitation of nuclear energy, which, coming in quanta of 200 Mev, is *too concentrated* for easy utilization.   Such technical difficulties, however, do not seem insurmountable.   Future research in nuclear physics may change the picture completely.

It may be anticipated that the release of nuclear energy will profoundly affect the course of human civilization.   This development will depend not so much upon the total amount of nuclear energy available as upon the ease with which this energy can be utilized; in other words, upon the cost of nuclear energy as compared with that of chemical energy.   As a starting point for the new development, we may expect that in industrialized countries where the coal deposits are depleted uranium power plants will prove efficient in the near future.   Apart from the *quantity* of the energy available we are sure that here energy of an entirely new *concentration* has been found.   The control of this energy should lead to the solution of problems that have seemed beyond our grasp.   Now that one such problem, the construction of the atomic bomb, has been solved, one may hope that human as well as physical energy will be expended upon problems of a different nature.   One forecast, however, is reliable.   The neutron intensity in a pile exceeds by a huge factor that which could be reached with the cyclotron.   These neutrons are available for the abundant production of artificially radioactive isotopes all over the periodic table.   In one of the next sections we shall discuss the use of these isotopes in a new method of attack upon problems of physics and chemistry as well as of biology and medicine.

Any rational plan for the future beneficial use of nuclear energy is in contrast to the events of recent years.   In 1939, the basic facts of nuclear fission were discovered as the outcome of research that was not directed to practical purposes.   During the Second World War, the arduous development from the observation of fission to the atomic bomb was accomplished by an unheard-of concentration of physicists, chemists, mathematicians, engineers, and many other experts.   The production of plutonium involved the waste of an enormous amount of energy, equivalent to the output of a big hydroelectric power plant.   The production of pure U^{235} may not have been more economical.   This gigantic effort was successfully directed toward the instantaneous and most efficient destruction of cities.   The decisive success of the atomic bomb has aroused a universal consciousness of the waste and danger inherent in the present situation.

19.6. Hydrogen Fusion in Stars.   *a. Carbon Cycle.*   In order to make clear the importance within the cosmos of the processes to be discussed in the present section, we start from a review of the thermal and chemical history of the earth.   When a mixture of reactive gases, like hydrogen and oxygen, is slowly cooled, starting from very high temperature, it ends up in the most stable configuration, *i.e.*, water (with a possible excess of one of the reactants). This is what we may expect for a gradually cooling earth. So we understand that almost no free hydrogen is available on the earth because most of it is bound with oxygen as water. We should expect the same to be true for carbon and oxygen, hence as much CO_2 as possible to be formed and not both the isolated elements, carbon and oxygen, to be available. As Gamow puts it, nobody would expect a natural deposit of dynamite. If this expectation were realized, no chemical energy would be available at the surface of the earth and no organic life could exist.

Everybody knows that actually the situation is entirely different. Carbon and oxygen do not all occur as CO_2, but the separate elements are available as well. The carbon is not evenly dispersed but highly concentrated and easily accessible in plants and as a mineral. We have discussed this before and found that all animal life depends on the availability of food energy supplied by plants (Sec. 12.4c). *What is the source of our chemical energy?* It all comes from solar radiation absorbed by the chlorophyll in the green leaves which, in photosynthesis, assimilates the carbon present in the air as CO_2. The energy of light breaks up the structure of this stable carbon-oxygen compound. This same process in which carbon compounds are formed in the plant liberates oxygen into the atmosphere. For millions of years this process has been going on.

This answer confronts us with the next question: *Where does the solar energy come from?* This we shall try to answer in the present section. The most trivial guess is that the sun is a hot body in which, according to its heat capacity, energy is stored and radiated from its surface. On this basis one computes that even within a few years the cooling of the sun's surface would be noticeable; it would be very appreciable during the known period of human history. Hence this guess is obviously wrong. The estimate is not much improved when we assume a chemical reaction, like the combustion of carbon, to be responsible for the heat production of the sun. With this estimate we compare the facts of biology. It is known that the evolution of living beings on the surface of the earth is an exceedingly slow process. It has been estimated that the present state of animal life is the result of an evolution reaching over 500 million years, during which the surface of the earth must have been at a temperature sufficiently uniform for organic life. Since this temperature depends directly on the solar radiation, we must assume that the sun has had a rather uniform temperature through this vast period. Although we are unable to judge the accuracy of this figure, there is no doubt that, in the sun, we must assume a source uniformly producing energy far exceeding any possible supply of chemical energy.

Next it was suggested that the sun is heated by nuclear transmutations; more specifically, that the combination of 4 hydrogen atoms forming a helium atom (or 2 protons and 2 neutrons forming a helium nucleus) would supply the solar energy (see Prob. 19.11). This assumption, however, has the obvious drawback that the process seems to require a simultaneous collision of four particles, which is a highly improbable event.

This great and old problem of the energy production in the interior of the sun has recently been solved by Bethe (1938), who went into the detail of all nuclear reactions involved. The same cycle of reactions was simultaneously suggested by von Weizsäcker. A sequence of nuclear reactions is assumed, each one of them requiring only the collision of two particles. The individual steps involved have not been invented for this purpose but have been really performed in experiments with the cyclotron; so their probabilities are known. Bethe accepts the calculation, made by astronomers, of a temperature in the interior of the sun of about 20 million degrees K. In selecting plausible reactions, preference is given to light nuclei since the smaller Coulomb repulsion gives better chances of close approaches. Hydrogen is outstanding partly because of its small nuclear charge, partly because of its overwhelming abundance in the sun. What are the possible reactions of a proton? It does not react with another proton or a helium nucleus; but it does react with the next heavier nuclei, Li, Be, and B, so readily that they presumably have disappeared at an early stage of the history of the sun and similar stars.* Thus the next element $_6C^{12}$ turns out to be the plausible partner for a nuclear reaction with fast protons. Although at 20 million degrees K the *average* energy of translation of any particle is only about 2,000 ev, hence much too small for any nuclear reaction, there are always present a few particles of much higher energy, as predicted by Maxwell's velocity distribution. From experiments with the cyclotron one derives the probability of collisions which actually lead to the nuclear reaction $_6C^{12} + _1H^1 \rightarrow _7N^{13} + \gamma$. This lengthy argument leads to an estimate of the lifetime of an individual $_6C^{12}$ nucleus which is exposed to the proton bombardment as it occurs in the interior of the sun. Because collisions of very high energy are very rare, the lifetime is as long as 2.5×10^6 years. The product of this reaction, which is accompanied by gamma emission, is $_7N^{13}$. Our diagram (Fig. 18.4) shows that this nucleus (consisting of 7 protons and 6 neutrons) is unstable and emits positrons. Its half-life, which is characteristic of the nucleus and independent of collisions, is 10 min. The nucleus so produced, $_6C^{13}$, is stable. To this nucleus a similar argument is applied as to the $_6C^{12}$ just mentioned. The continuation of the argument leads to a sequence of reactions shown in Table 19.1. On the left side we list the particles consumed, in the middle the particles produced.

* We do not enter into the closely related speculations concerned with the early history of stars. A highly recommended discussion is given by G. Gamow, "Atomic Energy in Cosmic and Human Life," The Macmillan Company, New York, 1946.

The lifetimes of the *unstable* nuclei, $_7N^{13}$ and $_8O^{15}$, are characteristic constants measured at the laboratory. On the other hand, the lifetimes of the *stable* nuclei (*i.e.*, stable at the laboratory) are estimated on the basis of observations made with the cyclotron; they depend on the concentra-

Table 19.1. *Carbon Cycle*

Consumed	Produced	Lifetime	
$_6C^{12} + _1H^1$	$_7N^{13} + \gamma$	2.5×10^6 years	(1)
$_7N^{13}$	$_{+1}e^0 + _6C^{13}$	10 min	(2)
$_6C^{13} + _1H^1$	$_7N^{14} + \gamma$	50,000 years	(3)
$_7N^{14} + _1H^1$	$_8O^{15} + \gamma$	4×10^6 years	(4)
$_8O^{15}$	$_{+1}e^0 + _7N^{15}$	2 min	(5)
$_7N^{15} + _1H^1$	$_2He^4 + _6C^{12}$	20 years	(6)

tion of protons and the temperature and are uncertain by about the factor 10 either way.

This sequence of processes is easily remembered when its significance is understood. The carbon nucleus $_6C^{12}$, which presumably is built of *three* alpha particles, assembles 4 protons by successive collisions. Whenever an unstable nucleus is formed, it soon loses its excess positive charge by the emission of a positron and so changes into a stable nucleus. This, in turn, waits until it swallows the next sufficiently fast proton. Thus gradually the charges and masses are collected for the building up in reaction (6) of the "compound nucleus" $_8O^{16}$ which, if stable, would be built of *four* alpha particles. However, because of the energy of the last collision, it is unstable and immediately goes to pieces into $_2He^4 + _6C^{12}$. Hence the over-all effect is the *consumption of four protons*, the *creation of one helium nucleus and two positrons* and the liberation of energy.

The carbon nucleus entering into the reaction emerges unchanged although it plays an essential part. This function of the carbon, instigating a reaction without ultimately being consumed, is typical of a "catalyst" in a chemical reaction. Therefore, all we have to assume is that in the interior of the sun carbon nuclei and protons are present at very high temperature. Instead of carbon, any other nucleus occurring in the scheme, *e.g.*, ordinary nitrogen, $_7N^{14}$, would serve the same purpose. In the computation of the energy output, the creation of three gamma-ray quanta must be taken into account.

The carbon cycle is a very slow process. This follows from the average lifetimes of the principal reactants given above. The low probabilities of the reactions (1) and (4) are responsible for the conclusion that the completion of one cycle, beginning and ending with an individual $_6C^{12}$ nucleus, may take about 6 million years. On the basis of reasonable assumptions regarding the abundances of hydrogen and carbon, Bethe was able to estimate the total energy production which satisfactorily agrees with the total energy loss by radiation from the sun.

What is the importance of the carbon cycle for organic life on the earth? Its importance is twofold. Solar radiation, ultimately fed by the carbon cycle, is *heating* the earth to a nearly constant temperature and is providing the *chemical energy* needed for organic life. Biologists claim that the evolution of organic life on the earth requires a *moderate* temperature, between the boiling point and the freezing point of water, that must have prevailed at the surface of the earth for several hundred million years. The *moderate value* of our temperature is due to the fact that the earth, which is heated by solar radiation, is located at an appropriate distance from the sun. Furthermore, our average temperature is as *uniform* as the solar temperature, which has gradually reached a stationary value determined by equal values of energy loss from the surface and energy production in the interior. It appears as a mere coincidence that this stationary temperature of the earth is within that narrow range required for the evolution of organic life. This, then, is the rare combination upon which organic life depends, the *constancy of the temperature and its value.*

Now we come back to our original question: Where does the *chemical energy* that feeds organic life come from? What agent separates carbon and oxygen at the surface of the earth? This is the other contribution made by solar radiation during the vast period of nearly stationary temperature. Solar radiation (within a narrow wavelength range in the red) continually provides the energy for photosynthesis and so separates the stable CO_2 into carbon and oxygen. Thus solar radiation has stored large energy treasures of plants and coal on one hand and, on the other hand, gaseous oxygen. This energy is indispensable for life as well as for industrial activity. Thus these three agents cooperate to create and maintain life: the carbon cycle generating energy in the sun, solar radiation keeping the temperature of the earth on a favorable level, and photosynthesis transforming a small part of the solar radiation into chemical energy available to organisms. Primitive religions worship the sun as the source of life. On a different background science concurs.

For stars of lower internal temperature than that of the sun another nuclear process has been proposed. It starts with the reaction $_1H^1 + _1H^1 \rightarrow _1H^2 + _{+1}e^0$ and, in a few more steps, leads to $_2He^4$. The proton-proton reaction just written occurs only with very low probability, although it does not require so high a temperature as the reactions of the carbon cycle.

b. Abundances of Isotopes and Elements. Bethe's theory of the carbon cycle, introduced in order to explain the stationary temperature of the sun, at the same time suggests the answer to another great problem.

What determines the relative abundances of the various isotopes measured in the mass spectrograph?   They are so well defined that, for a long time, the chemical atomic weights, depending upon these abundances, were considered to be fundamental constants of nature.   Now we find that, in the interior of the sun, the relative abundance of C^{12} and C^{13} is determined by the *relative probabilities of the various nuclear transmutations* induced by proton bombardment.   This follows from the lifetimes given in the survey of the carbon cycle. C^{13} is rare because it is highly receptive to proton bombardment; C^{12} is abundant because it is about fifty times as reluctant to change its status.   When convection within the body of the sun brings matter from the hot interior to cooler regions near the surface, the nuclear reactions stop altogether; hence, the relative abundance determined in the hot interior persists as a "frozen equilibrium."   The same applies to the nitrogen isotopes.   Also the relative concentrations of carbon and nitrogen, both partners in the same cycle, should be determined by similar considerations.   Our argument by no means *completely* explains the relative abundances but, as an outstanding factor, indicates the probabilities of the transitions occurring in the oven where the elements are cooked.

19.7. Hydrogen Fusion at the Surface of the Earth.   When we realize the vast periods during which solar energy has been stored, building up coal deposits, we are appalled by the fact that our present activity in industry and war consumes this treasure at a rate far exceeding the rate of replacement.   Our wastefulness places before the physicist the problem of how to utilize the vast reservoir of nuclear energy available at the surface of the earth.   How can we liberate energy at will by the combination of 4 hydrogens to form helium?   The carbon cycle just discussed is useless for industrial purposes because even in the interior of the sun one cycle takes many millions of years.   Are there other nuclear reactions which would give a better prospect for energy production?   To find the answer we must systematically explore all reactions among the lightest nuclei because they offer the best chances for close approaches of nuclei. Experiments with the cyclotron prove that the approach of 2 protons does not lead to any probable reaction.

The failure of 2 protons to react with one another is strikingly demonstrated by the underwater explosion of a uranium bomb.   The extremely high temperatures so produced failed to start a nuclear reaction among the protons which are abundantly present in the water.   Otherwise such a reaction would have spread and burned out the whole ocean, which evidently did not happen.

A proton and a deuteron react with low probability to generate the rare helium isotope

$$H^1 + H^2 \rightarrow He^3 + \gamma$$

However, the energy escapes as a gamma ray and fails to heat the mixture and so to promote the reaction of adjacent atoms. The same limitation applies to the combination of two deuterons

$$_1H^2 + {}_1H^2 \rightarrow He^4 + \gamma$$

The situation is different for the reaction of a deuteron and a triton (the artificially produced, radioactive $_1H^3$)

$$_1H^2 + {}_1H^3 \rightarrow {}_2He^4 + n$$

This rapid reaction produces an energy as high as 17 Mev. Moreover, this energy does not escape as a gamma ray but appears as kinetic energy of particles, which heats up the mixture and so may enable neighboring nuclei to continue the reaction. Presumably, this is the reaction that is basic for the hydrogen bomb. How can we start the reaction? It is believed that the heat generated in the explosion of the uranium or plutonium bomb is just sufficient to start the explosion of the deuterium-tritium mixture. Once it is started, it will generate enough heat to propagate the explosion. But for the start the uranium or plutonium explosion is indispensable. This combination illustrates the different characters of fission and fusion. While uranium fission is started by thermal neutrons at ordinary temperature, hydrogen fusion requires violent collisions of hydrogen nuclei and, therefore, needs the highest obtainable temperature. Hence hydrogen fusion is called a "thermonuclear reaction."

The nuclear reactions between hydrogen and lithium, which are discussed in Sec. 18.7, offer the great advantage of liberating unusually large amounts of energy, since the product nuclei are helium, representing the most stable nuclear structure. The constituents of these reactions, hydrogen and lithium, are vastly less expensive than U^{235} or Pu^{239} or H^3. It may be that the hydrogen bomb provides a sufficiently high temperature for the hydrogen-lithium mixture to explode. One may imagine that in the modern atom bomb a plutonium explosion produces the heat required for the explosion of the H^2-H^3 mixture, which, in turn, by its still higher temperature explodes a hydrogen-lithium mixture.

We are disappointed when we look back at the problem we started from, how to utilize the energy stored in the cheapest fuel, hydrogen. At great expense the rare isotope, deuterium, is separated from natural hydrogen. Still much more difficult is the production of tritium, which does not occur in nature. In order to produce it, we must expend uranium in the nuclear reactor. Furthermore, tritium cannot be stored indefinitely because of its half-life of only 12.4 years. This, then, is the present situation of our knowledge of hydrogen fusion. At a terrific cost in labor and uranium we have added to the uranium bomb a still more destructive constituent.   However, we still do not see any technique which would enable us to utilize the energy stored in ordinary hydrogen. Here all we can do is, on the basis of Einstein's equation, to calculate the vast energy which, for the time being, seems to be shielded by an insurmountable barrier.

19.8. Applications.   In this section we shall survey applications of the nuclear reactor as well as those of the cyclotron.   These applications enter into so many fields that, instead of a systematic survey, we can give only examples.*

The application of radioactive isotopes as *tracers*, which was started by Hevesy and Paneth (1913) using natural radioactivity, has developed into a wide field by the artificial production of radioactive isotopes of all elements.   The nuclear reactor produces such isotopes in large quantities. Typical is the investigation of self-diffusion.   Two lead cylinders of equal size are prepared, one of ordinary lead, the other of lead with a small addition of radium D (half-life 22 years), which is an isotope of lead.   These two cylinders, just fitting face to face into a glass tube, are melted and kept in the liquid phase for several days.   After cooling, the ordinary lead is cut in slices; the radioactivity of each individual slice indicates the amount of lead that has diffused into it from the active part.   So the coefficient of diffusion of lead atoms in lead is measured.   This is a problem that can be solved only with the help of a tracer, which may be either a radioactive atom as here described or (in similar problems) a rare isotope as discussed in the chapter on Isotopes (Sec. 16.9).   By the same method the surprising result has been obtained that atoms are diffusing, although only very slowly, even *in the solid state*.   For example, zinc atoms diffuse through zinc single crystals at 410°C (9°C below the melting point) at a slow rate which shifts a noticeable concentration of the activated atoms within a few hours over distances of a few thousandths of an inch.

An application of artificial radioactivity to spectroscopy has occasionally been mentioned before (Sec. 19.5c).   By the reaction $_{79}Au^{197} + _{0}n^1 \rightarrow _{79}Au^{198}$ and the subsequent spontaneous electron emission, the stable mercury isotope $_{80}Hg^{198}$ is produced which, in natural mercury, occurs mixed with six other isotopes.   This single isotope emits very sharp spectral lines that are well suited for primary standards of wavelengths (Wiens and Alvarez, 1940; Meggers).

The elements with atomic numbers 43, 61, 85, and 87, which are not found in nature although their existence is predicted by the periodic table and the Moseley diagram, are generated in the cyclotron.   They are called technetium, promethium, astatine, and francium, respectively.

---

* See the book of E. C. Pollard and W. L. Davidson, listed in Appendix 8.

Of particular importance in organic chemistry and biology are the radioactive isotopes of carbon, C^{11} and C^{14} (half-lives 20.5 min and 5,600 years, respectively). They have been used, *e.g.*, in the investigation of photosynthesis to trace the fate of carbon atoms.

The migration of phosphorus from the roots to the leaves of a plant can be demonstrated in the lecture room within 10 min by applying 1 millicurie of P^{32} to the solution that feeds a bean plant.

Figure 19.4 shows a "radioautograph." A leaf that had been fed with a solution of radio phosphorus is placed in contact with a photographic plate. The image on the plate shows the preferred location of phosphorus in the leaf.

The rate at which the blood stream carries sodium through the human body is measured by feeding a person a salt solution containing a trace of radioactive sodium. The counting rate of a Geiger counter placed in the person's hand begins to rise after a few minutes.

Many biologists consider the tracer method and its wide application as the greatest advance in the technique of biological and medical research since the discovery of the microscope. For therapeutic purposes neutrons may, in special cases, be preferable to X rays. The effect of neutrons as well as that of X rays is due to secondary particles, which produce ionization. But in the case of X rays the secondary *electrons* cause a dilute ionization, whereas in the case of neutrons the secondary *protons* produce a much more concentrated ionization. This contrast

Fig. 19.4. Radioautograph. Distribution of P^{32} in tomato leaf. (*Courtesy of J. G. Hamilton.*)

is evident on the cloud-chamber pictures (Figs. 17.10 and 18.3). (It is immaterial whether the secondaries are produced by gamma rays or X rays.) The more condensed effect due to neutrons may, in some cases, be preferable. The effects on the human body of the products of the pile are so strong that, in any work near the pile or in applying radioactive tracers, health protection presents a problem of great difficulty.*

An unexpected application of radioactive carbon, C^{14}, has been the determination of the age of archaeological findings. The argument is as follows: the carbon dioxide, *present in the atmosphere*, contains a small, uniform abundance of radioactive carbon, C^{14}. As C^{14} is spontaneously

* Detailed advice is given in "National Bureau of Standards Handbook 42," Superintendent of Documents, Washington, D.C.

decaying with a half-life of 5,600 years, we must assume that a replacement for the spontaneous loss is permanently provided, presumably by cosmic rays transmuting N^{14} into C^{14}. The equilibrium between generation and disintegration is responsible for the uniform, small abundance observed. The carbon of the air is built into all plants by photosynthesis (Sec. 12.4c) and thus into all animals feeding on the plants. However, after the death of the plant or the animal no new radioactive carbon is generated because the body is less accessible to cosmic rays than the upper atmosphere is. Moreover, the plant or animal body does not contain nitrogen, the mother substance, in an abundance comparable to that of the air. Hence *in the dead body* of an animal or plant C^{14} is disintegrating without replacement. This has the effect that, for example, wood from ancient Egyptian tombs shows less relative abundance of C^{14} than new wood. Thus the relative abundance of C^{14} serves as a time clock which is suitable for indicating ages of thousands of years for all dead organic material.

The same method has led to the result that living bodies found in great depths of the Atlantic contain less C^{14} than normal. The abundance indicates that these bodies picked up their carbon about 1,500 years ago at the surface and, in the meantime, had no chance of replacement of carbon. This argument leads to conclusions regarding water currents in the Atlantic.

Elaborate high-voltage X-ray generators that are used for the treatment of deep-seated tumors may be replaced by radioactive cobalt (Co^{60}, half-life 5.3 years), which is produced in the nuclear reactor and emits gamma rays as hard as those produced by a three-million-volt X-ray machine.

SUMMARY OF CHAPTER 19

1. Fermi's systematic investigation of neutron capture by nuclei leads to a method by which an atom is transmuted into that of the next higher atomic number. Neutron capture transmutes U^{238} into U^{239}, which, by successive electron emissions, leads to the transuranic elements, $_{93}Np^{239}$ and $_{94}Pu^{239}$.

2. The atom of $_{92}U^{235}$, when bombarded with slow neutrons, splits into two fragments of nearly equal atomic weight and several neutrons, with the liberation of an energy of about 200 Mev (fission). We can start this reaction at will (in contrast to natural disintegration). Since the reaction generates more free neutrons than it consumes, it lends itself to a chain reaction which may be explosive.

3. The forces acting in the nucleus are the Coulomb force repelling the protons from one another and the meson-exchange force which, for nuclear distances, is overwhelmingly larger than the Coulomb repulsion

and is the same in the pairs p-p, n-n, and p-n.   The nucleus may be compared with a drop of liquid.   The particles constituting the drop are kept together by a kind of surface tension, which here is due to nuclear forces of attraction.   Large nuclei compare with large drops in their lack of stability, which may cause fission.   The packing-fraction curve gives evidence of the energies liberated in certain reactions.   Heavy nuclei liberate energy by fission, light nuclei by fusion.   The activation energies are computed for heavy nuclei as the limiting energies of the vibrations leading to fission; for light nuclei they are the energies required by charged projectiles to overcome the Coulomb repulsion.   The very heaviest and lightest nuclei liberate energy with the smallest activation energy and, therefore, offer the best chance for the utilization of nuclear energy.

4.   The *bomb* consists of pure U^{235} or Pu^{239}.   In a block exceeding the critical size, the fission processes lead to a rapidly branching chain and so to an explosion.

5.   The *pile* consists of natural uranium (or uranium enriched by addition of U^{235}).   The fast neutrons originating from fission are slowed down by collisions with the nuclei of the moderator.   This makes them more effective for producing fission.   The critical size is such that the chain reaction is maintained without leading to an explosion.   Many neutrons not used for the chain reaction are captured by U^{238} and so transform this nucleus indirectly (see above) into Pu^{239}.   This process makes the nuclear energy of the isotope U^{238} (abundance, 99.3 per cent) available for the chain reaction.   The plutonium may be *chemically* separated from the pile and used in the bomb, or else it may be left in the pile to contribute to the energy production.   The vast amount of heat produced in the pile may serve industrial purposes.

The most important application of artificial radioactivity is in "tracer" work.   Examples are taken from physics, chemistry, and biology.   Neutrons are applied instead of X rays for therapeutic purposes.   The radioactive isotope C^{14} (half-life 5,600 years), which occurs in living organisms and gradually decays after death, serves to determine the age of archaeological findings.

6.   The energy radiated from the sun probably originates in the hot interior of the sun from a set of nuclear reactions in which a carbon nucleus, $_6C^{12}$, gradually captures 4 protons and so finally builds up a helium nucleus.   This sequence of processes liberates two positrons and two gamma-ray quanta and finally restores the $_6C^{12}$ nucleus, which, therefore, acts only as a catalyst.   Through many millions of years the energy *production* in the sun by this process and the energy *loss* by radiation have been balanced.   The uniform solar radiation so produced has provided a uniform temperature at the surface of the earth and so created

the conditions favorable for the origin and development of organic life. At the same time, by photosynthesis, solar radiation has stored the chemical energy indispensable for organic life. The abundances of the various elements and isotopes are determined by their susceptibility to proton bombardment at the high temperature in the interior of the sun. For example, an isotope that is easily transmuted by proton bombardment is present in only a small abundance.

7. The nuclear reaction $_1H^2 + {_1}H^3 \rightarrow {_2}He^4 + {_0}n^1$, which combines a small activation energy with large energy production, lends itself to a thermonuclear reaction and, hence, may serve for a hydrogen bomb. For starting, this reaction needs the high temperature of the uranium or plutonium explosion. The excessively high temperature produced in this H bomb may be sufficient to start the thermonuclear reaction of hydrogen and lithium. Thus these comparatively inexpensive elements may vastly intensify the effect of the bomb.

No steady reaction of light elements is known that lends itself to the exploitation of nuclear energy for industrial purposes.

PROBLEMS

19.1. *Half-life of* $_{94}Pu^{239}$. A sample of 50 mg of $_{94}Pu^{239}$ has a strength of 3.1 millicuries. Calculate the disintegration constant λ and half-life T (in years) of $_{94}Pu^{239}$.

19.2. *Mean free path of neutron in uranium.* Calculate the mean free path of a neutron in uranium, considering only nuclear collisions. The diameter of the uranium nucleus is 3×10^{-12} cm (Sec. 9.3). The neutron is small as compared to this nucleus. Use the result of Prob. 5.1. Density of uranium 18.7 g/cm³. Assume an arrangement of atoms as in a cubic crystal (Sec. 14.1f). Hence the number n of uranium nuclei per cm³ is computed with the help of Eq. (14.2).

19.3. *Effect of the moderator.* (a) What fraction of its *kinetic energy* is *given away* by a fast neutron in a head-on collision with a deuteron? (b) Answer the same question replacing the deuteron by a carbon nucleus. Use the result of Prob. 9.1.

19.4. *Energy of uranium fission.* Suppose that in uranium fission $_{92}U^{235} + {_0}n^1$ split into $_{56}Ba^{139}$, $_{36}Kr^{86}$, and 11 neutrons. Compute the total energy made available by this fission process; given the atomic weights: U^{235} 235.12; Ba^{139} 138.92; Kr^{86} 85.94; $_0n^1$ 1.009.

Actually only between 1 and 3 neutrons are liberated at once, and many others remain bound to the heavy fragment nuclei. Some of these neutrons come off within about 1 min as delayed neutrons; others remain bound to heavy nuclei which, after certain lifetimes, emit electrons.

19.5. *Power of the pile.* Suppose that in a pile each fission process contributes *one neutron* toward the transformation of U^{238} into Pu^{239}. Furthermore, the fission process liberates 200 Mev. How much power (in kw) is released when the pile produces 1 kg of plutonium per day?

19.6. *Comparison of energies.* How much coal must be burned to provide as much energy as the fission of 1 kg of U^{235} produces? Assume 200 Mev as the energy produced by one fission process and 8,000 cal/g as the heat of combustion of coal. 1 calorie = 4.19×10^7 ergs.

19.7. *Ordering radioactive material.* A hospital orders 10 μ curies = 10^{-5} curie of Co^{60} (half-life 5.3 years). Calculate the mass in grams of this quantity. (It will be delivered embedded in inactive cobalt.)

19.8. *C^{14} as a clock.* In a Geiger counter 1 mg of carbon taken from living material produces 20 counts per minute. In the same arrangement the same quantity of carbon taken from an ancient piece of wood produces 5 counts per minute. How old is this piece of wood?

19.9. *Basic idea of carbon cycle.* Reconstruct the carbon cycle, applying its basic idea as follows. Assume proton capture by the *stable* nuclei, beginning with $_6C^{12}$. Identify the *stable* nuclei by referring to Appendix 5. Determine the type of emission of the *unstable* nuclei as discussed in Sec. 18.4. Finally, to explain the last step, compare the energy liberated by $N^{15} + H^1$ with the energy required to decompose O^{16} into $_2He^4$ and $_6C^{12}$.

19.10. *Diagram of carbon cycle.* Enter the transmutations occurring in the carbon cycle into the diagram of Fig. 18.4.

19.11. *Energy content of hydrogen.* We estimate the enormous energy that will be made available if we succeed in combining hydrogen into helium as follows. We separate all the hydrogen contained in a glass of water (250 g of water) from the oxygen. We suppose that a future physicist will use half the hydrogen atoms available for making neutrons by combining the electrons with the protons. Furthermore, he will combine any 2 neutrons with 2 protons to form $_2He^4$ nuclei. Then he will have just the number of electrons left to form neutral He atoms. Calculate the total energy liberated (in ergs and kwhr). Calculate the value of this energy, assuming 2 cents for 1 kwhr. Use the results of Probs. 18.3 and 18.7.

19.12. *Consumption of hydrogen in the sun.* Calculate the consumption of hydrogen in the sun (in atoms per year and tons per year). Assume that the energy radiated per year (calculated in Prob. 6.12) is provided by the combination of hydrogen atoms (calculated in Prob. 19.11).

19.13. *Energy production by fission and fusion.* (a) How much energy is liberated by the fission of 1 g of U^{235}? Assume an energy of 200 Mev for each fission process. (b) How much energy is liberated by the fusion of 1 g of the mixture $H^2 + H^3$?

19.14. *Producing tritium.* A nuclear reactor supplies 200 g of $_1H^3$ per day to our stock. (This is an arbitrary figure.) $_1H^3$ has a half-life of 12.4 years. (a) Calculate the final ("equilibrium") accumulation. (b) Calculate the accumulation reached after 12.4 years of operation. Use the result of Prob. 17.19.

CHAPTER 20

COSMIC RAYS

Cosmic rays are rays, occurring in nature, that have a penetrating power far exceeding that of any other radiation known.   Their study is of outstanding interest for two reasons: (1) Since cosmic rays consist largely of particles and quanta endowed with much larger energies than can be produced in the laboratory, they give rise to processes otherwise unknown. The investigation of these particles and processes by the methods of nuclear research represents a field of major importance.   (2) The occurrence of cosmic rays gives evidence of processes in the cosmos that still are a mystery and accessible only to speculation.

We shall discuss first results obtained with the simple technique by which cosmic rays were discovered, *i.e.*, by observing the *discharge of an electroscope*.   Then we shall report the much more refined results obtained with *Geiger-Müller counters, cloud chambers*, and *photographic plates*.   In the following sections we shall deal with the evidence obtained by the various methods regarding the nature of the primary and secondary rays and the conversion of primaries into secondaries.

20.1. Fundamental Observations.   It is known that every charged condenser, in spite of the most careful insulation, gradually loses its charge.   This was first explained by the presence of traces of radioactive substances emitting rays that cause a weak ionization of the air.   However, during balloon flights it was discovered that this loss of charge takes place much more rapidly at high altitude.   This cannot be explained by a greater concentration of radioactive gases present because, at high altitude, this concentration is actually much smaller than that at sea level. From such observations, Hess (1910) concluded that the ionization of the air is continually being produced by rays coming from outside, later called "cosmic rays."   This radiation has an extraordinary penetrating power which enables it to reach the surface of the earth.

· This may not seem unusual since we are used to the penetration of sunlight through the whole atmosphere.   However, this complete transparency of the atmosphere for visible light is a specific property of certain gaseous molecules in a limited wavelength range.   It is due to the fact that the first absorption lines of the atmospheric gases are located in the ultraviolet.

Cosmic rays penetrate water to such an extent that at any depth yet investigated traces of them are found.   They likewise penetrate thick lead plates. We measure the rate of discharge of an electroscope protected by various layers of lead. The resulting curve, representing the rate of discharge versus the thickness of the lead, is not simply an exponential curve. It shows that some parts of the radiation are readily absorbed in about 10 cm of lead while other parts have much greater "hardness."

The various components, however, are related to each other as is revealed by their absorption in the atmosphere. For its investigation, Millikan and his collaborators sent an electroscope carried by sounding balloons into the stratosphere. Once every 4 min the electroscope was charged and then its rate of discharge measured. The ionization of the air so measured follows a rather complex law since it is affected by two

factors: the intensity of the cosmic rays and the density of the air, decreasing with altitude. In order to correct for the decrease of the density of the air, a curve was derived from the data representing the ionization as it would be if the air had a uniform density all over. (For the sake of this computation the sounding balloons carried recording barometers and thermometers in addition to the electroscopes.) Thus, in Fig. 20.1 the abscissa represents the thickness of the layer of air traversed by the rays, measured by the total mass per unit area of the atmosphere above any altitude.

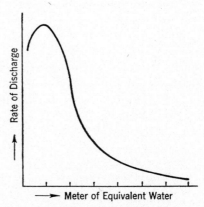

FIG. 20.1. Cosmic-ray ionization at various altitudes (computed for a uniform atmosphere).

This is expressed in terms of an equivalent water column (see Prob. 20.2). On this scale the layer zero means the top of the atmosphere. The highest altitude reached in these experiments is represented by 20 cm and sea level by 1,030 cm of water column. The ordinate represents the intensity as measured by the rate of discharge of the electroscope (in ions produced per cm^3 and sec). If the incident radiation consisted, e.g., of X rays the decay with depth would be represented by an exponential decay curve. The actual curve, however, has a maximum at high altitude as shown in the diagram. This is explained as follows: It is assumed that at the highest altitude the cosmic rays consist of particles or quanta of exceedingly high energy which are known to dissipate their energy in collisions with molecules only at a low rate (see Sec. 17.2b; Fig. 17.9 shows that the straight track due to a fast electron has a smaller density of water droplets than the curved tracks belonging to slower electrons). Gradually these particles generate secondaries so that the few particles of highest energy are replaced by many particles of lower energy that, on the average, ionize more heavily. This explains the increase of ionization when, starting from the highest altitude reached (absorbing layer 20 cm of water equivalent), we go down to the maximum ionization which occurs at 80 cm water equivalent. The powerful decrease of ionization toward sea level (10.3 m water equivalent) is explained by the gradual dissipation of the energy of the cosmic rays. The low residual ionization at sea level is only 1 per cent of the maximum value shown by the diagram. Further investigation of individual rays shows that this residual ionization is due to secondaries.

The intensity of the rays, measured by the rate of discharge of an electroscope, is uniform with time and not affected by the position of the sun, the moon, the planets, or the galaxy. We conclude that the rays originate in the cosmos. This justifies their name without explaining their origin (see Sec. 20.5).

The study of the ionization as a function of the altitude leads to the total ionization produced in the atmosphere. If tentatively the production of each ion pair is associated with an energy of 30 ev (see Prob. 17.3), one can calculate the *total energy* incident on the earth. This is of the same order of magnitude as the total energy incident as starlight.

The results so far discussed have all been obtained with the simplest technique, that of recording the rate of discharge of an electroscope. The *Geiger-Müller counter* permits a demonstration of cosmic rays in a laboratory experiment. We have already discussed the coincidence counter (Sec. 18.5). This acts like a combination of two Geiger-Müller counters connected in series, which responds only when both counters are made conducting *simultaneously*. Two such counter tubes are placed in a parallel position (geometrically, not electrically) at a short distance from each other, forming the two opposite sides of a square. First the two coincidence counter tubes are placed in a *vertical* plane, each tube horizontal, one above the other; next they are placed in a *horizontal* plane. In a vertical plane they register many more coincidences per minute than in the horizontal plane. This simple measurement indicates that the cosmic rays arrive largely in the *vertical* direction. One should not conclude, however, that *outside the earth* the cosmic rays show such a preference for the vertical direction, but only that vertical rays have to pass through the minimum layer of air and, therefore, have the best chance of reaching the surface of the earth.

Most instructive observations of individual particles are made with the *cloud chamber*. The atmosphere is not so densely filled with cosmic rays that any random cloud-chamber photograph would show them. In order to avoid waste, the cloud chamber is operated with the help of coincidence counters just described. For this purpose two parallel counter tubes, each horizontal, are placed in a vertical plane, one counter above, the other below the cloud chamber (Fig. 20.2). Hence a cosmic ray shooting through this "counter telescope" is sure to pass through the chamber. Through a relay, the coincidence counters operate the expansion and illumination of the chamber and so restrict its operation to the moments when a ray has just passed through. This elaborate arrangement is called the "counter-controlled cloud chamber."

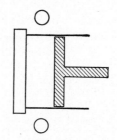

Fig. 20.2. Counter-controlled cloud chamber. The pair of coincidence counters, through a relay, operate the cloud chamber.

The *photographic emulsion technique* discussed in the section on mesons (Sec. 18.8) was originally developed for cosmic-ray research. Its great advantage over the cloud chamber, apart from its simplicity, is due to the fact that the emulsion is permanently ready to register ions. Moreover, in rockets photographic plates can be sent to very high altitudes.

20.2. Primary Rays. After discussing the experimental methods and some fundamental results, we want to explore the nature of the primary and secondary rays. Are the primaries photons or, possibly, neutrons or charged particles? The answer is found by using the magnetic field of the earth as that of a gigantic mass spectrograph. The intensity of the total incoming cosmic radiation is measured all over the earth with the ionization chamber. In order to obtain comparable data, A. H. Compton (1931) sent the same carefully built chamber with a built-in electroscope over long trips from the Northern to the Southern Hemisphere. The outstanding result, known as the *latitude effect*, is that the intensity of the radiation is lower at the equator than at the poles by about 10 per cent. The latitude effect is much more pronounced on mountain tops where the rays contain a larger percentage of their primary constituents than at sea level.

In the theory of this effect, the primary cosmic rays are assumed to be charged particles that shoot toward the earth from all directions and are deflected by the magnetic field of the earth. The atmosphere of the earth occupies only a thin layer; 97 per cent of the mass of the atmosphere is contained in a layer of 25 km thickness; this amounts to only 1/250 of the radius of the earth. However, the magnetic field of the earth, considered as a large permanent magnet, reaches much farther out. Hence the primary rays, when approaching the earth, travel long distances through the magnetic field before they strike the atmosphere.

We consider particles approaching in the direction perpendicular to the surface because they suffer the least absorption. Furthermore, we restrict our discussion to two special cases: to particles approaching either in the direction of the magnetic axis or in the plane of the magnetic equator. Particles shooting *along the magnetic axis* toward one of the magnetic poles are not affected by the magnetic field because the particles travel in the direction parallel to the field. On the other hand, particles approaching in the plane of the *magnetic equator* are deflected, the angle of deflection depending on their kinetic energy (Fig. 20.3). Particles of low kinetic energy do not reach the earth at all. Only the fastest particles suffer so little deflection that they penetrate the magnetic field to the surface of the earth. It has been computed that an electron approaching in the equatorial plane must shoot toward the earth with an energy of at least 10 billion electron volts (abbreviated Bev) in order to reach sea level (neglecting absorption in the atmosphere.) But we should not expect particles observed at sea level to follow this theory accurately since what we observe is secondaries. However, this comparison is sufficient to explain the fact that the cosmic-ray intensity at the equator is lower than that at the poles; at the equator the charged particles of lower energy are lost

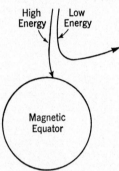

High Energy Low Energy

Magnetic Equator

FIG. 20.3. Paths of positively charged cosmic-ray particles arriving in the magnetic equatorial plane of the earth, seen from the geographic South Pole.

altogether. Most important is the conclusion that the primary cosmic rays consist principally of *charged particles*.

The *sign* of their charges is manifest in the *east-west effect*. Figure 20.3 shows that the primary particles are incident on the magnetic equator under a certain angle whose direction (east or west) depends on the sign of their charges. Johnson investigated these angles using an elaborate apparatus which was essentially a row of parallel counters in a coincidence circuit. This "counter telescope" could be pointed in the various directions. He found a preference for particles coming from the *west* indicating a preference for *positive charges*. Although this effect is barely noticeable at sea level because of the preponderance of secondaries, it is so pronounced at high altitude that one assumes the majority of the primaries to be *positively* charged particles. Here positrons are ruled out by the very high penetration of the primaries discussed below. This is incompatible with the assumption of light particles like positrons, which are readily deflected when passing near nuclei and thus dissipate their energies by generating gamma rays and secondaries. Hence the primaries consist largely of protons and other nuclei.

The analysis by the magnetic field of the earth gives evidence of the energies of the primary rays. Protons approaching in the equatorial plane must have at least 9 Bev in order to reach sea level. The higher intensity observed near the poles proves that primaries of lower energy are also incident.

Of particular interest is the absorption of the *primary protons*. One may try to measure their absorption in the atmosphere by measuring the change with altitude of effects that may be attributed to the action of primaries. Such an effect is, for example, a typical nuclear disintegration into many particles which produce tracks in the form of a "star" (see Sec. 20.4). The frequency of occurrence of such stars as a function of the altitude leads to a decrease of the primary radiation by the factor $1/e$ in about 1.2 m water equivalent.

In the comparison of alpha rays with X rays (Sec. 17.2a) we noticed that X rays follow an *exponential decay* while alpha rays are characterized by a *well-defined range*. Therefore, we are surprised to find *particles*, the primary protons, which decay according to an *exponential law* like X rays. This observation forces us to assume that these high-energy protons lose their energies by single rare events rather than by the gradual process of ionization as alpha particles do. Presumably disintegrations producing "stars" (see Figs. 20.7 and 20.8) represent such events.

In high-altitude flights cloud chambers and photographic plates give evidence of the constitution of the primaries. To more than 90 per cent they consist of protons of an energy range 1 to 10^5 Bev. There are less than 10 per cent helium nuclei and less than 1 per cent heavier nuclei (with atomic numbers up to 41) present. An indication of rare cosmic rays of vastly higher energy is found as follows. Coincidence counters give evidence of large showers of cosmic rays (see below), each one of which is endowed with high energy. Their simultaneous incidence forces us to assume that they represent numerous secondaries, all generated in the air and originating more or less directly from one primary. The energies and number of the secondaries lead to the estimate of the energy of the primary. The result is as high as 10^6 or even 10^7 Bev; it vastly surpasses the energy of any particle measured heretofore.

20.3. Conversion Processes. The study of the individual conversion processes will make the over-all picture of the secondary rays understandable. These processes, which are observed in the cloud chamber and photographic emulsions, reveal the existence of new particles, positrons and the various types of meson. Finally we shall study outstanding events, evident as stars and cascade showers.

Anderson discovered the *positron* as a cosmic-ray secondary in the cloud-chamber picture discussed in Sec. 18.3 (Figs. 18.5 and 18.6). Soon afterward the positron was found to be an abundant product of artificial radioactivity (Sec. 18.4). A few years later Anderson discovered the *meson* whose production in the cyclotron and systematic investigation was discussed above (Sec. 18.8). In a cloud-chamber picture mesons were first identified by three outstanding characteristics of a cloud track: its *density* (number of drops per centimeter), its *curvature in a magnetic field*, and its *range*. These three quantities permit at least an approximate determination of the *charge*, the *mass*, and the *energy* of the particle. We presuppose that charges occur in multiples of the electronic charge. The accuracy of the result does not compare with that obtained by the mass spectrograph. However, electrons and protons differ in their cloud-chamber tracks so vastly that they can easily be distinguished and an intermediate particle can be identified. This is illustrated by one of the first cloud-chamber photographs of such a particle taken by Anderson and Neddermeyer (1936; Fig. 20.4). From the lead plate (0.35 cm, visible as a horizontal strip) a group of particles are ejected, one of them shooting upward, showing a strikingly heavy ionization, much heavier

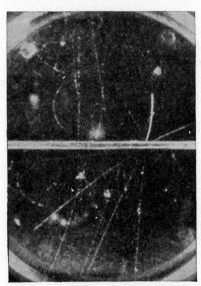

Fig. 20.4. Cloud-chamber picture of a meson and several electrons. (*Courtesy of C. D. Anderson and S. H. Neddermeyer.*)

than that due to electrons. Let us tentatively assume this particle to be a proton. For protons the relation between the range and the kinetic energy has been empirically determined and, for the range here observed, leads to an energy of 1.5 Mev (or more, if a part of the track is located within the lead plate). From these data one *predicts* the radius of curvature ρ of the path of the particle in the magnetic field ($B = 7,900$ gauss) to be $\rho = 20$ cm. However, the *observed* radius ρ is only 7 cm. Consequently our guess, interpreting the particle as a proton, is wrong. A more detailed examination leads to a mass about 200 times that of an electron. In Sec. 18.8 the artificial production of mesons in the cyclotron is reported and a survey given of meson research which is based on experiments with the cyclotron and observations on cosmic rays. The two distinct types of meson, each characterized by its mass, were discovered on emulsion pictures of cosmic rays (Powell). A striking event is the decay of the heavy pi meson into the light mu meson, which, in turn, decays into an electron (Fig. 20.5).   (The neutrinos, whose simultaneous ejection is predicted by the theory, fail to leave tracks.)

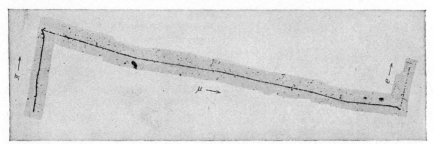

Fig. 20.5. Emulsion picture of the tracks of mesons; a pi meson (heavy track) decays into a mu meson, which, in turn, decays into an electron.   (*Courtesy of C. F. Powell and G. P. S. Occhialini.*)

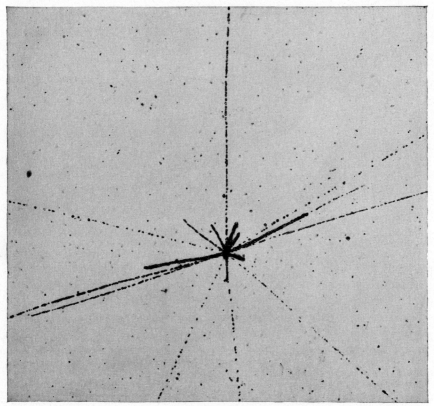

Fig. 20.6. Emulsion picture of evaporation star.   (*Courtesy of C. F. Powell and G. P. S. Occhialini.*)

The conversion of primary cosmic rays (protons and other ions) into secondaries, followed by numerous further conversion processes, takes place in the atmosphere, whereas our cloud chambers, counters, and plates give ample evidence of the same processes taking place in the instruments themselves. We shall discuss a few important examples of conversion processes, *"stars," "meson showers,"* and *"cascade showers."*

Figure 20.6 is a typical picture of a *"star"* (microphotograph of an emulsion picture). Here a high-energy particle, presumably one of the

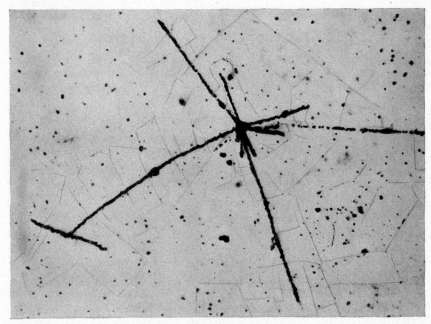

Fig. 20.7. Emulsion picture of evaporation star with disintegration of a secondary particle. (*Courtesy of C. F. Powell and G. P. S. Occhialini.*)

primaries, causes a complete disruption of a nucleus and so creates secondaries, many of them protons. This is called an "evaporation star." Some of the secondaries are unstable. Occasionally one of them manifests its later disintegration in a branch of the same picture. This explains the so-called "hammer track" (Fig. 20.7). Here one of secondaries, a short time after emerging from the star-shaped explosion, disintegrates; presumably it is a $_3Li^8$ nucleus (half-life, 0.9 sec) disintegrating into an electron (not visible) and two alpha particles whose tracks are in a straight line since the Li nucleus has no momentum when disintegration takes place. Long before these cloud-chamber and emulsion pictures were known, the simple technique of the ionization chamber had already shown rare, heavy "bursts" which are superimposed on the usual, more uniform ionization. They are called "Hoffmann bursts" after the discoverer. They represent a more primitive observation of evaporation stars and electronic showers that are analyzed in much greater detail by cloud-chamber and emulsion pictures.

A different, much rarer type of shower is given in Fig. 20.8. Here, in addition to evaporation into any direction, a distinct shower of mesons is generated, aimed at the same direction as that of the shower-producing particle. Since the creation of a meson requires a great energy (several 100 Mev), this *"meson shower"* is presumably produced by a much more energetic primary than the "evaporation star" is.

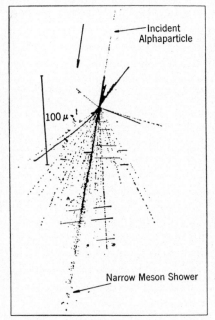

Fig. 20.8. Emulsion picture of a meson star. (*Courtesy of B. Peters.*)

Fig. 20.9. Cloud-chamber picture of a cascade shower (multiplied in lead plates). (*Courtesy of L. Fussell, Jr.*)

Another important conversion process is evident in a *"cascade shower"* (Fig. 20.9). Here several rays originate from one spot at the top of the chamber and multiply by producing more secondaries in thick lead plates mounted in the chamber. In cascade showers an alternation between gamma-ray quanta and electron pairs is due to the following sequence of processes. A gamma-ray quantum changes into a positron-electron pair (Sec. 18.5); each of these particles, in turn, when deflected near a nucleus, generates a gamma-ray quantum. The large momentum of the initial particle is manifest in the downward components of all constituents of the cascade shower. Gradually less energetic particles and quanta are produced, which are likely to lose their energies by other processes (ionization and Compton effect, respectively) until, finally, the whole energy of the shower is consumed.   Whereas the lead plates of the cloud chamber concentrate numerous conversion processes within a few millimeters, in the atmosphere the same processes are distributed over many kilometers and hence spread over large volumes.   The atmospheric showers are observed by coincidence counters placed hundreds of meters apart.   The total energy of an intense shower gives evidence of the vast energies of some primary rays mentioned above.

20.4. Secondary Rays.   The conversion processes which are individually analyzed in the preceding section are responsible for the production of the great variety of the secondary cosmic rays observed at sea level where practically all rays are secondaries.   They are incident at a rate of about one particle or photon hitting each square centimeter per minute.   Cloud-chamber observations, supplemented by the application of magnetic fields, give evidence of all possible particles and quanta known in nuclear physics.

In spite of the great variety of particles two outstanding components of the secondary radiation can be distinguished, a highly penetrating (or "hard") and a less penetrating (or "soft") component.   At sea level the hard cosmic rays consist largely of mu mesons, the soft rays of positive and negative electrons, and gamma rays.   This observation is correlated with the conversion processes just discussed as follows.   In the upper atmosphere the primary particles disrupt nuclei of nitrogen or oxygen in a nuclear explosion which gives rise to many particles as seen in a star or meson shower (Figs. 20.6, 20.7, and 20.8).   In the shower charged pi mesons are generated which, because of their short half-lives, decay in flight after traveling less than 100 m.   They produce mu mesons which have a much longer half-life and represent the greater part of the "hard" component.   In agreement with this interpretation, at very high altitude cosmic rays show a preponderance of pi mesons, while at sea level the mu mesons are the common variety.   (The meson shower of Fig. 20.8, started by an alpha particle, was observed in 100,000 ft altitude.)

A *spontaneous* decay of mu mesons occurring in the atmosphere is indicated by the following argument: It is observed that the cosmic-ray intensity at sea level decreases slightly with increasing temperature, corresponding to the thermal expansion of the air.   If in the atmosphere the mu mesons would suffer losses only by collisions, the expansion would only distribute the collisions over a greater path length without contributing to their losses.   The actually observed effect of the heat on the intensity is explained by spontaneous disintegration of mu mesons during their flight, which increases by the thermal expansion of the air.   The quantitative treatment leads to a half-life of the mu mesons of 10^{-6} sec.

In the same nuclear explosion that generates pi mesons or in a star gamma-ray quanta are produced (possibly indirectly as decay products of neutral pi mesons). The gamma rays give rise to an atmospheric cascade shower, similar to that observed in the cloud chamber (Fig. 20.9). The gamma rays and electrons of this shower contribute to the "soft" component observed at sea level.

Our discussion of cosmic rays shows the great significance of the fact that here we are dealing with particles and quanta endowed with energies far surpassing those generated at the laboratory. Whereas recent synchrotrons produce protons of a few Bev, the cosmic-ray primaries may be endowed with several million Bev.

20.5. Origin. The origin of the primary cosmic rays is a mystery. Not even annihilation of heavy nuclei, if it should ever occur, would provide energies of this high order of magnitude. As mentioned above, their direction fails to show a relation to our solar or galactic system. Here, however, a very exceptional observation leads to a guess. In several instances an unusually violent eruption, observed as a bright flare on the surface of the sun, was accompanied by a distinct increase of cosmic radiation. One may assume that a developing sunspot which is the core of a developing magnetic field (Sec. 11.1a) may have accelerated charged particles by an effect compared to the action of a betatron. In this process most particles would soon be lost because the tuning condition would be fulfilled only incidentally for a small fraction of the particles which would be speeded up to cosmic-ray energies. The idea of cosmic rays as coming from solar flares leads to difficulties which have not yet been fully resolved. If the particles constituting the rays come from the sun, why do they arrive at the earth uniformly from all directions? The magnetic field of the earth is not strong enough to change their initial directions so completely, in particular those of the high-energy rays which are hardly deflected by the field of the earth and yet seem to arrive from all directions. This indicates that the sun does not contribute the high-energy particles. A related difficulty is as follows. The total intensity of cosmic rays is so high that, presumably, they do not fill uniformly the whole cosmos but preferentially the galactic system. But then we must explain why they do not escape in straight lines from our galaxy. Are we allowed to assume extended magnetic fields bending the rays and trapping them for considerable lengths of time in the galaxy?

SUMMARY OF CHAPTER 20

The unavoidable slow discharge of all electroscopes, which is much more pronounced at high altitude than at sea level, is attributed to the ionization of the air by cosmic rays, *i.e.*, rays coming from the cosmos and able to penetrate the atmosphere, many meters of water, and even heavy lead plates. The ionization plotted against the depth of the atmosphere in terms of the equivalent water column shows a maximum at high altitude. This indicates that in the atmosphere a gradual conversion of the high-energy primaries into secondaries of less energy takes place. Cosmic rays are investigated with ionization chambers, Geiger counters, in particular coincidence counters, cloud chambers, and photographic plates.

The deflection in the magnetic field of the earth is responsible for the "latitude effect," which indicates that the primary cosmic rays are charged particles of energies of 10 Bev or more. The east-west effect proves that the great majority of the particles are positively charged. The primary rays when passing through the atmosphere are absorbed at such a rate that their intensity decreases by about the factor $1/e$ when they pass through an equivalent of 1.2 m of water.

Positrons and *mesons* were first discovered on cloud-chamber photographs. Later, photographic emulsions gave evidence of the distinction between the heavy pi meson, a product of a nuclear disintegration, and the light mu meson, the product of the spontaneous decay of the pi meson. The mu meson, in turn, has a comparatively long life which ends either in a nuclear reaction or in a spontaneous disintegration in which an electron is generated.

Stars observed in photographic emulsions give evidence of the conversion of the primaries (protons and heavier ions) into secondaries. There are two types of star, "*evaporation stars*" (disruption of a nucleus into neutrons, protons, other ions and electrons) and "*meson stars*" (generating a shower of well-directed pi mesons in addition to all other possible fragments). The pi mesons very soon decay into mu mesons, the penetrating (or "hard") component of cosmic rays observed at sea level.

Another outstanding conversion process is the *cascade shower*, in which gamma-ray quanta alternate with pairs of positive and negative electrons. These showers represent the less penetrating (or "soft") component observed at sea level. Certain atmospheric cascade showers of unusually high total energy give evidence of primaries of an energy as high as 10^6 or 10^7 Bev.

Since in a few cases an increase of cosmic radiation was observed at the same time as a violent eruption at the surface of the sun, it is inferred that cosmic rays *originate in the sun and similar stars*. Possibly a betatron effect caused by the growing magnetic field of a sunspot near the eruption accelerates the charged particles. This hypothesis, however, does not adequately explain the uniform incidence of the rays from all directions.

PROBLEMS

20.1. *The meson.* On a cloud-chamber picture taken by Anderson and Neddermeyer a heavy track is tentatively interpreted as due to a proton. On the basis of the empirical range versus energy diagram, its energy is determined as 1.5 Mev. Compute the radius of curvature given to the path of this particle by a magnetic induction of 7,900 gauss. (Your result will deviate slightly from that given in the text, owing to the fact that the track is not exactly in the plane of the paper, hence not exactly perpendicular to the magnetic field. This is investigated by stereoscopic photographs.)

20.2. *Water equivalent of the atmosphere* (calculus problem). Millikan *measured* the total mass per unit area of the atmosphere above any arbitrarily selected height h_0 by measuring the pressure and temperature in various heights (Fig. 20.1). You are asked to *compute* the same quantity, presupposing an isothermal atmosphere and applying the result of Prob. 3.9, which can be written $n = n_s e^{-mgh/RT}$ where $h =$ height above sea level; $n =$ density of molecules at any height; $n_s =$ same at sea level; R, T, m, g as usual.

a. For an arbitrarily selected height h_0 above sea level calculate the total number of molecules contained in a column of unit cross section above h_0.

b. Suppose that all this air be compressed to the uniform density of molecules n_s under standard conditions. Calculate the thickness l_a of this layer of air in terms of the height h_0.

c. How thick (l_w) is a layer of water of equal mass?

d. Introducing numerical values ($T = 273°\text{K}$; $m = 29.0$), calculate l_w for sea level ($h_0 = 0$) and for $h_0 = 20$ km.

e. Millikan's curve has a maximum near 1 m of equivalent water. Calculate the corresponding height using the same data.

PART VII
WAVE NATURE OF MATTER

In our discussion of the nature of light we were left with an intolerable discrepancy. For more than a century the old controversy between the corpuscular theory and the wave theory of light seemed to have been decided since the phenomena of *diffraction and interference* gave clear evidence of its *wave nature* (Young, 1801; Fresnel, 1815). Much later, however, the *photoelectric effect* and the *Compton effect* furnished proof of the quantum structure of light and so revived the *corpuscular theory* (Einstein, 1905; Compton, 1923). These two theories appear to be incompatible.

Before, however, we try to reconcile the theories of *light*, we must report an observation which, at first glance, seems to make the situation worse. The discovery of electron diffraction by Davisson and Germer (1923; final results, 1927) introduced a similar discrepancy in the description of *matter* by two opposing theories. We shall first describe the experiments and afterward give a brief outline of wave mechanics, which reconciles the corpuscular nature and the wave nature for matter as well as for light.

CHAPTER 21

DIFFRACTION OF ELECTRONS

In a systematic investigation of "secondary electrons" produced by electron impact on metals, Davisson and Germer explored the scattering of a well-defined beam of electrons impinging on a single crystal of a metal (Fig. 21.1).   In high vacuum, a beam of electrons emanating from a glowing filament is accelerated by a potential difference of the order 50 volts.   Two diaphragms narrow the beam down to a thin pencil.   When this beam is incident on the surface of a single crystal of nickel or another metal, many of the impinging electrons flow into the metal while others bounce back.   The observer measures the intensity of the beam of electrons scattered into any direction by collecting them on a small, isolated piece of metal which can be turned around the point of incidence on the crystal.   A retarding field (not indicated on the diagram) keeps away from the collector all electrons that have lost some energy so that the electrons recorded are only those that bounce off the crystal with their full initial energy.

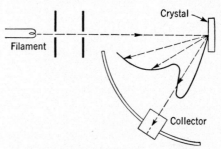

Fig. 21.1. Davisson-Germer experiment. The collector is rotated about the point of incidence on the crystal.   The electron currents scattered in the various directions (broken lines) show intensities given by the curved solid line.

This experiment, simple in principle but difficult in performance because of secondary effects, gives results that are indicated on the same diagram.   The intensity of the electron beam scattered into any direction is represented by the length of the vector drawn in this direction.   The ends of the various vectors are connected by a line.   The entirely unexpected result is that the scattered electrons do not show the diffuse distribution that might have been expected; instead they show a pattern with a well-defined maximum and minimum resembling a diffraction pattern.   When the accelerating potential difference is varied, the maximum mentioned shows up more or less distinctly (Fig. 21.2); it is best defined at a potential difference of 54 volts and at an angle $\phi = 50$ deg from the incident electron beam.

Let us tentatively attribute this maximum to diffraction and defer the more thorough discussion of this explanation to the next chapter. We derive the wavelength indicated by the maximum as follows: Diffraction

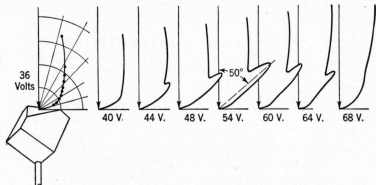

FIG. 21.2. Electron-diffraction pattern for different voltages.

by a crystal grating, as distinct from the ruled grating, is discussed in the chapter on X Rays (Sec. 14.1*f*). There we argued that this *diffraction* is identical with an apparent *reflection* of the X ray on a crystal plane, *i.e.*, a plane rich in atoms. (Since the rays enter into the body of the crystal, this plane is not necessarily identical with the surface plane.) In the experiment described, the angle ($\phi = 50$ deg) between the incident beam, which is normal to the surface, and the diffracted beam indicates that "reflection" takes place (at an angle $\theta = 65$ deg) not from the surface but from an interior plane as shown in Fig. 21.3. From X-ray data the grating constant d of nickel in this plane is known to be 0.91×10^{-8} cm. Since only one maximum shows up, we assume $n = 1$. Bragg's equation leads to a wavelength $\lambda = 1.65 \times 10^{-8}$ cm. For the interpretation of this wavelength, a fundamentally new idea will be introduced in the next chapter.

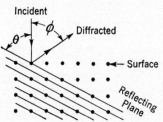

FIG. 21.3. Electron diffraction treated as Bragg reflection on a crystal plane. θ = angle between ray and reflecting crystal plane; ϕ = angle of deflection.

Davisson and Germer report the history of their discovery as follows: "The investigation reported in this paper was begun as the result of an accident. A liquid air bottle exploded at a time when the target was at high temperature. The target was heavily oxidized by the inrushing air. By prolonged heating the oxide was eventually reduced. When the experiments were continued it was found that the distribution-in-angle of the scattered electrons was completely changed."

Are these patterns that resemble diffraction patterns a specific property of electrons or can they be observed for other particles too? With great experimental effort traces of such patterns were found for helium atoms and hydrogen molecules by Stern and his collaborators (1929). Hence, the patterns represent a more general property of very small particles.

Another method for the observation of electron diffraction has been developed by G. P. Thomson (1927). In our discussion of X rays we mentioned the crystal powder method in which two narrow holes (not two slits) limit a narrow pencil of X rays, which are reflected from all the various crystal planes presented by a powder. Accordingly, in Thomson's experiment a narrow pencil of *electrons* is incident on a crystal film which is so thin that most of them pass through. The numerous, very small single crystals of which the film is composed act like the crystal

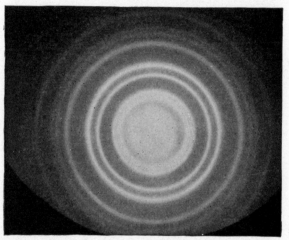

FIG. 21.4. Electron diffraction by gold foil, method of G. P. Thomson (photographic positive). (*Courtesy of G. P. Thomson.*)

powder and are responsible for the ring-shaped diffraction pattern observed behind the crystal film. Figure 21.4 shows the diffraction of 60,000-volt electrons by a film of simple cubic crystals (gold). This picture of *electron* diffraction may be compared with that of diffraction of monochromatic X *rays* by a powder of simple cubic crystals (Fig. 14.10).

From the sharp pattern observed and the known crystal constant of gold, Thomson was able to derive the wavelength which must be attributed to 60,000-volt electrons in order to make the pattern explicable by diffraction. In the next chapter we shall correlate this result with de Broglie's idea of matter waves.

Since electrons as well as X rays are diffracted according to Bragg's law, a beam of electrons is just as suitable as a beam of X rays for the exploration of regular structures like crystals. However, electrons have much less penetrating power than X rays. This distinction makes the diffraction of an electron beam useful for the investigation of the structures of surfaces and complex organic molecules. Such molecules are made to travel as a beam of low density (see Sec. 4.1) which, when traversed from the side by a beam of electrons, causes their diffraction. The diffraction pattern gives evidence of regularities in the molecular structure.

A summary of the present chapter will be found at the end of Chap. 22.

CHAPTER 22

REPORT ON WAVE MECHANICS

Wave mechanics has removed the discrepancy between the wave theory and the corpuscular theory of light. Moreover, it has reconciled the new discovery of electron diffraction, which is described in the preceding chapter, with the older concept of matter. This young branch of theoretical physics, which requires an advanced mathematical treatment, does not readily lend itself to an elementary discussion; nevertheless, we shall try to give an outline of the underlying ideas.

When we discussed the Compton effect, caused by X-ray or gamma-ray quanta colliding with free electrons or atoms (Sec. 14.3), we associated a momentum $= h\nu/c$ with a quantum. Quanta of the shortest wavelengths, *i.e.*, hard gamma rays, have the largest momenta. The relation between the wavelength λ and the momentum is easily written (replacing ν/c by $1/\lambda$)

$$\text{Momentum} = \frac{h}{\lambda}$$

This relation, which is no longer new for *quanta*, was applied to *corpuscles* in a purely speculative way by L. de Broglie (1922) before Davisson and Germer discovered the pattern of scattered electrons resembling diffraction. De Broglie argued as follows:

Determination of the stable motion of electrons in the atom introduces integers; and up to this point the only phenomena involving integers in physics were those of interference and of normal modes of vibration. This fact suggested to me the idea that electrons, too, could not be regarded simply as corpuscles, but that periodicity must be assigned to them.

While dealing with light, we *measure its wavelength* λ (*e.g.*, by an interferometer) and introduce the hypothetical momentum by the above equation. Conversely, according to de Broglie, while dealing with particles we *measure their momentum mv* and use the same equation to attribute to them a hypothetical wavelength where

$$\lambda = \frac{h}{\text{momentum}} = \frac{h}{mv}$$

In 1922, this definition of the "de Broglie wavelength" λ seemed a mathematical speculation, remote from any direct relation to experiment.

383

After the publication of the preliminary experiments of Davisson and Germer, Elsasser (1925) found that the de Broglie wavelength of the electrons incident on the nickel crystal gives a striking explanation of the complicated pattern observed among the scattered electrons (Fig. 21.2). In the preceding chapter we computed the wavelength 1.65×10^{-8} cm from the observed diffraction pattern. On the other hand, for 54-volt electrons the de Broglie wavelength is computed to be 1.66×10^{-8} cm, in excellent agreement with the experimental value. The simple equation correctly predicts the shift of the diffraction maxima brought about by an increase of the accelerating potential. Furthermore, G. P. Thomson's diffraction pattern (Fig. 21.4) is in good agreement with the de Broglie wavelength. This is a surprising fruit of what appeared to be a mere mathematical speculation.

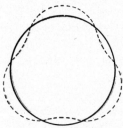

Fig. 22.1. Quantized state of hydrogen atom; $n = 3$.

The discrepancy between Newtonian mechanics and wave mechanics will be evident from an example. Suppose that a wide beam of atoms is incident on a metal plate in which a small hole is drilled. No electric fields are applied. According to Newtonian mechanics, the hole transmits a narrow beam of atoms traveling in their original direction. According to wave mechanics, however, the electrons passing through the hole form a diffraction pattern like that formed by light or X rays.

The value of de Broglie's hypothesis is evident from the fact that it is equivalent to Bohr's quantum condition defining the stationary states of the hydrogen atom. To begin with, as in Bohr's theory, we define the orbits as given by classical physics, i.e., by the following condition: centripetal force = Coulomb attraction (Sec. 10.4).

$$\frac{mv^2}{r} = \frac{Ze^2}{r^2} \quad \text{or} \quad v^2 = \frac{Ze^2}{mr}$$

Hence any of the orbits can be characterized as well by its velocity v as by its radius r. Now we wish to invent a hypothesis, based on the de Broglie wavelength, in order to select certain quantized orbits from the continuous range of orbits given by the above equation. It is plausible to introduce the following hypothesis. For any orbit we define the de Broglie wavelength as $\lambda = h/mv$. Only for certain specific orbits can a *whole number* of waves be accommodated on the periphery of the circular path of radius r as sketched in Fig. 22.1, for the case of three full waves. (We can visualize these orbits as accommodating standing waves.) Our hypothesis is that these are the quantized orbits. Our new quantum condition is expressed by the equation

$$n\lambda = 2\pi r \qquad \text{or} \qquad \frac{nh}{mv} = 2\pi r$$

This equation, although derived from a different physical idea, is mathematically identical with Bohr's quantum condition [Eq. (10.5)]. Since the two equations given above form the whole basis of Bohr's theory, the computation of the energy levels and frequencies of the spectral lines is identical with that given by Bohr. Hence, in this simple case, the de Broglie quantum condition is fully equivalent to Bohr's quantum condition.

De Broglie's hypothesis of matter waves has been the starting point of *wave mechanics* (Schrödinger, 1926), which replaces Newtonian mechanics in the description of the motion of the lightest particles, hence, in particular, of processes within the atom. An equivalent description of such processes has been given by Heisenberg's "matrix mechanics" (1925). We shall report some results of Schrödinger's wave mechanics as well as can be done briefly without integrating differential equations. In wave mechanics Schrödinger gives a mathematical form to de Broglie's hypothesis by introducing a "wave equation" and postulating that the stationary states are defined by integrals of this equation meeting certain conditions. Wave mechanics covers a wider ground than the older quantum theory. This will be clear when we briefly survey the successes of the new theory. First of all, it explains electron diffraction. The spectrum of the hydrogen atom (including the effects of magnetic and electric fields and fine structure) is represented as well as by the older theory of Bohr and Sommerfeld. Wave mechanics surpasses the older theory by giving account of the *intensities* as well as the *frequencies* of the spectral lines. The spectrum of the "two-electron system," *i.e.*, the helium atom, which is not covered by Bohr's theory, is correctly predicted as far as we are able to carry through the mathematical treatment. Many general features of the spectra of more complicated atoms and of molecules are correctly described. An outstanding success of wave mechanics consists of the description of the chemical bond (Heitler and London, 1927). In our brief discussion of polar molecules (Sec. 13.5) we emphasized the fact that the Coulomb attraction between positive and negative ions is only one aspect of the chemical bond because this force fails to describe the molecules of elements like H_2. Wave mechanics, however, predicts the properties of the hydrogen molecule and thus gives the general idea of the "nonpolar bond." In nuclear theory likewise, the successes of wave mechanics are great.

It is no objection to the validity of wave mechanics that our mathematical technique fails in the solution of the more complex problems. The theory of the hydrogen atom has been carried through in great detail. But the helium atom, consisting of a nucleus and 2 electrons, offers mathematical difficulties as great as the "three-body problem" in astronomy which has been solved by approximations only for special cases. Hence, for more complicated atoms and molecules we are unable to integrate the equations. But the successes are so great that there is no doubt of the validity of the general idea.

Wave mechanics explains the great advantage of the electron microscope (Sec. 6.2c) over the well-known optical microscope. For both instruments the resolving power is limited by the wave nature of the light and of the electrons to about one-half of the wavelength applied. This limit is about 2.5×10^{-5} cm for visible light and about 2.5×10^{-10} cm for 60,000-volt electrons used in an electron microscope. The limiting resolving power has technically been reached many years ago for the optical microscope, while the electron microscope in its present state of development, although it surpasses the optical microscope (Fig. 6.9), is far from its theoretical limit.

Our starting point was the discrepancy between the two opposed theories of *light*. By introducing wave mechanics, *i.e.*, by introducing the same discrepancy into the description of *particles*, we have apparently only made the situation worse. What is the significance of *waves* in describing motion of *quanta* or *particles?* The following answer was given by Born (1926). As we cannot interpret the experimental facts by assuming that quanta and particles are governed by the laws of Newtonian mechanics, we must discard this idea as too primitive and find another fundamental law. This is given by the hypothesis that the *light waves* guide the motion of *quanta* and similarly the *de Broglie waves* guide the motion of *particles*. Thus when electrons (mass m) of a certain velocity v are incident on a nickel crystal, we predict their motion by computing the propagation of the waves of wavelength $\lambda = h/mv$ that are diffracted by the nickel crystal and so form the characteristic pattern described. The maxima indicate the points through which plenty of electrons travel, while the minima indicate the places through which few or no electrons travel. Strictly speaking, the hypothesis is made that the *square of the amplitude, computed for any spot in the diffraction pattern, is proportional to the probability of finding electrons traveling through the spot.* Hence the de Broglie waves are not identical with matter. They have only the rather abstract significance of describing a probability. Thus they define the law of motion of electrons diffracted by a crystal. When we assume a very weak beam of electrons, on the average, say, 1 electron per second hitting the crystal, we may be able to observe the individual electrons (*e.g.*, by scintillations on a screen) showing up here or there. By observing the distribution of billions of electrons, we should expect to find the same diffraction pattern that would show up at once if the electron beam were billions of times more intense. This example illustrates that we think of the waves and their diffraction pattern as a permanently existing mathematical construction which predicts the probable events even if the electrons whose probable paths are described by the waves arrive only rarely.

According to Born's interpretation, the same basic idea applies to the diffraction of *light waves* by a grating or of *X rays* by a crystal (Sec. 14.1*f*). Here the waves are not supposed to be uniformly covered with energy; they only furnish the guidance for the quanta in which the energy is concentrated. Again, in the case of an extremely weak light ray, we think of the waves as existing permanently although only once in a while there comes a quantum that needs guidance. The concepts of *waves*, on the one hand, and *quanta* or *particles*, on the other, are not mutually exclusive but complementary to each other. Our old warning (Sec. 8.3) still holds that the analogy between light waves and matter waves should not lead to the conclusion that light is a special kind of matter. A striking distinction is given by the fact that light in vacuum always travels with the velocity 3×10^{10} cm/sec; matter never does.

We shall better appreciate how this theory resolves the discrepancy when we consider the extreme cases of short and long waves, first light waves and next matter waves.

1. For *very short light waves* the theory predicts a diffraction pattern so narrow that practically rectilinear propagation results. This is observed for gamma rays. The distribution of the energy is far from uniform since the individual quantum carries a very large energy which, for example, may be delivered to an individual nucleus and so show up by an individual cloud-chamber track in nuclear photoelectric effect or by pair production.

2. *Very long light waves* are identical with radio waves. They show pronounced diffraction and so readily go around corners. The distribution of the energy is practically uniform all over the wave front since the individual quantum carries an energy of only, say, $1/10^8$ that of a quantum of visible light. Since no effects of these individual, exceedingly small quanta are to be expected, radio waves are in every respect satisfactorily described by Maxwell's classical theory of electromagnetic radiation.

3. *Very short matter waves* pertain to all motion observed in daily life (see Prob. 22.1). The theory predicts rectilinear propagation. This agrees with the statement of Newton's first law that all bodies not subjected to forces travel in straight lines. Here is the connecting link

between wave mechanics and Newton's mechanics; the latter is only approximately valid.

We mentioned in Sec. 6.4 that Newtonian mechanics breaks down for velocities approaching that of light; here we find another limitation coming into effect for the lowest velocities or, rather, the lowest momenta. Between these extremes, there is an immense range in which not the slightest deviation from Newton's mechanics has ever been observed.

Now we understand why the observation of these diffraction patterns is restricted to the lightest particles. They are the only ones that show diffraction that is just observable with X-ray technique. All heavier bodies have de Broglie wavelengths so extremely short that we fail to observe any diffraction.

4. Finally, *very long matter waves* do not occur. They would belong to very slow electrons, which, however, cannot be handled experimentally. The fact that practically all matter waves are so much shorter than light waves explains why electron diffraction has been observed two and a half centuries later than the diffraction of light.

Wave mechanics has introduced a fundamentally new concept into physics by describing the motions of particles in terms of certain *probabilities*. Here it is important that wave mechanics does not claim at all to predict the motion of one individual particle. Going back to the example mentioned above, we consider 1 electron traveling from the filament to the nickel crystal. Into what direction will it be diffracted? The theory fails to give the answer since it makes only a statement regarding the statistical distribution of very many electrons.

The theory, however, goes one great step further. Heisenberg, in his *uncertainty principle*, argues that this is not a deficiency of our theory which may be remedied but that it is *fundamentally impossible* to describe the motion of the individual particle in every detail. More specifically, it makes no sense to give an accurate statement regarding the *position and velocity* of a particle. This will be understood when we consider the problem of measurements from the "operational point of view," emphasized as a general guiding idea by Bridgman. He argues that the definition of a physical quantity makes sense only if the operations required for its measurement are fully described. From this point of view Heisenberg asks the question: How is the position of a particle measured by the ideal physicist who has mastered techniques unknown to us? He observes the position under a microscope. Since the resolving power is limited to about one half wavelength of light he has a choice; either he uses visible light and so determines the position only with low accuracy, or he constructs a special microscope for gamma rays and so obtains an accuracy a million times higher, but still limited. But here he runs into a fundamental trouble that he cannot overcome by refinement of his apparatus. The gamma ray, which shows the *position* of the particle, knocks it out of the way by the Compton effect. Hence he loses his chance of observing the *velocity* since this requires two determinations of the positions separated by a certain time interval. So this is his dilemma: If he uses light of long wavelength, then the velocity is hardly disturbed but the position is not exactly measured; if he uses light of short wavelength, the situation is reversed. In any case he is fundamentally unable to measure both quantities, the position and the velocity, with unlimited accuracy. This is an outstanding example of Heisenberg's uncertainty principle.

The principle deeply affects the fundamentals of thought in physics. It shows a limitation of the principle of causality which seemed to be the foundation of all research in science. This will be evident when we compare wave mechanics with Newtonian mechanics. The causal principle found its mathematical expression in Newtonian mechanics. There we learn that, when we know all positions and velocities of an isolated system of masses, we can predict its future. Heisenberg's uncertainty principle takes exception to this statement. His principle claims that this statement, although not *wrong*, is *void* because we are fundamentally unable to fulfill the condition, *i.e.*, to know accurately both the positions and the velocities; hence we shall never be able to predict the future, *e.g.*, of an individual electron or hydrogen atom, except with a certain lack of accuracy. This applies especially to individual, very light particles; the limitation imposed by the uncertainty is negligible for heavy bodies.

This result may seem abhorrent to the reader. Indeed, the abrogation of the law of causality seems to go beyond the province of the physicist because this law may be considered to be the one and only law which the student tacitly takes for granted before undertaking the study of physics. The physicist, however, is skeptical. He claims that the law of causality is only apparently self-evident to the human mind. Actually it is abstracted from countless experiences in daily life and experiments in physics, all concerned not with single atoms but with larger bodies. We cannot be certain a priori that the same law holds for the behavior of the smallest particles and quanta, a realm remote from direct experience. The physicist assumes that all processes involving the smallest particles and quanta are governed by well-defined probabilities, which cooperate in such a fashion that they ultimately explain all large-scale observations, and not by the law of causality.

The claim of wave mechanics that the law of causality is subject to a limitation will seem less radical when we analyze the situation in detail. This claim is based on the operational point of view which limits physics to the discussion of quantities which are accessible to measurement. Anything that is not accessible to measurement is not recognized as belonging to physics and is termed "metaphysics." The physicist realizes that the operation by which he measures the *position* of a small particle affects the motion of the particle and so prevents him from measuring its *velocity*. Hence this undesirable effect of his measurement deprives him of the chance of predicting the future. The operational point of view itself, however, does not express a law of nature but rather provides a useful definition of what the physicist, considering his limitations, wants to deal with. From a different point of view the situation may be described as follows: A philosopher may postulate the principle of causality for all processes in nature, including the smallest particles and quanta, keeping in mind, however, that there exists a certain range beyond which the position and the velocity of a particle cannot both be measured. The physicist cannot prove by an experiment that the philosopher's statement is wrong. He only offers the criticism that nobody will ever prove by an experiment that it is right. Therefore he excludes it from the realm of physics, calling it metaphysics. In other words, the physicist has no way of proving that the law of causality *is void in nature*. He only claims that it is *void in physics*, *i.e.*, void in the limited part of nature which is accessible to measurement. Therefore, the physicist *recognizes his limitations* when he refrains from predicting the motion of individual particles or quanta and, instead, applies to particles and quanta only the laws of probability.

The physicist doing experimental research with the most refined tools *practically available* need not be worried by the uncertainty principle because the observations practically accessible to our instruments are much cruder than what the theoretical physicist is able to visualize; for the time being, there is no gamma-ray microscope. But it is important to distinguish this *practical* limitation from the *fundamental* limitation that would make the gamma-ray microscope useless for our purpose. Therefore, this practical consideration does not detract from the great importance of the principle. After finding the limitations of so many apparently well-established laws of physics like Newtonian mechanics and the conservation of mass, finally we come to a limitation even of the principle of causality.

This then is the outstanding result of wave mechanics. Particles as well as quanta of light do not follow the laws of ordinary mechanics but, instead, are governed by waves, which by their amplitudes predict the probability that a particle or quantum will travel in one or the other direction. For matter this effect of waves is noticeable only for the lightest particles when traveling with low velocities. For light as well as for matter there is no *alternative* between the corpuscular theory and the wave theory; instead both aspects *supplement* each other. The uncertainty principle makes the claim, which would have seemed preposterous to earlier generations of physicists and philosophers, that all *measurable* phenomena are satisfactorily described by the probability statements of wave mechanics, whereas the quantities which would allow us to predict the future of one particle cannot all be concurrently measured.

The reader should judge how great a change in the foundation of physical theory is brought in by wave mechanics. During the nineteenth century the idea prevailed that Newtonian mechanics, which was considered to be exactly correct, would ultimately explain all the actions of atoms. The success of mechanics is illustrated by the theory of the dispersion of light in which it is assumed that each atom is a damped vibrator in which forced vibrations described by Newtonian mechanics are induced by the incident light waves. However, gradually it became clear that this atomic theory, which now is termed "classical," fails to explain spectroscopic observations, i.e., the spectrum of the black body and those of atoms and molecules. Planck, Einstein, Bohr, and others replaced classical atomic physics by the quantum theory and thus introduced the basic ideas needed for the explanation of spectra. Wave mechanics finally provides the comprehensive new picture, on one hand bordering on Newtonian mechanics for the case of heavy bodies, on the other hand completely departing from Newtonian mechanics in the description of electrons, atoms, and quanta. This then is the present claim of theoretical physics: for each atom we know the constituent parts, the nucleus and electrons; moreover, we know the laws which govern their motion, laws which fundamentally depart from Newtonian mechanics and were characterized by J. H. Jeans as follows: "The laws which nature obeys are less suggestive of those which a machine obeys in its motion than of those which a musician obeys when writing a fugue."

SUMMARY OF CHAPTERS 21 AND 22

When electrons of uniform velocity impinge on a single nickel crystal, the scattered electrons show a striking pattern resembling a diffraction pattern that varies with their velocity (Davisson-Germer experiment). Similar patterns have been discovered for rays of helium atoms and hydrogen molecules scattered by crystal surfaces.

These patterns are quantitatively explained by attributing to each particle (mass m, velocity v) the wavelength $\lambda = h/mv$, called "de Broglie wavelength," and applying the theory of X-ray diffraction.

De Broglie's idea of matter waves leads to Bohr's condition for the stationary states of a revolving electron when we postulate that the only stationary orbits are those for which the circumferences of the circles are multiples of the de Broglie wavelengths of the electrons.

The idea of waves attributed to particles has been generalized and mathematically expressed in Schrödinger's wave mechanics. This theory covers a much wider range of atomic phenomena than the older theory of Bohr and Sommerfeld.

The dilemma between the corpuscular theory and the wave theory is solved by the hypothesis of Born, who assumed that the amplitudes of matter waves indicate the probabilities for particles like electrons to travel in one or the other direction. When the electric current is exceedingly weak, only once in a while is an electron traveling; nevertheless the waves have the permanent significance of guides for electrons although they are not permanently covered with uniformly distributed mass or energy.   The analogous statement applies to the relation between light waves and light quanta.

Wave mechanics makes only a statement regarding the statistics of many processes, not regarding the individual process, *e.g.*, the scattering of 1 individual electron from a nickel crystal.   Heisenberg's uncertainty principle claims that this is not a deficiency of wave mechanics but that we are fundamentally unable to predict the fate of individual particles because we cannot measure both their positions and velocities with unlimited accuracy.

PROBLEMS

22.1. *Matter waves.*   Compute the de Broglie wavelengths of the following bodies: (*a*) 1-volt electron; (*b*) 10-volt electron; (*c*) electron in Bohr's first orbit; (*d*) hydrogen atom at 0°C; (*e*) 100,000-volt proton; (*f*) mass of 1 g moving at a velocity 1 cm/sec; (*g*) automobile (2 tons) at 50 mph.

22.2. *Scale of wavelengths.*   On a logarithmic scale on which one power of 10 (10^{-5} to 10^{-4}, 10^{-4} to 10^{-3} cm, etc.) occupies 1 cm, mark the wavelengths of the de Broglie waves calculated in the preceding problem; gamma rays (up to 0.1 A); X rays (0.1 to 20 A); ultraviolet; visible light; infrared (up to 10^7 A); microwaves ($\frac{1}{10}$ to 30 cm); radio waves (from 30 cm upward).

APPENDIX 1

UNITS

The difficulty experienced by the beginning student dealing with units is not inherent in nature but was arbitrarily introduced by the physicists who found that for different purposes different systems are convenient (as speeds are measured in cm/sec or mph). The difficulty vanishes when we consistently apply one system of units, keeping in mind that the choice is arbitrary. For our purpose it will be convenient to use metric absolute units; specifically in electricity we employ absolute electromagnetic units which bear a simple relation to practical units. (In recent issues of *Physical Review* we have not found one paper on atomic physics in which mks units were applied.) If the experimental physicist supplies the data for a problem in inconsistent units (mile, electron volt, calorie), the student must convert all of them to a uniform system.

1. Electromagnetic System. The electromagnetic system of units is based on the set of definitions given below under A. The definitions are given in such an order that each equation contains only *one new* quantity. Notation: r = distance between poles; d = distance between condenser plates; t = time. We attribute no dimensions to the dielectric constant ϵ and the permeability μ. As we are dealing only with measurements in vacuum or near vacuum, we assume throughout $\epsilon = 1$ and $\mu = 1$. On the basis of Table A the student is advised to express all units in terms of powers of cm, g, and sec.

A. Definitions

Quantity to Be Defined	Definition
Magnetic pole strength m	Force $= mm'/r^2$
Intensity of Magnetic field H	$H = m/r^2$
Magnetic induction B	$B = \mu H$
Current I (circular coil)	$H = 2\pi I/r$
Electric charge Q	$Q = I \times t$
Potential difference V	$V = \text{work}/Q$
Electric field E (between plates a distance d apart)	$E = V/d$
Capacitance C	$C = Q/V$
Resistance R	$R = V/I$
Inductance L	Induced emf $= L \times dI/dt$
Impedance Z (at the frequency f)	$Z = \sqrt{R^2 + \left(2\pi fL - \dfrac{1}{2\pi fC}\right)^2}$

B. Other Equations.   In the electromagnetic system Q is defined before Coulomb's law for electric charges is mentioned.   Therefore, this law represents a relation which cannot serve for the definition of Q but, instead, correlates quantities (force, Q, and r) all of which are already defined.   Hence this law carries a factor of proportionality determined by experiments.   The law is as follows:

$$\text{Force} = c^2 \frac{QQ'}{r^2} \qquad (c = 3 \times 10^{10} \text{ cm/sec})$$

The electric field E (defined above as V/d) at the distance r from the charge Q is derived as $E = c^2 Q/r^2$.   Furthermore, in em units the following equations apply:

Energy of a condenser $= \dfrac{1}{2} QV = \dfrac{Q^2}{2C} = \dfrac{V^2 C}{2}$

Power due to electric current $IV = I^2 R = \dfrac{V^2}{R}$

Energy of an inductance $= \frac{1}{2} L I^2$

Force exerted by magnetic induction B on wire of length l (perpendicular to B) carrying current I:

$$\text{Force} = l I B$$

Faraday's law of induction:

$$\text{Induced emf} = \frac{\Delta (B \times \text{area})}{\Delta t}$$

2. Practical System.   Another (less comprehensive) system is formed by the practical units: ampere, coulomb, volt, ohm, farad, henry.   They are defined in combination with the units joule and watt, so that a group of frequently used equations, namely, the equations for electric circuits, can be used with these practical units as well as with absolute electromagnetic units.   The oersted and gauss do not belong in this system; they are other names for emu of the magnetic field H and the magnetic induction B, respectively.   For the following group of equations (the equations for electric circuits, selected from the above equations) you may use practical units or emu.   In any computation you must consistently apply one or the other system.

$Q = I \times t$	$\text{Emf} = L \, dI/dt$
$V = \text{work}/Q$	Energy of condenser $= \frac{1}{2} QV$
$E = V/d$	Power of electric current $= IV$
$C = Q/V$	Energy of inductance $= \frac{1}{2} L I^2$
$R = V/I$	

WARNING: It is a minor inconvenience that experimental physicists introduce their voltmeter readings, etc., into the same equations with quantities not covered by the practical system, such as a magnetic field or induction. Such equations require extra numerical factors and definitions.

Examples: magnetic field in center of circular wire $H = 2\pi I/10r$ (I in amp; H in emu = oersted); induced emf $= \dfrac{1}{10^8} \dfrac{d(B \times \text{area})}{dt}$ (emf in volt; B in emu = gauss).

Electromagnetic and Practical Units

Quantity	1 emu Equals
Magnetic pole m	No practical unit
Magnetic field H	No practical unit*
Magnetic induction B	No practical unit*
Electric current I	10 amp
Electric charge Q	10 coulombs
Potential difference V	10^{-8} volt
Electric field E	10^{-8} volt/cm
Resistance R	10^{-9} ohm
Capacitance C	10^9 farad
Inductance L	10^{-9} henry
Energy W	10^{-7} joule
Power P	10^{-7} watt

* Oersted and gauss do not belong in the practical system but are names for emu of magnetic field and magnetic induction respectively.

APPENDIX 2

DEMONSTRATION AND LABORATORY EXPERIMENTS

REFERENCES

G. P. Harnwell and J. J. Livingood, "Experimental Atomic Physics," McGraw-Hill Book Company, Inc., New York, 1933.

J. D. Hoag and S. A. Korff, "Electron and Nuclear Physics," 3d ed., D. Van Nostrand Co., Inc., 1947.

R. W. Pohl, "Einführung in die Physik," Springer-Verlag OHG, Berlin.

R. M. Sutton, "Demonstration Experiments in Physics," McGraw-Hill Book Company, Inc., New York, 1938.

A. LECTURE-ROOM DEMONSTRATIONS

3.1. *A force as produced by a bombardment.* The experiment is described in the text. An inexpensive two-pan balance is good enough. The motion of the pan that carries

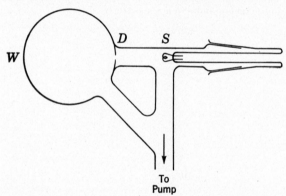

To Pump

FIG. APP. 2 (scale 1:3). Demonstration of the long mean free path at low pressure. Aluminum atoms evaporating from the bead S form a deposit with the shape of the diaphragm D on the wall W.

the steel plate is damped by a horizontal disk mounted under the pan, dipping into oil. The pointer of the pan is mounted upward, and the force is measured by the deflection of this pointer. A shadow of the whole apparatus can well be projected by an arc lamp.

3.2. *Model of a gas.* After R. W. Pohl.

4.1. *Microprojection of Brownian motion.* After R. W. Pohl. The last two experiments are described by N. H. Black, *J. Chem. Educ.*, **5**, 868 (1928).

4.2. *Long free path of atoms at low pressure.* An aluminum bead S is fixed on a tungsten helix and evaporated in high vacuum (Fig. App. 2). The aluminum transmitted through a cross-shaped diaphragm D is deposited on the glass wall W and there forms a cross. The apparatus is connected with a diffusion pump.

6.1. *Low-pressure electric discharge.* This shows a cathode ray and a positive ray (Central Scientific Company, experiment of Knipp and Kunz).

6.2. *Measurement of e/m.* K. T. Bainbridge, *Am. Phys. Teacher*, **6**, 35 (1938).

6.3. *Field electron microscope.* Apparatus available at Leybold, Nachf., Köln, Germany.

6.4. *The cathode-ray oscilloscope.* Electric deflection, magnetic deflection; both deflections compensating one another.

7.1. *Stokes' law.* Fall of small steel spheres through glycerin, to be projected.

8.1. *Photoelectric effect.* Sutton, p. 488.

9.1. *Penetrating power of alpha and/or beta particles.* Discharge of an electroscope by rays from a radium sample, Sutton, 502. For a radium D sample, see Hoag and Korff, p. 295.

10.1. *Balmer series.* A powerful discharge (0.4 amp) through a water-cooled low-pressure discharge tube is needed to project the two or three first lines of the Balmer series on the screen.

12.1. *Excitation of neon by controlled electron impact.* G. Hertz, *Z. Physik*, **22**, 18 (1924). A difficult experiment.

12.2. *Ionization of mercury vapor by controlled electron impact.* Sutton, p. 474.

12.3. *Arc, spark, low-pressure discharge.* The arc should be projected on the screen.

12.4. *Potential drop near cathode of low-pressure discharge.* D-c discharge of Fig. 12.4, 2 in. wide, 10 in. long, pressure of air so low that the dark space in front of the cathode is 3 or 4 cm long; electrostatic voltmeter to be connected with electrodes or cathode and probe at a distance from the cathode of about 3 or 4 cm at the edge of the dark space. The probe consists of a thin metal wire sealed through the cylindrical glass wall.

12.5. *Absorption spectrum of sodium vapor.* Sutton, p. 476.

12.6. *Absorption spectrum of chlorophyll.* Sutton, p. 415.

12.7. *Fluorescence radiation of iodine vapor.* A few iodine crystals are distilled into a highly evacuated glass bulb (diameter 8 in.); the bulb is sealed off. The light from a carbon arc concentrated by a condenser lens produces intense fluorescence radiation.

12.8. *Fluorescence radiation of sodium.* R. W. Wood, *Phys. Rev.*, **56**, 1172 (1939). (W. M. Welch Co., Chicago, Ill.)

12.9. *Fluorescence radiation of kerosene.* Excited by ultraviolet light (Stokes' law). Sutton, p. 417.

12.10. *Phosphorescence.* Illumination of certain powders excites phosphorescence radiation.

12.11. *Fluorescence radiation of iodine vapor, quenched by air* (impacts of the second kind). Another bulb is prepared like the one just described; before the sealing off, 1 atm of air, made dustfree by filtering through glass wool, is admitted. This bulb shows absorption of light but no fluorescence radiation.

14.1. *X rays.* Sutton, p. 495. P. Kirkpatrick, *Am. J. Phys.*, **9**, 14 (1941), and **10**, 233 (1942). O. Oldenberg, *Am. J. Phys.*, **20**, 111 (1952).

14.2. *The turning-crystal spectrometer.* In the spectrometer described by Harnwell and Livingood (p. 351) the line K_α of molybdenum can be demonstrated with the help of a well-shielded Geiger counter.

15.1. *Space-charge and saturation current.* Hoag and Korff, pp. 103 and 116.

15.2. *Cloud of electrons in heated crystal.* R. W. Pohl, *Naturwissenschaften*, **21**, 261 (1933).

17.1. *Geiger counter.* See A. L. Hughes, *Am. Phys. Teacher*, **7**, 271–292 (1939). Alpha and beta rays can be distinguished by a counter with mica window and various absorbers. The counter can be made sensitive for alpha rays only by applying a subnormal voltage. Beta and gamma rays can be distinguished by their widely different penetrating power.

17.2. *Range of alpha particles.* Sutton, p. 502.

17.3. *Wilson cloud chamber for projection.* Sutton, p. 504. A weak radium D sample shows tracks of the alpha rays from polonium. For the preparation of the sample, see Hoag and Korff, p. 295. The continuously sensitive cloud chamber, *Rev. Sci. Instr.*, **21**, 991 (1950); **22**, 673 (1951).

19.4. *P^{32} as a tracer.* To the water in which the roots of a three-week-old bean plant are immersed, an aqueous solution of 1 millicurie of P^{32} is added. After 15 min. the Geiger counter responds to the radioactivity of a leaf. P^{32} can be obtained from the Oak Ridge National Laboratory. The sample here used requires ample precautions.

Neutron demonstration. Described by R. Döpel, *Physik. Z.*, **38**, 980 (1937). A strong neutron source permits very impressive demonstrations of artificial radioactivity and uranium fission by slow or fast neutrons (J. R. Dunning).

The processes occurring in the atomic bomb and the pile are visualized in the film "Atomic Energy" (Encyclopaedia Britannica Instructional Film, No. 370).

21.1. *Electron diffraction.* Hoag and Korff, p. 63.

B. LABORATORY EXPERIMENTS

4.1. *Distinction between monatomic, diatomic, and polyatomic gases.* Determination of c_p/c_v, method of Clément and Desormes; method of Kundt's tube.

6.1. *The specific charge of ions* (Faraday constant). Measured with the copper voltameter.

6.2. *The specific charge of the electron.* K. T. Bainbridge, *Am. Phys. Teacher*, **6**, 35 (1938).

7.1. *The charge on the electron.* Millikan's oil-drop experiment. Hoag, p. 14; Millikan (see reference in Sec. 7.1). O. Oldenberg, *Am. J. Phys.*, **17**, 35 (1949).

8.1. *Photoelectric effect.* Planck's constant can be derived with an error of about 10 per cent. A. J. O'Leary, *Am. J. Phys.*, **14**, 245 (1946).

8.2. *Black-body radiation.* J. G. McCue and O. Oldenberg, *Am. Phys. Teacher*, **5**, 173 (1937).

10.1. *The Balmer series of hydrogen.* Determination of the Rydberg constant R and h^3/me^4.

10.2. *Comparison of the spectra of light and heavy hydrogen.* A spectrograph that resolves lines 2 A apart is needed.

11.1. *Sodium spectrum in emission.* In the spectrum of the carbon arc, amply supplied with Na_2CO_3, the distinction between the sharp and the diffuse series is evident. Self-reversal of the yellow line is noticeable.

12.1. *Excitation potential of mercury vapor.* Method of Franck and Hertz. W. Rudy, *Am. J. Phys.*, **16**, 188 (1948). A tube built for this purpose (the grid close to the plate) may be preferable.

12.2. *Electric discharge through a low-pressure gas.* The probe method (see Sec. 12.2a). The discharge tube is connected with a pump; a rotary mechanical pump, if in good condition, is sufficient. The dark space should be 3 or 4 cm long.

12.3. *Sodium spectrum in absorption.* D. C. Stockbarger, *J. Opt. Soc. Amer.*, **30**, 362 (1940). A quartz spectrograph is needed. With a medium-size Hilger quartz spectrograph 28 members of the principal series can be photographed. The positive crater of an arc between pure carbon electrodes supplies the continuous spectrum that serves as the background.

12.4. *Mercury spectrum in absorption.* A glass tube, 10 or 20 in. long, with quartz windows contains air and a few droplets of liquid mercury. No heating is needed. Other details the same as in the preceding experiment. For the determination of Planck's constant, see Sec. 12.1.

12.5. *Raman effect.* The mercury line 4,358 is scattered by CCl_4. A high-intensity (low-dispersion) glass spectrograph is needed.

For X-ray laboratory experiments see P. Kirkpatrick, *Am. Phys. Teacher*, **9**, 14 (1941) and **10**, 233 (1942).

17.1. *Range of alpha particles.* Hoag and Korff. With a polonium source and d-c amplification (*e.g.*, by the F-P54) the Bragg curve (Hoag and Korff, p. 283) is measured.

17.2. *Decay of thorium emanation.* Hoag and Korff, p. 267. A simple gold-leaf electroscope may be used.

18.1. *Annihilation of a positron-electron pair* (Sec. 18.5). Coincidence counters and a positron source are required. J. S. Levinger, *Am. J. Phys.*, **20**, 71 (1952).

20.1. *Cosmic rays* (Sec. 20.1). The experiment requires a coincidence counter.

For more laboratory experiments in nuclear physics see E. C. Pollard and W. L. Davidson, "Applied Nuclear Physics," 2d ed., John Wiley & Sons, Inc., New York, 1951.

APPENDIX 3

CONSTANTS*

(The last digit of any figure here given is uncertain.)

Velocity of light in vacuum c..................... 2.99793×10^{10} cm/sec

Gas constant R................................ 8.3166×10^7 erg/(degree mole)†

Avogadro's number N_0.......................... 6.0247×10^{23} mole^{-1}

Boltzmann constant $k = R/N_0$.................... 1.3804×10^{-16} erg/degree

Faraday constant F............................. 96,520 coulomb/gram atom†

Electronic charge e............................. 1.60207×10^{-20} emu

Specific electronic charge e/m................... 1.75888×10^7 emu/g

Mass of electron m............................. 9.1085×10^{-28} g

Mass of H^1 atom.............................. 1.67334×10^{-24} g

Mass of proton/mass of electron................. 1836.13

Energy of 1 ev................................. 1.60207×10^{-12} erg

Energy equivalent of mass of unit atomic weight.... 931.3 Mev

Planck's constant h........................... 6.6252×10^{-27} erg sec

* DuMond, J. W. M., and E. R. Cohen, *Revs. Mod. Phys.*, **25,** 706 (1953).
† Physical scale.

APPENDIX 4

Periodic Table of Elements*

Period	Group I	Group II	Group III	Group IV	Group V	Group VI	Group VII	Group VIII		
I	1 H 1.0080									2 He 4.003
II	3 Li 6.940	4 Be 9.02	5 B 10.82	6 C 12.01	7 N 14.008	8 O 16.000	9 F 19.00			10 Ne 20.183
III	11 Na 22.997	12 Mg 24.32	13 Al 26.97	14 Si 28.06	15 P 30.98	16 S 32.06	17 Cl 35.457			18 A 39.944
IV	19 K 39.096	20 Ca 40.08	21 Sc 45.10	22 Ti 47.90	23 V 50.95	24 Cr 52.01	25 Mn 54.93	26 Fe 55.85	27 Co 58.94	28 Ni 58.69
IV	29 Cu 63.57	30 Zn 65.38	31 Ga 69.72	32 Ge 72.60	33 As 74.91	34 Se 78.96	35 Br 79.916			36 Kr 83.7
V	37 Rb 85.48	38 Sr 87.63	39 Y 88.92	40 Zr 91.22	41 Nb 92.91	42 Mo 95.95	43 Tc	44 Ru 101.7	45 Rh 102.91	46 Pd 106.7
V	47 Ag 107.880	48 Cd 112.41	49 In 114.76	50 Sn 118.70	51 Sb 121.76	52 Te 127.61	53 I 126.92			54 Xe 131.3
VI	55 Cs 132.91	56 Ba 137.36	57 to 71 Rare earths†	72 Hf 178.6	73 Ta 180.88	74 W 183.92	75 Re 186.31	76 Os 190.2	77 Ir 193.1	78 Pt 195.23
VI	79 Au 197.2	80 Hg 200.61	81 Tl 204.39	82 Pb 207.21	83 Bi 209.00	84 Po 210	85 At			86 Rn 222
VII	87 Fa	88 Ra 226.05	89 Ac 227.05	90 Th 232.12	91 Pa 231	92 U 238.07	93 Np	94 Pu 95 Am	96 Cm 97 Bk	98 Cf 99 100

* Atomic weights based on O = 16.000.

† Rare earths:

57 La 138.92	58 Ce 140.13	59 Pr 140.92	60 Nd 144.27	61 Pm	62 Sm 150.43	63 Eu 152.0	64 Gd 156.9	65 Tb 159.2	66 Dy 162.46	67 Ho 164.94	68 Er 167.2	69 Tm 169.4	70 Yb 173.04	71 Lu 174.99

APPENDIX 5

PARTICLES AND STABLE ISOTOPES OF LIGHT NEUTRAL ATOMS

Isotope	Atomic weight*	Per cent abundance
Neutron	1.008982	
Electron	0.000549	
Proton	1.007593	
Deuteron	2.014186	
Alpha particle	4.00279	
$_1H^1$	1.008142	99.98
$_1H^2$	2.014735	0.02
$_2He^3$	3.01711	10^{-4}
$_2He^4$	4.00389	100
$_3Li^6$	6.01684	7.4
$_3Li^7$	7.01818	92.6
$_4Be^9$	9.01494	100
$_5B^{10}$	10.01633	18.8
$_5B^{11}$	11.01295	81.2
$_6C^{12}$	12.00384	98.9
$_6C^{13}$	13.00766	1.1
$_7N^{14}$	14.00756	99.62
$_7N^{15}$	15.00486	0.38
$_8O^{16}$	16.00000	99.76
$_8O^{17}$	17.00453	0.04
$_8O^{18}$	18.00469	0.20
$_9F^{19}$	19.00452	100
$_{10}Ne^{20}$	19.99896	90.5
$_{10}Ne^{21}$	20.99968	0.3
$_{10}Ne^{22}$	21.99864	9.2
$_{11}Na^{23}$	22.9968	100
$_{12}Mg^{24}$	23.99189	78.6
$_{12}Mg^{25}$	24.99277	10.1
$_{12}Mg^{26}$	25.99062	11.3
$_{13}Al^{27}$	26.9916	100
$_{14}Si^{28}$	27.9866	92.3
$_{14}Si^{29}$	28.9864	4.7
$_{14}Si^{30}$	29.9832	3.0
$_{15}P^{31}$	30.9843	100

*Based O^{16} on = 16.00000.

APPENDIX 6

MEASUREMENT OF NUCLEAR CHARGES BY SCATTERING OF ALPHA PARTICLES

We shall first discuss the deflection of one alpha particle passing near a highly charged, heavy nucleus and then the probabilities of the various deflections of many particles incident on a film of a heavy element. An alpha particle is aimed at the neighborhood of a nucleus. If undeflected, it would pass the nucleus at the smallest distance p (Fig. Appendix 6). The nucleus is supposed to be so heavy that no appreciable kinetic energy is transferred to it. The computation of the deflection is a problem of mechanics, well known to the astronomer because it is the same as the computation of the deflection of a comet passing near the sun. The angle of deflection θ is determined on the basis of the same fundamental equations that describe planetary motion. The result is

$$\tan \frac{\theta}{2} = \frac{2Ze^2}{mv^2p} \qquad (9.1)$$

where θ = angle between incoming and outgoing directions

$2\,e,\, m,\, v$ = charge, mass and velocity of alpha particle

Ze = charge of nucleus

p = shortest distance between nucleus and incoming direction.

FIG. APP. 6. Deflection of alpha particle by a heavy nucleus.

We want to predict the angular distribution of all particles that have passed through a thin foil. Since no two particles are deflected by *exactly* the same angle, we must allow a small margin and inquire what fraction F of all particles is deflected by angles between θ and $\theta + d\theta$. As most particles are observed as undeflected, we are sure that successive deflections of the same particle by 2 or more nuclei can be disregarded. If the foil presents n atoms per square centimeter of its surface to the incoming beam or alpha particles, we may attribute to each nucleus an area of $1/n$ and investigate the deflection

403

of many alpha particles that hit this area. In order to apply the above equation, we must find out how many particles, when arriving at random, are passing the nucleus at distances between p and $p + dp$—in other words, how many are hitting a ring of the area $2\pi p\, dp$ described about the nucleus. Assuming N alpha particles per square centimeter and sec, we calculate as follows:

Area attributed to each nucleus..................... $1/n$
Number per second incident on area................ N/n
Number per second incident on ring $2\pi p\, dp$........ $2\pi p\, dp\, N$
Fraction of all particles incident on ring.......... $= \begin{cases} 2\pi p\, dp\, N/(N/n) \\ 2\pi p\, dp\, n \end{cases}$

This fraction computed for 1 nucleus is identical with the fraction of all particles passing at distances between p and $p + dp$ from any nucleus.

In order to introduce observable quantities, we want to compute the fraction F of all particles deflected by angles between θ and $\theta + d\theta$. For this purpose, applying Eq. (9.1), we introduce θ instead of p into the last equation and $d\theta$ instead of dp. The relation between these small quantities is given by the derivative

$$\frac{dp}{d\theta} = \frac{-Ze^2}{2mv^2} \frac{1}{\sin^2 (\theta/2)}$$

We are not interested in the negative sign, since the observer does not differentiate between positive or negative values of $d\theta$. The final result is

$$F = \frac{4\pi n Z^2 e^4}{(mv^2)^2 \tan (\theta/2) \sin^2 (\theta/2)}\, d\theta$$

This equation indicates to the experimenter what he must measure. For various angles θ (with an arbitrarily selected small margin $d\theta$) the number of deflected particles is counted and divided by the total number of particles constituting the alpha ray. This ratio represents the fraction F. The number n of metal atoms per square centimeter of the foil is computed from the thickness, the density of the metal, and the mass of each atom.

The resulting equation is tested as follows: (1) For alpha particles of uniform velocity the dependence of the fraction F on the angle θ and the thickness of the foil (involved in n) agrees with the observations. (2) Comparing alpha rays of different velocities, the dependence on v agrees with the observations. These successes give us confidence in the validity of the underlying hypothesis, i.e., the idea of the nuclear atom. Now for an alpha ray of given properties we evaluate the only unknown in the last equation, i.e., the nuclear charge Ze. (In Sec. 9.3 deviations from the last equation are interpreted by the bodily collisions of very fast alpha particles with nuclei.)

APPENDIX 7

EQUIVALENCE OF MASS AND ENERGY

Because of its great importance, we want to give a derivation of Einstein's law of the equivalence of mass and energy. We largely follow the book of M. Born, "Einstein's Theory of Relativity," E. P. Dutton & Co., New York. We start from a simple problem of mechanics, the *firing and stopping of a bullet*. Presupposing that light consists of quanta (Chap. 8) and that each quantum is endowed with a momentum, we shall apply essentially the same argument to the *emission and absorption of a quantum*.

A railroad car is standing still, able to move without friction. At its front wall a gun (mass M) is rigidly mounted and aimed toward the rear wall where, at the distance L, the bullet is intercepted by a target of the same mass M, rigidly mounted in the car, too. It is convenient to assume that the mass of the car proper is negligible as compared with the mass $2M$ of the gun and target. When the gun shoots the bullet (mass m, velocity v), by the reaction the whole car is given a velocity V, easily computed from the conservation of momentum $2MV = mv$. As soon as the bullet hits the rear wall, it transfers its momentum mv to the car. The momentum so given to the car is just equal and opposite to its momentum $2MV$; hence the car stops again. By what distance is the car shifted? It has moved with the velocity $V = mv/2M$ during the time of flight of the bullet (L/v); hence the shift of the car equals $LV/v = Lm/2M$. (In the expression for the time of flight we disregard the fact that the bullet does not quite cover the full length of the car since, during the same time, the car itself is moving in the opposite direction.)

What has happened to the center of gravity of the car? Before the shot, because of the symmetrical distribution of the masses, the center was right in the middle between the gun and the target. After the shot, the car has been shifted by the distance d; furthermore the gun has lost and the target gained the mass m. The student is asked to compute the new position of the center of gravity as seen from an outside observer. The result is that the center has remained unchanged. We could have predicted this simple result because a general theorem of mechanics (simplified for our special case) states: The center of gravity (or mass center) of a system that is at rest to begin with will remain at rest as long as no external forces are acting on the system.

Now we apply the same argument to the flight of a quantum of light (energy $E = h\nu$; momentum $= h\nu/c = E/c$).   Here we *presuppose* the theorem of mechanics just confirmed by our computation; as the unknown we compute the mass which the energy E transfers from the emitter to the absorber.   In a closed container (Fig. App. 7) of negligible mass, which is at rest with respect to the observer, two *equal* bodies, A and B (each of mass M), are rigidly mounted at the mutual distance L, both able to emit and absorb light.   When A emits a quantum of energy E in the direction toward B, the whole rigid body suffers a reaction since the quantum carries the momentum E/c.   Thus the container is given a velocity V, computed from the law of conservation of momentum $2MV = E/c$.   During the time of flight L/c of the quantum, the container moves with the velocity V.   When the quantum is absorbed by

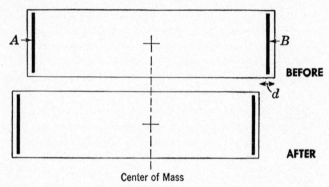

FIG. APP. 7. The box recoils through the distance d while a quantum travels along the box.

the body B, it gives just the opposite momentum to the container; hence, now it stops.   During the time of flight it has been shifted by the distance $d =$ time of flight of bullet $\times$ velocity of container $= LE/2c^2M$.   All this is seen by the observer who is at rest, outside the container.

The theorem of mechanics referred to above states that the center of gravity of the system has not been shifted by the emission and absorption of the quantum.   To start with, this center was exactly midway between the bodies A and B because these are assumed to have equal masses at the beginning.   Although the center of gravity remains unchanged, finally both bodies are shifted to the left by the distance d.   Hence we are forced to assume that the transfer of the quantum of energy E has taken away mass from the body A and has given it to the body B.   Thus we conclude that the addition of energy contributes to the mass of a body.

We compute the mass equivalent μ of the energy E of the quantum on the basis of the same theorem of mechanics; μ must be such that the center of gravity of the system remains unchanged with respect to the observer; hence it is shifted by the distance d with respect to the bodies A and B. We express this shift by the equation:

$$(M - \mu)\left(\frac{L}{2} + d\right) = (M + \mu)\left(\frac{L}{2} - d\right)$$

As everything else is known, we compute the only unknown μ:

$$\mu = \frac{2Md}{L}$$

and, introducing the above value of d,

$$\mu = \frac{E}{c^2}$$

This is the amount by which the mass of any body increases when it absorbs the energy E.

This computation is special in that it attributes a mass to energy of *light*. We generalize it by considering that in the body A or B a ready exchange takes place between light and other forms of energy. For example, in the body A, before the emission, the energy E possibly consisted of kinetic energy of two atoms which, in an inelastic collision, was changed to energy of excitation of one of the atoms and subsequently emitted as a quantum. This internal change occurring before the emission process does not affect the position of the body A. Hence, our argument is not specific for light but applies to any form of energy.

Einstein's theory of relativity enters only into the last step of the present argument. When saying that the quantum travels with the velocity of light c, we failed to specify the frame of reference with respect to which the velocity is measured. Since Huygens (1678) up to the time of Einstein (1905) it was assumed that light, being a wave motion, must be carried by a medium invented for this purpose and called "ether." Since the container was assumed to travel through the ether with a certain velocity, before Einstein one would have taken into account the velocity of the box with respect to the ether, called the "ether wind," and so would have obtained a more complicated final equation. Einstein established as a principle that the velocity of light is independent of the relative velocity of the observer and the source of light. Therefore, it is basically impossible to measure the velocity of light with respect to the hypothetical ether; in other words, there exists no effect that would be affected by the motion of the apparatus with respect to the ether. Hence the equation mass $= E/c^2$ does not depend upon the motion of our box with respect to the ether and represents the general law.

APPENDIX 8
REFERENCES

GENERAL REFERENCES

M. Born, "Atomic Physics," 5th ed., Hafner Publishing Co., Inc., New York, 1951.

T. B. Brown, "Foundations of Modern Physics," John Wiley & Sons, Inc., New York, 1948.

J. A. Crowther, "Ions, Electrons, and Ionizing Radiations," 8th ed., Longmans, Green & Co., Inc., New York, 1949.

W. Finkelnburg, "Atomic Physics," McGraw-Hill Book Company, Inc., New York, 1950.

W. Heisenberg, "Philosophic Problems of Nuclear Sciences," Pantheon Books, Inc., New York, 1952.

J. B. Hoag and S. A. Korff, "Electron and Nuclear Physics," 3d ed., D. Van Nostrand Company, Inc., New York, 1948.

G. F. Hull, "Elementary Modern Physics," 2d ed., The Macmillan Company, New York, 1949.

F. O. Rice and E. Teller, "The Structure of Matter," John Wiley & Sons, Inc., New York, 1949.

F. K. Richtmyer and E. H. Kennard, "Introduction to Modern Physics," 4th ed., McGraw-Hill Book Company, Inc., New York, 1947.

E. Schrödinger, "What is Life?" The Macmillan Company, New York, 1945.

H. Semat, "Introduction to Atomic Physics," 2d ed., Rinehart & Company, Inc., New York, 1946.

J. D. Stranathan, "The Particles of Modern Physics," The Blakiston Company, New York, 1942.

S. Tolansky, "Introduction to Atomic Physics," 3d ed., Longmans, Green & Co., Inc., New York, 1949.

Scientific American, numerous recent articles.

PART I

L. Pauling, "General Chemistry," W. H. Freeman and Co., San Francisco, 1948.

PART II

E. H. Kennard, "Kinetic Theory of Gases," McGraw-Hill Book Company, Inc., New York, 1938.

L. B. Loeb, "Kinetic Theory of Gases," 2d ed., McGraw-Hill Book Company, Inc., New York, 1934.

PART III

P. G. Bergmann, "Introduction to the Theory of Relativity," Prentice-Hall, Inc., New York, 1942.

R. A. Millikan, "Electrons, Protons, Photons, Neutrons, and Cosmic Rays," 2d ed., University of Chicago Press, Chicago, 1947.

PART IV

V. K. Zworykin and E. G. Ramberg, "Photoelectricity," John Wiley & Sons, Inc., New York, 1949.

PART V

A. H. Compton and S. K. Allison, "X Rays," D. Van Nostrand Company, Inc., New York, 1935.

G. Herzberg, "Atomic Spectra and Atomic Structure," 2d ed., Dover Publications, New York, 1944.

W. Shockley, "Electrons and Holes in Semiconductors," D. Van Nostrand Company, Inc., New York, 1950.

PART VI

H. A. Bethe, "Elementary Nuclear Theory," John Wiley & Sons, Inc., New York, 1947.

J. M. Cork, "Radioactivity and Nuclear Physics," 2d ed., D. Van Nostrand Company, Inc., New York, 1950.

G. Gamow, "Atomic Energy in Cosmic and Human Life," The Macmillan Company, New York, 1946.

General Electric Co. Chart of the Nuclides, 4th ed., November, 1952.

S. Glasstone, "Source Book on Atomic Energy," D. Van Nostrand Company, Inc., New York, 1950.

D. Halliday, "Introductory Nuclear Physics," John Wiley & Sons, Inc., New York, 1950.

M. D. Kamen, "Radioactive Tracers," Academic Press, New York, 1947.

S. A. Korff, "Electron and Nuclear Counters," D. Van Nostrand Company, Inc., New York, 1946.

R. E. Lapp and H. L. Andrews, "Nuclear Radiation Physics," Prentice-Hall, Inc., New York, 1948.

D. J. X. Montgomery, "Cosmic Ray Physics," Princeton University Press, Princeton, N. J., 1949.

E. C. Pollard and W. L. Davidson, "Applied Nuclear Physics," 2d ed., John Wiley & Sons, Inc., New York, 1951.

B. Rossi, "High Energy Particles," Prentice-Hall, New York, 1952.

PART VII

D. Bohm, "Quantum Theory," Prentice-Hall, Inc., New York, 1951.

V. Rojansky, "Introductory Quantum Mechanics," Prentice-Hall, Inc., New York, 1938.

BIOGRAPHIES

"A. Einstein," by P. Frank, Alfred A. Knopf, Inc., New York, 1947.

R. A. Millikan, "Autobiography," Prentice-Hall, Inc., New York, 1950.

"Rutherford," by A. S. Eve, The Macmillan Company, New York, 1939.

"J. J. Thomson," by Lord Rayleigh, Cambridge University Press, London, 1943.

APPENDIX 9

ANSWERS

1.1. (a) N_2 and NO; (b) 1 volume nitrogen + 2 volumes oxygen = 1 volume nitrogen tetroxide.

1.2. 1 volume H_2O_2 = 1 volume H_2 + 1 volume O_2.

2.2. NaCl or Na_2Cl_2, etc.

2.3. Analysis by weight leads to CH_2 or C_2H_4, etc. The density leads to the molecular weight 28, hence the formula C_2H_4.

2.4. (a) 46.7 g N_2 + 53.3 g O_2; (b) 30.4 g N_2 + 69.6 g O_2; (c) 36.8 g N_2 + 63.2 g O_2.

3.2. 23.6 per cent oxygen, 76.4 per cent nitrogen.

3.3. (a) 1,083 kg; (b) 14.0 kg.

3.4. $F = 2mn\sqrt{2gh}$; $h = 48.0$ cm.

3.5. $F = nmc$.

3.9. (a) $\Delta p = -\Delta hg\rho$; (c) $\Delta p/p = -(gm/RT) \times \Delta h$; (f) $p = p_0 e^{-(gm/RT) \times h}$.

3.10. $\dfrac{\Delta p}{p} = -\dfrac{mg}{R}\dfrac{\Delta h}{a+bh}$; $p = p_0\left(\dfrac{a}{a+bh}\right)^{mg/Rb}$; $\rho = \dfrac{p_0 m}{R}\left(\dfrac{a}{a+bh}\right)^{mg/Rb} \times \dfrac{1}{a+bh}$

At 400 km: $p = 5.5 \times 10^{-7}$ mm; $\rho = 7.8 \times 10^{-14}$ gcm^{-3}.

4.2. 1.98×10^{-5} cm.

5.1. $l = 1/\pi nr^2$.

6.3. (a) $v \times \Delta t$; (b) $nv\,\Delta t$; (c) $i = env$; (d) force on length $L = env \times L \times H$; (e) evH.

6.10. $v = E/B$.

6.11. $r = 10^{-4}$ cm; magnification = 30,000.

6.12. 1.335×10^{14} metric tons/year.

6.13. (a) $y = eVz^2/2mdv^2$; (b) 0.218 cm; (c) 0.200 cm.

6.14. $x = eBz^2/2mv$; 0.203 cm.

6.15. $x^2 = y \times el^2dB^2/2mV$; $e/m = 419$ emu/g; presumably Na^+.

6.16. $dy/dx = eVx/mdv^2$; $b = 32.1$ cm.

6.17. (a) 1 per cent; (b) 2; 1; 2 per cent.

7.2. $E = 3\,mg/q$; 200 volt/cm.

7.3. (a) $x = \dfrac{1}{2}\dfrac{e}{m}\dfrac{V}{d}t^2$; (b) $v = \dfrac{e}{m}\dfrac{V}{d}t$; (c) $v = \sqrt{2\dfrac{e}{m}\dfrac{V}{d}x}$; (f) $t = d\sqrt{\dfrac{2m}{eV}} = 6.15 \times 10^{-9}$ sec.

7.6. 1 kcal/mole = 0.0434 ev/molecule = 0.695×10^{-13} erg/molecule.

7.7. 1.745×10^{-7} dyne.

7.8. 0.264×10^{-8} per cent.

7.9. 2.3×10^{-7} per cent.

7.10. (a) $n = i/Ave$; (b) 5.00×10^{-13} Coul/cm^3.

7.11. 9.15 sec.

7.13. 2.71×10^{10}.

7.14. 2.69×10^{19} molecules/cm^3.

7.15. 47.5×10^{-24} cm^3; 2.25×10^{-8} cm.

7.16. 1.28×10^{-3}.

7.17. (a) 5.85×10^{-6} cm; (b) $u = 4.13 \times 10^4$ cm/sec; (c) 1.42×10^{-10} sec; (d) 7.04×10^9 collisions per second.

7.18. $n = 3.54 \times 10^9$ molecules/cm^3.

7.19. $v = 2c \sqrt{\dfrac{e}{m} q \log_e \dfrac{r}{r_f}}$.

8.1. (a) 6.62×10^{-27} erg sec; (b) 1.74 ev; (c) $7{,}110$ A.

8.3. 2.13×10^{18} quanta.

8.4. 1.45×10^{14} quanta per square centimeter and second.

8.5. $1{,}700$ quanta per sec.

8.6. $n = I/ch\nu$; 8.01×10^{-7} quanta per cubic centimeter.

8.7. 1.2 per cent.

9.1. (a) $\frac{1}{2}m_1u_1{}^2 = \frac{1}{2}m_1v_1{}^2 + \frac{1}{2}m_2v_2{}^2$; (b) $m_1u_1 = m_1v_1 + m_2v_2$; (c) $v_1 = u_1 \times (m_1 - m_2)/(m_1 + m_2)$; $v_2 = u_1 \times 2m_1/(m_1 + m_2)$; (d) (1) $v_1 = 0$; $v_2 = u_1$; (2) $v_1 = -u_1$; v_2 negligible; (3) $v_1 = u_1$; $v_2 = 2u_1$.

9.2. I. $u_1{}^2 = v_1{}^2 + v_2{}^2$; II. $u_1 = v_1 \cos \phi + v_2 \cos \theta$; III. $0 = v_1 \sin \phi + v_2 \sin \theta$; $v_1 = u_1 \cos \phi$; $v_2 = u_1 \sin \phi$; $\theta = \pi/2 - \phi$; $v_1 = 0.866 \, u_1$; $v_2 = 0.500 \, u_1$; $\theta = 60°$.

9.3. Equate initial W_k and maximum W_p; 3.0×10^{-12} cm.

9.4. Fraction 2.5×10^{-5}.

10.3. $W = -13.58$; -3.39; -0.136 ev; 0; $W_p = -27.16$; -6.78; -0.272 ev; 0; $W_k =$ same figures as W but with positive sign.

10.6. $79{,}000°$K; because of the velocity distribution.

10.7. $f = 4\pi^2 mZ^2 e^4/n^3 h^3$.

10.11. $v = 1.118 \times 10^6$ cm/sec; 0.706×10^6 cm/sec.

10.12. (a) (1) $mr\omega^2 = Ze^2/(r + R)^2$

        (2) $MR\omega^2 = Ze^2/(r + R)^2$

        (3) $mr^2\omega + MR^2\omega = nh/2\pi$

  (b) $mr^3\omega^2(1 + m/M)^2 = Ze^2$

      $mr^2\omega(1 + m/M) = nh/2\pi$

(c) $r = n^2h^2/4\pi^2 mZe^2$; (d) $v = 2\pi Ze^2/nh(1 + m/M)$; (e) $W = W_k + W_p = \frac{1}{2}mv^2 + \frac{1}{2}MV^2 - Ze^2/(r + R)$; (f) Introducing $R = rm/M$ and $V = vR/r = vm/M$, $W = \frac{1}{2}mv^2(1 + m/M) - Ze^2/r(1 + m/M)$; (g) $\nu_{th} = \dfrac{2\pi^2 mMZ^2 e^4}{h^3(m + M)} \left(\dfrac{1}{n''^2} - \dfrac{1}{n'^2} \right)$; (h) $R_{\mathrm{H}}/R_{\mathrm{He}} = \left(1 + \dfrac{m}{M_{\mathrm{He}}} \right) \Big/ \left(1 + \dfrac{m}{M_{\mathrm{H}}} \right)$.

Theoretical ratio $= 1 - 0.000407$; observed ratio $= 1 - 0.000408$.

10.13. $\lambda_H - \lambda_D = \lambda_H \times m(M_D - M_H)/(M_D \times M_H) = 1.78$ A.

10.14. (a) $\Delta W = GmM\Delta r/r^2$; $W = GmM(1/r_1 - 1/r_2)$.

12.3. $12{,}390$ ev $\times$ A.

12.5. 0.0268 ev; 0.0390 ev.

12.6. 5×10^{-8} sec.

12.7. (a) $u_1{}^2 = v_1{}^2 + v_2{}^2 + 2W/M$; $u_1 = v_1 + v_2$; (c) $Mu_1{}^2/2 \geqq 2W$.

12.8. $dn = -\alpha n^2 \, dt$; $n = n_0/(1 + n_0\alpha t)$.

12.9. (a) $\Delta I = -\mu \Delta l I$; (b) $I_1 = I_0 e^{-\mu l_1}$.

14.1. 0.0367 roentgen.

14.5. 0.00178 radian.

14.7. 0.1650 A; $1°40'$.

14.10. 0.222 A (observed 0.213 A).

14.11. (a) 5.82×10^4 volts; (b) 6.96×10^4 volts.

14.12. 93.3; 87.3; 77.8; 1.54; 2.38×10^{-2}; 5.6×10^{-6} per cent; 12.3 cm aluminum.

14.13. (a) 0.0113; (b) 1.44×10^{-6}; (c) density of Hg $= 20.06 \times 10^{-3}$ g/cm^3; $I/I_0 = 0.718$; (d) density of Hg $= 3.88 \times 10^{-3}$ g/cm^3; $I/I_0 = 0.682$.

14.15. (b) $\dfrac{h^2}{\lambda^2} + \dfrac{h^2}{\lambda'^2} - \dfrac{2h^2}{\lambda\lambda'} \cos \phi = m^2 v^2$;

(c) $\dfrac{2h^2}{\lambda\lambda'} (1 - \cos \phi) = m^2 v^2 \left(1 - \dfrac{v^2}{2c^2}\right)$;

(d) Eq. (IV) is conveniently rewritten as $hc \dfrac{\lambda' - \lambda}{\lambda\lambda'} = \dfrac{mv^2}{2}$ and divided into the last

equation (neglecting $v^2/2c^2$). Result: $\dfrac{h(1 - \cos \phi)}{c(\lambda' - \lambda)} = m$; $\lambda' - \lambda = \dfrac{h}{mc} (1 - \cos \phi)$.

14.18. $\tan \theta = -\lambda/\lambda' = -0.985$; $v = h/\lambda m \cos \theta = 6.62 \times 10^8$ cm/sec.

14.19. Pressure $= 2nh\nu/c$; force $= 6.77 \times 10^{-7}$ dyne.

16.2. $e/m = 419$ emu/g; Na^+.

16.3. Separation of Li isotopes, 0.82 cm; of Hg isotopes, 0.025 cm.

16.7. Packing fraction $= (-8 \pm 1) \times 10^{-4}$; atomic weight 39.968 ± 0.004.

16.8. 16.0044.

16.10. 931 Mev.

16.12. 19,000 years.

16.13. $\Delta W = $ torque $\times \Delta\alpha = mlH \sin \alpha \Delta\alpha$; $W = 2mlH$.

17.4. 6.4×10^{-5} per cent.

17.6. Average 53.0 kev.

17.7. $\lambda = 0.71 \times 10^{-8}$ cm.

17.8. 0.92 min.

17.9. $T = (\log_e 2)/\lambda$; $T' = (\log_e 1.111)/\lambda$.

17.10. (a) 1.383×10^{-9} per cent; (b) 3.69×10^7 atoms per second; (c) 12.2 per cent; (d) $\frac{1}{32}$.

17.11. 0.062 per cent.

17.12. (a) 3.7×10^{10} sec^{-1}; (b) 1.18×10^{-8} amp; (c) 18.5×10^{10} sec^{-1}.

17.13. 6.5×10^8 years.

17.16. $\lambda = 1.30 \times 10^{-5}$ sec^{-1}; $N = 2.84 \times 10^{10}$; mass $= 1.13 \times 10^{-12}$ g.

17.17. Final product $_{82}Pb^{208}$.

17.18. $\Delta n = -\lambda n \Delta t$.

17.19. $dn = \lambda_1 N \, dt - \lambda_2 n \, dt$; $n = N \dfrac{\lambda_1}{\lambda_2} (1 - e^{-\lambda_2 t})$.

17.20. In intervals of 3.82 days.

18.1. (1) 55 Mev; (2) 89 Mev.

18.2. $m_1 = 1.16 \times$ mass of proton; $u_1 = 3.1 \times 10^9$ cm/sec.

18.3. 0.78 Mev liberated.

18.4. 4.14; 8.35 Mev.

18.6. W_k of $p = (h\nu - D)/(1 + $ mass of $p/$mass of $n)$.

18.7. 1.11; 7.05; 7.66; 7.95; 8.44; 8.66; 7.46 Mev per nucleon.

18.8. (a) Decrease by 2.002/2.015; (b) increase by 2.015/1.008.

18.9. (a) $N = B^2 R^2 e/2Vm$; (b) N proportional $1/V$; W independent of V; (c) $N = 1{,}109$; $W = 11.09$ Mev.; (d) $N = 1{,}118$; $W = 22.36$ Mev.

18.12. -1.14; $+5.60$; $+17.2$; $+22.1$ Mev.

18.13. 1.34×10^{-26} cm^2.

18.14. $_1H^3 - _2He^3 = 2 \times 10^{-5}$.

18.15. (a) $v_c = v_p m/(m + M)$; (c) $\frac{1}{2}mv_p^2 M/(m + M)$; (d) 0.109 Mev.

19.1. $T = 24{,}100$ years.

19.2. 1.5 cm.

19.4. 160 Mev.

19.5. 9.3×10^5 kw.

19.6. 2,400 metric tons.

19.7. 8.9×10^{-9} g.

19.8. 11,200 years.

19.11. 1.78×10^{20} ergs $= 4.94 \times 10^{6}$ kwhr; \$98,800.

19.12. 1.13×10^{46} atoms per year; 1.89×10^{16} tons/year.

19.13. (a) 0.82×10^{18} ergs; (b) 3.4×10^{18} ergs.

19.14. (a) 1.31×10^{6} g; (b) 0.65×10^{6} g.

20.1. 22.3 cm.

20.2. (a) $\displaystyle\int_{h_0}^{\infty} n\, dh = \frac{n_s RT}{mg}\, e^{-mgh_0/RT}$;

(b) $l_a = \dfrac{RT}{mg}\, e^{-mgh_0/RT}$; (d) 1,030 cm; 83.4 cm;

(f) 18.7 km.

22.1. (a) 12.25×10^{-8} cm; (b) 3.86×10^{-8} cm; (c) 3.32×10^{-8} cm; (d) 1.52×10^{-8} cm; (e) 9.05×10^{-12} cm; (f) 6.62×10^{-27} cm; (g) 1.5×10^{-36} cm.

INDEX

415